Praise for **Predictions**

'There is something for everyone in this entertaining series
. . . good value for such a thrill' Sebastian O'Kelly, *European*

'For the price of a pint of lager, browsers can bone up on
likely developments in science, geopolitics, religion and war'
Robert Winder, *New Statesman*

'The styles are different . . . but [the contributors] share an
impressive commitment to explaining the toolkits used by
medical, demographic and meteorological forecasters'
Francis Spufford, *Independent*

'Distinguished writers and compelling subjects are the series'
hallmarks' *New Scientist*

'Well-researched and knowledgeable' *Yorkshire Evening Post*

'Predictions is a series of slim volumes with a powerful punch
. . . a summary of modern trends and an intelligent guess at
future trends in various subjects of importance by commentators of stature. They are sometimes alarming, sometimes
reassuring, always provocative and hugely educative
Oxford Times

'The language in each is fresh and direct, appealing to the
general reader without losing interest for the specialist
Independent on Sunday

The Future Now

PREDICTING THE 21ST CENTURY

PHŒNIX

A PHOENIX PAPERBACK

First published in Great Britain
by Weidenfeld & Nicolson in 1998
This paperback edition published in 1999 by Phoenix,
an imprint of Orion Books Ltd,
Orion House, 5 Upper St Martin's Lane,
London WC2H 9EA

A CIP catalogue record for this book is available
from the British Library.

ISBN 0 75380 902 8

Typeset by SetSystems Ltd, Saffron Walden, Essex

Printed in Great Britain by The Guernsey Press Co. Ltd, Guernsey, C.I.

Contents

1 Cosmology JOHN GRIBBIN   1

2 Religion FELIPE FERNÁNDEZ-ARMESTO   41

3 Warfare FRANÇOIS HEISBOURG   95

4 The Middle East BERNARD LEWIS   143

5 Terrorism CONOR GEARTY   191

6 Europe HUGH THOMAS   237

7 Moral Values A. C. GRAYLING   283

8 Manipulative Reproduction ROBERT WINSTON   331

9 Disease MATT RIDLEY   383

10 Media PADDY BARWISE AND KATHY HAMMOND   425

Further Reading   475

Index   481

1 Cosmology
JOHN GRIBBIN

The Birth of the Big Bang

If you look at the sky on a dark, clear moonless night, far away from the dazzle of any city lights, with the unaided human eye you will be able to see no more than a couple of thousand individual bright stars. You will also see a band of hazy light circling the sky, forming the Milky Way; a modest pair of binoculars, or a small telescope like the one built by Galileo in 1609, will show that the Milky Way is made up of a myriad of stars, too faint to be picked out individually by eye. Astronomers estimate that there are at least 100 billion stars in the Milky Way, forming a disc-shaped system so large that light would take 100,000 years to cross it from one side to the other. Those stars are all objects like our Sun – some are bigger, some are smaller, but they are all balls of hot gas, radiating energy that is produced by nuclear fusion reactions (the same sort of process that powers a hydrogen bomb) going on in their hearts. The Sun is an ordinary star, about two-thirds of the way out from the middle of the disc-shaped system of stars that is known as the Milky Way, or as 'our' Galaxy. If each star were the size of a rice grain, the Galaxy would have a diameter the same as the real distance from the Earth to the Moon.

But this impressive island of stars is just one among many. Until well into the twentieth century, it seemed that the Milky Way was the entire Universe. But in 1919 the 100-inch (2.5 metre) diameter Hooker Telescope, the largest built up to then, began operating at Mount Wilson, in California. With this instrument, the American astronomer Edwin Hubble showed in the 1920s that many fuzzy patches of light seen on the sky could be resolved into stars, and that they are, in fact, other galaxies, beyond the Milky Way. Some are disc-shaped, like our own Galaxy; others are spheroidal or ellipsoidal; still others are irregular in shape. As telescope technology has been improved, so that we can see fainter objects further away, deeper into space, more and more galaxies have been found. It is estimated that 100 billion galaxies are in principle visible to our modern instruments, including the Hubble Space Telescope; but only a few thousand of these islands in space have yet been studied systematically.

We live on an ordinary planet, orbiting an ordinary star, in an ordinary part of an ordinary galaxy – the Milky Way Galaxy is, if anything, slightly smaller than the average spiral. There is nothing special about our place in the Universe, and to a cosmologist a whole galaxy, containing hundreds of billions of stars, is merely a test particle, whose motion shows how the Universe as a whole is changing. And it *is* changing. The most important single discovery in the whole of cosmology was also made by Hubble and his colleagues, using the Hooker Telescope in the 1920s. The galaxies are moving apart from one another; the Universe is expanding.

The evidence comes from a phenomenon known as the redshift, an expression that has become part of the language but is often misunderstood. And we know about the redshift because it is possible to analyse the light from distant stars and galaxies, splitting it up into the rainbow pattern of the spectrum in just the same way that light from the Sun can be spread out to make a rainbow pattern using a simple triangular prism.

The rainbow pattern of the spectrum represents a spread of wavelengths of light, from longer wavelengths at the red end of the spectrum to shorter wavelengths at the blue end of the spectrum. It just happens that the way our eyes and brains perceive this part of the electromagnetic spectrum is as a series of colours. There is also much more to the spectrum than we can see; it extends beyond the red end into the still longer infrared and radio wavelengths, and beyond the blue end into the still shorter ultraviolet, X- and gamma-ray regions. To astronomers, all of this is the spectrum, and all of the electromagnetic spectrum is now available for analysis using instruments such as radio telescopes and X-ray telescopes, hoisted (if necessary) above the obscuring layers of the atmosphere on rockets, satellites or balloons. But the essential cosmological redshift was discovered using the visible part of the spectrum and conventional optical telescopes.

What makes spectroscopy so informative for astrophysicists is that each variety of atom (hydrogen, oxygen, iron and all the rest) produces a characteristic pattern of lines in the spectrum. These may be bright lines, if the atoms producing them are hot and radiating energy, or dark lines if the atoms are cold and absorbing energy from light coming from behind them. But they are always produced at precisely the same wavelengths, and each set of lines is as characteristic as a fingerprint, identifying the presence of particular substances in the light from a distant star or galaxy, or in cold clouds of gas and dust in space. It is thanks to spectroscopy that we know what those stars, galaxies and clouds are made of; but in cosmology that is of secondary importance. We know, from spectroscopic studies of different substances on Earth, the precise wavelengths at which these lines are produced. But in the light from distant galaxies the whole pattern of lines is shifted bodily towards the red end of the spectrum – to longer wavelengths. This is the famous redshift; and it tells us how distant galaxies are moving.

When Hubble and his colleagues discovered the cosmological redshift in the late 1920s, astronomers were already familiar with one way to produce this effect. It is called the Doppler effect, and it is caused by motion through space. The Doppler effect is familiar in everyday life from the way the sound of a siren on a vehicle (for example, an ambulance) changes pitch as the vehicle rushes past you. When the vehicle is approaching, the note made by the siren sounds higher, because the sound waves from it are squashed together (making the wavelength shorter) by the motion of the vehicle. As the vehicle passes, the note deepens, because as the vehicle moves away from you the sound waves coming from it are being stretched to longer wavelengths by its motion. In exactly the same way, light from an object moving away from you through space would be stretched, and lines in the spectrum of that light would move to longer wavelengths (towards the red end of the spectrum). It was natural for Hubble to think of the cosmological redshift as a Doppler effect, caused by the galaxies moving outward through space, as if from the site of a great explosion. But this is *not* the cause of the cosmological redshift.

Even before Hubble discovered the cosmological redshift, Albert Einstein had developed his general theory of relativity. This is a theory of gravity, space and time; and since the whole Universe is held together by gravity, the general theory can be applied to give a mathematical description (a so-called model) of the behaviour of the Universe at large. Einstein solved the appropriate equations as early as 1916. This was towards the end of the era when it was still thought that the Milky Way was the entire Universe, and that, although individual stars might be born and die, the system as a whole was unchanging, in the same way that a forest may last for millennia even though each individual tree in the forest lives for only a few decades or centuries. So Einstein was completely baffled when the equations of his new theory insisted that the universe could not be static. The equations told him that according to the general theory of relativity space itself (as part of four-dimensional spacetime, but we don't need to go into that here) must be either expanding or contracting, like a block of rubber being stretched or squeezed. In order to hold everything still, Einstein had to introduce an extra term into the equations, a fiddle factor called the cosmological constant. He later described this as the greatest blunder of his career.

Although Einstein didn't believe what his own equations were trying to tell him, the Russian Aleksandr Friedmann followed up the implications over the next few years, and published, in 1922, his solutions to Einstein's equations, without the fiddle factor and complete with the idea of an expanding Universe. Friedmann had found a family of variations on the theme, all involving expansion. In some models, the universe expands for ever. In others, it expands from a very small size, reaches a maximum size, and then shrinks, possibly 'bouncing' and repeating the whole cycle. In one special case, known as the 'flat' model, it expands ever more slowly, until it hovers for an eternity on the brink of recollapse.

In 1927, unaware of Friedmann's work, Georges Lemaître, in Belgium, made essentially the same discovery, and even suggested that if Einstein's theory were correct the expansion of the real Universe might be discovered by studying the way galaxies moved. Hubble didn't know about any of this work when he discovered the cosmological redshift; but it didn't take long for astronomers to put two and two together and realize the true importance of his discovery.

Although Hubble himself did not know it at first, the redshift had actually been predicted by the general theory of relativity. This is a very powerful reason to believe that the general theory is a good mathematical description of the way the Universe works, and modern cosmology is entirely based on Einstein's theory, which has been tested against ever improving observations of the real Universe and passed every test. What this combination of theory and observations tells us is that the very fabric of the Universe, space itself, is expanding and carrying galaxies along for the ride, like raisins being carried further apart from one another in the rising dough of a loaf of raisin bread. The cosmological redshift is caused by this stretching of space, which stretches light to longer wavelengths on its journey to us from those distant galaxies.

Strictly speaking, we should think of clusters of galaxies being carried apart in this way. Galaxies tend to congregate in clusters, like swarms of bees, held together by gravity. The expanding Universe carries individual swarms apart, producing the cosmological redshift; but within the swarm each galaxy has its own motion through space, like the motion of the stars around our Milky Way. This shows up in the measured redshifts of galaxies in a cluster.

Each cluster has an average redshift, caused by the expansion of the Universe. But each galaxy in the cluster is moving through space, and this motion produces a Doppler effect which shifts its spectral lines slightly (by an amount less than the cosmological redshift). Depending on whether a particular galaxy is moving towards us or away from us, this Doppler effect may decrease or increase the observed redshift, so we see a spread of redshifts around the average for the cluster. There *is* a Doppler shift in the light from distant galaxies, but it is quite independent of, and (except for our very nearest neighbours in space) much smaller than, the cosmological redshift.

The fact that we see the Universe expanding now tells us that it must have been smaller in the past – clusters of galaxies must have been closer together. Using the equations of the general theory of relativity, we can wind the expansion backwards to calculate what the Universe would have been like long ago. We can imagine a time when galaxies touched one another and mingled; a time before that when the stars touched one another and formed a huge fireball; and we can go even further back, using not just our imagination but calculations within the framework of the general theory of relativity, matched against observations of the way the Universe is expanding today. It is this combination of theory and observations which tells us that the Universe must have been born out of a hot, dense fireball (the Big Bang) in the distant past; and the great triumph of cosmology in the forty years following Hubble's discovery of the cosmological redshift was that by the end of the 1960s it could tell us how hot and dense that fireball was, and when the Big Bang occurred.

Apart from revealing the fact that the Universe is expanding, the most important feature of the cosmological redshift discovered by Hubble and his colleagues is that it is proportional to distance. In other words, a galaxy twice as far away from us is being carried away from us twice as fast by the expanding Universe, one three times as far away is receding three times as fast, and so on. This does not mean that we are at the centre of the universal expansion. As it happens, this kind of redshift–distance relation, with redshift proportional to distance, is the only pattern of expansion (apart from no expansion at all) which would look the same from any point in the expanding Universe. It is also the kind of expansion predicted by Einstein's general theory of relativity. *Whichever* galaxy you sit on, you will see the same pattern of behaviour, with the redshifts of other galaxies proportional to their distances from you.

A useful way to picture what is going on is to imagine the surface of a smooth sphere, painted with dots to represent galaxies. If the sphere expands, like a balloon, the distances between the dots will increase, even though the paint blobs do not move through the material the sphere is made of. Suppose that the sphere expands uniformly so that in the time it takes to expand two spots that were 10 centimetres apart become 20 centimetres apart. In that case, two spots that were 20 centimetres apart become 40 centimetres apart, in the same time. The further away a spot is from *any* chosen spot, the faster it seems to recede as the sphere expands. From whichever point you choose to measure, you will see a 'recession velocity' proportional to distance, and there is no centre to the expansion, anywhere on the surface. Except that space has three dimensions and the surface of a sphere has only two dimensions, this is exactly the pattern we see in the real Universe – uniform expansion with no centre.

We know this because it is possible to measure distances to relatively nearby galaxies. Measuring redshifts is easy, and can be done, in principle, for any object we can see, no matter how far away it is. But measuring distances to other galaxies is difficult, and still depends in large measure on a technique used by Hubble in the 1930s. Fortunately, there is a family of stars, called Cepheids, which vary in a regular way. Each of these stars has a brightness related to the period of its variation (the time it takes to brighten, dim and brighten again). There are Cepheids in our own Galaxy, and in its near neighbours, two irregular galaxies called the Magellanic Clouds. So it has proved possible to calibrate the relationship between the real brightness of a Cepheid and its period. This means that when Cepheids are detected in other galaxies (no mean feat even for nearby galaxies, even today, using the Hubble Space Telescope), their periods can be measured, and their true brightnesses calculated. By measuring their apparent brightnesses, this tells us how far away they are, just as you could, in principle, determine the distance to a hundred-watt light bulb by measuring its apparent brightness (or dimness!).

Once you have done this for nearby galaxies, you can determine the redshift–distance relation. And once you have done *that*, you can determine the distance to any galaxy by measuring its redshift and plugging the number in to the known redshift–distance relation.

The snag is that relatively nearby galaxies have such small cosmological redshifts that their random motion through space produces speeds which are a sizeable fraction of their recession velocities (for historical reasons, cosmologists still talk of recession velocities, even though they know the redshifts are not caused by motion through space). This makes it hard to calibrate the redshift–distance relation, because we don't know exactly how much of the redshift is caused by the expansion of the Universe and how much is caused by random motion.

The key parameter is a number now known as the Hubble Constant (H), and in the units used by cosmologists this has a value somewhere between 50 and 70 kilometres per second per Megaparsec. That is, the parameter has a unique value somewhere in that range, but we have not yet been clever enough to pin down exactly where. A Megaparsec is a million parsecs, about 3.25 million light years; if the value of H is indeed 50, that would mean that a galaxy 1 Megaparsec away would have a redshift corresponding to a recession velocity of 50 km/sec, and so on. A widely accepted estimate today is that H is between 60 and 65, and the accuracy of the measurement is likely to be improved dramatically over the next few years, thanks to the Hubble Space Telescope.

Of course, astrophysicists want to pin the number down so they can have accurate measurements of the distances to other galaxies. But cosmologists are more interested in the value of the Hubble Constant for another reason. The number tells us how fast the Universe is expanding. That means it tells you how much time has elapsed since the Big Bang. The bigger the value of H, the smaller the age of the Universe; the smaller the value of H, the bigger the age of the Universe. It is because of the uncertainty in the measurement of H that there is uncertainty in the estimates of the age of the Universe, and all we can say for sure is that between 10 billion years and 20 billion years have elapsed since the Big Bang. My own work, carried out with Simon Goodwin (of the University of Sussex) and Martin Hendry (of the University of Glasgow) in 1997 suggests that the value of the Hubble Constant may be as low as 55 in the usual units, implying that the Universe is at least 13 billion years old. But I shall try to be agnostic about the exact value of the Constant, giving equal weight to other studies.

The widely quoted uncertainty, by a factor of two, in the value of the Constant is sometimes held up to ridicule by people who do not appreciate what a breathtaking achievement it is to measure the age of the Universe even to this accuracy. Certainly, if you only knew the balance of your bank account to within a factor of two you might get into financial difficulties; and an airline pilot who wasn't sure whether the distance from New York to London was nearer 1,500 miles or nearer 3,000 miles would be unlikely to make a success of his profession. But we are talking here about the age of the Universe, the time that has elapsed since the Big Bang. We know that it isn't as small as 1 billion years, and we know that it isn't as large as 50 billion years. We can pin it down to a factor of two, and give as a reasonable round number an age of 15 billion years.

If you stop to think about it, this is an utterly staggering achievement of science, that any generation before the mid-twentieth century would have looked upon in wonder.

What's more, the number we get fits in with other highly significant cosmic ages determined entirely independently. Geologists tell us, on the basis of solid evidence, that the age of the Earth is about 4.5 billion years, comfortably less than the age of the Universe (it would certainly be worrying if the numbers came out the other way around, with geologists telling us that the Earth was 15 billion years old and cosmologists telling us that the Universe was 4.5 billion years old). And astrophysicists calculate that the oldest stars are also around 15 billion years old. To be sure, this does present problems if you prefer the higher values of the Hubble Constant, implying that the Universe is about 10 billion years old. But the way to interpret this 'conflict' is to infer that almost certainly the stellar ages are telling us that the value of H must be low, closer to 50 than to 80, but still in the range suggested by redshift studies.

And, again, it is, in everyday terms, utterly amazing that studies of stars should tell us that the ages of the oldest stars are roughly the same as the age of the Universe. The two numbers are calculated entirely independently, using entirely different techniques. If there was something wrong with our understanding of stars, or our understanding of the Universe, we might have ended up with wildly different 'answers' – stars 100 billion years old in a universe 1 billion years old, perhaps. But we don't. The numbers are in the same ball park, and that gives scientists confidence both in their understanding of astrophysics and in their understanding of cosmology. The remaining differences are significant, and suggest that fine-tuning of their theories is needed; but they suggest that *only* fine-tuning is needed, and that we really do know where we came from, and roughly when.

The Universe was born in a hot fireball some 15 billion years ago. The clinching evidence that persuaded most astronomers that the Big Bang really happened came in the 1960s, when they discovered a faint glow of radiation coming from all directions on the sky. This cosmic microwave background radiation is interpreted as the afterglow of the Big Bang itself – and, astonishingly, it had been predicted twenty years earlier, but the prediction had been forgotten.

The first person to attempt to describe the conditions in the Big Bang quantitatively, using the equations of the general theory of relativity and the best understanding of the behaviour of matter under extreme conditions, was George Gamow (a Russian-born American cosmologist), in the 1940s. Even then, it was obvious that you couldn't take the general theory itself literally as the guide to everything back to the beginning itself, time zero. Winding the present expansion of the Universe backwards mathematically using those equations would imply that it was born out of a mathematical point, a singularity with zero volume and infinite density. This is generally accepted as indicating that there is a flaw in the theory, and that something better (specifically, a quantum theory of gravity) is needed to describe the very earliest stages of the expansion.

Of course, this does not mean that the general theory is wrong in all those applications (and there are many) where it has been tested, and passed the tests with flying colours. Even Newton's theory of gravity is still perfectly good if you want to calculate the load on a bridge, say, and no civil engineer bothers with Einstein's equations. You need Einstein's equations under more extreme conditions, where gravity is stronger, and they also provide a description of the whole Universe. But Einstein's theory includes Newton's theory within itself. A quantum theory of gravity will be able to solve problems involving still greater densities of matter, and puzzles like the birth of the Universe; but it will contain Einstein's theory within itself, as the version that applies under less extreme conditions.

The first people to study the details of the physics of the Big Bang (like Gamow) didn't worry too much about the region close to time zero where the general theory breaks down, but restricted themselves to the period a little later in the history of the Universe, when conditions were less extreme and could be understood in terms of experiments that had been carried out on Earth.

The most extreme form of matter around today is the matter in the nucleus of an atom, the tiny central core, made up of protons and neutrons, that is so dense that a cubic centimetre of nuclear material would have a mass of 100 billion kilograms. The behaviour of matter at such high densities (actually, at rather higher densities) has been studied by experimenters using giant particle accelerators, like those at CERN, in Geneva, and Fermilab, in Chicago.

The behaviour of protons, neutrons and nuclear matter is very well understood, and physicists are confident that they can describe how the Universe at large changed as it expanded away from a state in which the entire Universe had the density of nuclear matter. And that corresponds to a time only one ten-thousandth of a second (0.0001 sec) after time zero itself. As far as the physics is concerned, we understand everything that has happened to the Universe since that time, although working out the details of how a hot fireball of energy with nuclear density produced the galaxies, stars, planets and people we see today is no easy task. It's rather like a game of chess – even a ten-year-old can learn the basic rules of the game, including such subtleties as how the knight moves, and even tricks like castling; but not even a grand master can use those rules to reconstruct the play of a game of chess solely by studying the end game. We know the rules the Universe has operated under since the first ten-thousandth of a second, but we haven't yet used those rules to describe every move in the 'game' that has been played out over the past 15 billion years.

Curiously, it is relatively easy to describe what happened when the Universe was young, and much harder to describe later events (such as the origin of life). This is because a hot fireball is much simpler than a cool Universe. People are complicated systems, in which many different kinds of atom interact with one another chemically in interesting and subtle ways. But if you heat a person up to even a few thousand degrees, all that complexity is broken down and they disappear in a puff of smoke, which is a much simpler substance. Similarly, the Sun is much simpler than the Earth, and the Big Bang was even simpler than the Sun.

So, even back in the 1940s, Gamow and his colleagues were able to calculate how the Big Bang fireball would have cooled as it expanded. They showed that nuclear reactions in the fireball would have produced a mixture of 25 per cent helium and 75 per cent hydrogen in the gas that emerged – exactly the mixture of hydrogen and helium seen (using spectroscopy) in the oldest stars. And they found (updating the numbers slightly) that about 300,000 years after time zero an important change occurred in the Universe.

Before that time, the Universe was so hot that stable atoms could not exist. There were hydrogen nuclei and helium nuclei (each carrying positive electric charge) and there were electrons (each with negative charge), ricocheting around like balls in a crazy pinball machine, in a hot mixture called a plasma. But as the temperature of the whole Universe fell to about 6,000°C, the positively charged nuclei began to cling on to the negatively charged electrons to make electrically neutral atoms. Electromagnetic radiation, including light, can interact with electrically charged particles. So, before atoms formed, the radiation was also involved in the crazy pinball dance, being bounced around from particle to particle. But when atoms formed, there were no charged particles left for it to interact with, and the radiation streamed uninterrupted through the Universe. It decoupled from the matter, and the Universe became transparent.

It is no coincidence that 6,000°C is roughly the temperature at the surface of the Sun; radiation deeper inside the Sun, where it is hotter, is also bounced around between charged particles, to such an extent that it takes 10 million years to get from the core of the Sun to its surface, following a crazy zig-zag path. It only flies freely out into space when it reaches the point where the temperature is low enough for neutral atoms to begin to form. At the time matter and radiation decoupled, when the Universe was 300,000 years old, the entire Universe was in roughly the same state that the surface of the Sun is in today.

Gamow and his colleagues realized that the radiation from the fireball would still fill the Universe today. But because it must have expanded as the Universe expanded, it would have got a lot colder – in effect, being redshifted to much longer wavelengths. It started out, 300,000 years after time zero, with a temperature of a few thousand degrees; using the general theory of relativity, it is straightforward to calculate how much it has cooled as the Universe has expanded. The answer Gamow's team came up with was that the radiation must have a temperature today of a few degrees on the absolute, or Kelvin scale – the scale on which zero is

−273°C. Radiation with a temperature of 6,000°C corresponds to orange light, like the light from the Sun. Radiation with a temperature of −270°C corresponds to radio waves in the microwave part of the spectrum, like a very cool microwave oven. Gamow and his colleagues made the prediction that the Universe is filled with this radiation, but did not realize that, even in the 1950s, the technology existed to search for it, using radio telescopes.

In the 1960s, microwave radiation with a temperature of 2.7 K (−270.3°C) was found, by accident, by radio astronomers looking for something else entirely. The radiation comes from everywhere on the sky, and it was soon realized that it was the radiation Gamow had predicted, the afterglow of the Big Bang.

The nature of the cosmic background radiation, which has now been studied in great detail by many instruments (including the COBE satellite) is exactly what we expect from the expanding fireball described by the known laws of physics. Those same laws explain the production of hydrogen and helium in the Big Bang (and also how heavier elements, including the oxygen and nitrogen in your body, were made inside stars later in the life of the Universe), how radiation and matter decoupled after 300,000 years, and why we see that cool glow of background radiation today. There is even a developing understanding of how clouds of gas in the expanding Universe could have been held together by gravity, resisting the expansion, contracting and breaking up to make stars, galaxies and clusters of galaxies. By the end of the 1970s, the Big Bang was firmly established as the best understanding of the Universe.

Cosmology Now

But how did it all begin? Where did that seed of the entire Universe, a hot fireball with the density of nuclear matter, come from? Cosmologists have begun to probe that question in recent decades, and have what they think are some pretty good answers. Not as precise and accurate as their understanding of what happened after the first hundred-thousandth of a second, but intelligent speculations that have made even the subject of the origin of the Universe itself, at time zero, part of serious scientific study, no longer solely the preserve of metaphysicians and theologians. Everything I have told you so far is solid scientific fact, as well established as any theory which attempts to describe what happened long ago and far away can be. What I am about to tell you contains an element of speculation and informed guesswork; but, if anything, that makes it even more intriguing.

There are rival versions of the story of the birth of the Universe, and I shall not go into details of all of them here. But there are two particularly intriguing, and closely related, ideas. All you need to understand the first variation on the theme is a little bit of quantum physics, and a little bit of gravity.

The little bit of quantum physics has to do with quantum uncertainty, a phenomenon discovered in the 1920s by the German quantum pioneer Werner Heisenberg. It turns out that in the quantum world there are certain pairs of related physical properties which can never both be precisely determined at the same time. The classic example is the pairing of position and momentum (which, for our purposes, is synonymous with velocity). We are used to thinking of objects in the everyday world (such as snooker balls) being in a certain place and moving in a certain direction at each instant of time. But in the quantum world, an object such as an electron does not behave in this way.

If the position of an electron were precisely known, then it could be moving in any direction at any speed. If the direction and speed with which an electron were moving were precisely known, it would be impossible to say at any instant just where along that path the electron was.

Of course, usually the electron is in a less extreme state, and we can specify both roughly where it is and roughly where it is going; but the more accurately one property is determined, the less precisely the other one is defined.

This is not simply the result of imperfections in our measuring instruments. The uncertainty is built into the laws of physics, so that the electron itself does not 'know' both where it is and where it is going at the same time.

Intriguing though the implications are, this is not the place to go into them. What matters for cosmologists speculating about the birth of the Universe is that there is another pair of these so-called conjugate properties, involving time and energy. It turns out to be impossible to specify the precise energy of a system at a precise time. The more accurately the energy is determined, the more uncertainty there is about exactly when it was determined; the more precise the timing of the determination of the energy, the less certainty there is about the amount of energy.

One astonishing implication of this is that even a region of empty space cannot be said to have zero energy, because that would be a precisely determined amount of energy. Instead, a bubble of energy can flicker into existence out of nothing at all, provided it flickers back out of existence in the time allowed by quantum uncertainty – in effect, before the rest of the Universe has noticed its existence. Because energy and mass are related by Einstein's famous equation $E = mc^2$, this means that for a very brief time even material particles can be created out of nothing at all, provided they disappear very quickly.

It sounds bizarre, but the existence of these so-called virtual particles has a measurable effect on the real particles of the everyday world. In particular, electrically charged particles such as electrons have to be regarded as surrounded by a cloud of virtual particles, and the behaviour of electrons and their interactions with electromagnetic fields can be fully explained only by taking account of the influence of the virtual particles. Each virtual particle exists only for a tiny fraction of a second; but as one disappears another takes its place.

The amount of mass-energy that there is in one of these virtual bubbles of energy determines how long the bubble can survive. The greater the mass-energy, the shorter the lifetime of the bubble – so it is relatively easier to make electrons than it is to make protons, which are much heavier than electrons.

This is where the little bit of gravity comes into the story. It may surprise you to learn that the total energy of the entire Universe may be precisely zero. This is hard to believe, if you think in terms of all those stars and galaxies, containing vast amounts of mass, and therefore vast amounts of mc^2. But all those stars and galaxies are held together by gravity; and gravity turns out to have negative energy. Not just negative energy, but precisely the amount of negative energy required to cancel out the mc^2 in all the mass in the Universe.

The full details are best appreciated using the general theory of relativity; but there is a nice physical way to picture how this happens. To start, you have to get hold of the idea that when a cloud of material shrinks under the influence of gravity, gravitational energy is released. This is how a collapsing cloud of gas and dust in space forms a star – it shrinks, and the gravitational energy that is released as a result gets turned into heat, so the collapsing cloud gets hotter. When it is hot enough in the middle (about 15 million degrees centigrade), nuclear reactions begin, and these provide the energy which stops the star collapsing any further, as long as it has nuclear fuel to burn.

The second part of the picture comes from imagining all the material in such a cloud of gas, or in a star, broken down into its component atoms, and dispersed outward in all directions to infinite distance. Because gravity obeys an inverse square law, the strength with which these particles at infinite distance affect one another is zero – the force that matters is proportional to 1 divided by (infinity squared), and that is definitely zero. This means that there is no gravitational energy in the system. But if the cloud of widely dispersed particles is allowed to fall together gradually (obviously, it would need some kind of a nudge to get it going), as it does so energy will be released. You start out with zero energy, and then some energy is taken away. So what you end up with is less than zero.

If you carry the appropriate calculation through fully, using Einstein's equations, you find that if the cloud of particles has a mass m, by the time it has contracted to a point it has given out precisely mc^2 in energy. In other words, the gravitational energy associated with a mass m is $-mc^2$, equal and opposite to its mass energy.

If you find this hard to swallow, you are in good company. During the Second World War, George Gamow worked as a consultant to the US government. One of his jobs was to take a briefcase full of papers up to Albert Einstein, in Princeton, every couple of weeks. The papers were full of crackpot ideas from inventors who claimed to have devised new wonder weapons that would shorten the war; Einstein, a former patent officer (and a good one), seemed the ideal man to find the flaws in their arguments. The kind of calculation about gravity that we have just described, showing that a star born at a point contains zero energy overall, was first carried out by one of Gamow's colleagues, Pascual Jordan. In his autobiography *My World Line*, Gamow tells how he was walking with Einstein one day, from Einstein's home to the Institute for Advanced Study in Princeton. Gamow casually mentioned to Einstein that Jordon had calculated that a star could be created out of nothing at all, since if all the matter appeared at a point its negative gravitational energy would be numerically equal to its positive rest mass energy.

'Einstein stopped in his tracks,' Gamow tells us, 'and, since we were crossing a street, several cars had to stop to avoid running us down.'

This idea that stopped Einstein dead in his tracks has now been applied to the whole Universe, not to a single star; some cosmologists see this as the answer to the origin of the Universe itself. It could have been created out of nothing at all, as a quantum fluctuation with zero energy overall. And if a quantum fluctuation lives longer if it has less energy, then a quantum fluctuation with zero energy could, in the words of the song, live forever.

The idea surfaced in the 1970s, but was not taken seriously at the time, because there is one big snag. Obviously, neither the Universe nor a star could be created 'at a point' (a singularity), but that is where you hope quantum gravity will come to your aid, and you assume instead that it might have been created in a state slightly larger than a mathematical point, as a kind of quantum seed, but still much, much smaller than the nucleus of an atom. If you imagine all of the matter in the Universe, all those tens of billions of galaxies, packed together in such a quantum seed, one thing is blindingly obvious. The seed will have an absolutely enormously strong gravitational field, and gravity doesn't blow things apart, it makes them collapse.

At first sight, it seemed that a quantum fluctuation on the scale of the Universe would be as short-lived as any other quantum fluctuation, crushing itself out of existence almost as soon as it was born. But then, in the 1980s, cosmologists found a way to take such a quantum seed and blow it up into the kind of expanding Universe we see around us. The trick is called inflation.

One of the most impressive things about inflation is that the physics behind it comes not from cosmology, but from particle physics. Physicists working at the other extreme of the scale from cosmology, the world of the very small, not the very large, found this mechanism as a natural consequence of their efforts to unite the mathematical description of the forces of nature in one package, a so-called grand unified theory, or GUT.

Like the agreement between the measured ages of the oldest stars and the calculated age of the Universe, this meshing of ideas from the particle world and the world of cosmology is taken as a strong indication that physicists really are on the right track with their theories of how the Universe works. At the end of the twentieth century, particle physics has become part of cosmology, as the theory of the forces and particles of nature has gone beyond the point at which it can be tested by experiments in even the largest accelerators on Earth. The theory deals with energies and temperatures so extreme that in the entire history of the Universe they have existed only in the first split second of the life of the Universe, the interval between the appearance of a quantum seed of superhot energy at superhigh density, and the time, just 0.0001 of a second later, when everything was at the density of an atomic nucleus. The very early Universe is the only laboratory in which the most extreme ideas of particle theory can be tested, and it is tested by seeing (that is, by calculating) how the physics described by those ideas would have shaped the evolution of the Universe, and comparing the predictions of those theories with what we see around us in the real Universe.

Gravity is still the odd one out on this picture, because we do not yet have a complete quantum theory of gravity. And the very beginning of the Universe – the beginning of time – is a mystery. There is a kind of quantum of time, the smallest unit of time that has any meaning, which is called the Planck time, in honour of the quantum pioneer Max Planck. It is ludicrously small – 10^{-43} of a second, which is written in decimal notation as a decimal point followed by 42 zeroes and a 1. The best we can say at present is that the quantum seed from which the Universe has grown came into existence – was born, if you like – with an age of 10^{-43} seconds, and with gravity already established as an independent force. The size of this primordial seed would have been 10^{-33} centimetres, a distance known as the Planck length. So why didn't gravity crush the seed out of existence?

The answer offered by the particle physicists concerns the behaviour of the other forces of nature. There are three of them – electromagnetism, which is a familiar force in the everyday world, and two forces which only operate on a scale smaller than the size of an atomic nucleus, the so-called strong and weak nuclear forces. The weak force is responsible for radioactivity, and the strong force is what holds atomic nuclei together. According to grand unified theory, under the extreme conditions that existed just after the Universe was born all three of these forces were equivalent in strength to one another, and behaved in the same way, as long-range forces. As the Universe cooled, this symmetry was lost, and the forces split apart to take on the characteristics that we know today. The process is called a phase transition, by analogy with the kind of change that occurs when a liquid (such as water) freezes into a solid (in this case, ice).

When water vapour condenses to make liquid water, or when liquid water freezes to make ice, it gives up energy in the form of latent heat, because the state it is changing into stores less energy than the state it is changing from. In an analogous way, phase transitions in the very early Universe released energy, which gave an enormous outward push to the quantum seed, acting as a kind of antigravity and expanding the Universe vastly in a very small interval of time.

The key feature of this expansion is that it was exponential. This means that, while the inflation lasted, in each split second the Universe expanded twice as much as in the previous split second, assuming each split second was the same size. This is like walking down a road in some kind of super seven-league boots. The first step you take covers, say, a metre; the second steps covers two metres; the third step covers four metres; and so on. At that rate, the tenth step would cover more than a kilometre, and the hundredth step would cover more than 10^{30} kilometres, which is more than 10^{17} light years. Such exponential doubling very quickly runs away with itself.

According to one version of inflation, each doubling in the very early Universe took 10^{-34} sec (some versions of inflation suggest even more rapid doubling). But the whole process may have lasted for only 10^{-32} sec. It sounds as if it were over in less than the blink of an eye, and it was; but in that brief interval there was time for a hundred doublings. A hundred doublings means that what you end up with is 2^{100} times bigger than what you started with. In very round terms, it means that if you start with a quantum seed about 10^{20} times smaller than a proton, you end up with a sphere 10 centimetres across, about the size of a grapefruit. At that point, the exponential inflation stops, and the expansion becomes no more than a coast, just as a rocket fired upward stops accelerating when it has used up all its fuel and can only coast upward, gradually being slowed by the tug of gravity; but, once inflation has done its work, the Universe is left expanding so rapidly that gravity will take hundreds of billions of years to halt the expansion. What we see today is a more or less linear expansion, the coasting era, in which each step down the road takes you the same distance as the one before (in fact, each step takes you a tiny bit less far than the one before, because gravity is gradually slowing the expansion). And that is how, many physicists think, a quantum seed smaller than a proton but containing all the mass-energy of all the visible Universe may have got blown up into a grapefruit-sized Universe experiencing a Big Bang. Astonishing though it may seem, this is the new standard model of the early Universe, which forms the basis of most current research in cosmology. But that still leaves intriguing questions for the next generation of cosmologists to tackle.

Into the Future

If you don't like the idea of the primordial quantum seed appearing out of nothing at all, there is another way in which it could have been born, one which some cosmologists find even more appealing. This is the idea that our Universe is just one among many, and that there was no unique 'beginning', just an interconnected web of universes extending forever in both time and space. The way to get a handle on this idea is to think about what may happen inside a black hole in our Universe. Now, we are entering deeper into the realms of informed speculation, and some of the ideas I will discuss are by no means fully worked out scientific theories. They are not even, strictly speaking, predictions. Instead, they are signposts into the future, pointing the way for researchers who may develop those fully worked out theories in the decades ahead.

A black hole is a place where matter collapses indefinitely, under the influence of gravity, towards a singularity. It is a mirror-image in time of the way in which the Universe expands outwards from something close to a singularity, and is described by exactly the same equations, but with the direction of time reversed. We can only say that the matter falling into a black hole heads 'towards' a singularity, not into a singularity, because just as with the birth of the Universe we expect quantum gravity to become important very close to the singularity, at about the Planck length.

Without a complete quantum theory of gravity, it is impossible to say exactly what happens in the heart of a black hole. But two researchers based in the United States, Lee Smolin and Andrei Linde, have independently come up with the idea that some kind of 'bounce' may occur, turning the collapse into an expansion, and shunting the material falling in towards the singularity sideways into a new set of dimensions – its own space, and its own time. It is as if the black hole is the entrance to a tunnel through what the science fiction writers call hyperspace. Less elegantly, the cosmologists call such a tunnel a wormhole, and suggest that it connects to another region of spacetime (another universe), in which the matter from the black hole blasts outward in just the same way that matter burst out from close to a singularity at the birth of our own Universe.

And they do mean *just* the same way. Remember that if you start from a singularity, negative gravitational energy cancels out the positive mass energy of whatever it is that comes out. So you could make a black hole with, say, ten times as much mass as there is in our Sun, and what would emerge at the other end of the wormhole would not be a tiny universe containing only ten solar masses of matter, but a full-sized universe, containing perhaps as much matter as our own – or more. The few solar masses that go into the black hole in the first place are simply a catalyst, needed to trigger the formation of the singularity.

If this can happen to matter that falls into a black hole in our Universe (and all the evidence is that it can), then our Universe could have been born in the same way, from matter falling into a black hole in some other region of spacetime. It is possible that the overall structure of spacetime (sometimes called the 'Metaverse') is a series of interconnected bubbles, resembling froth on a glass of beer, with no beginning and no end.

Another way to picture this is to go back to the analogy between the expanding Universe and the skin of an expanding balloon. A baby universe would correspond to a piece pinched off from the skin of 'our' balloon, making a little blister which then begins expanding in its own right, with new baby universes budding off from its own skin, and so on indefinitely.

Strange though these ideas are, and they are admittedly speculative, they represent the serious speculations of respectable cosmologists today, and they are about as well developed as the idea of the Big Bang itself was in the 1940s. As we stand today, it seems clear that some form of inflation happened to put the Universe into the state that is generally referred to as the Big Bang; but nobody can say for sure just what it was that got inflation going. What we do know is that inflation is hugely successful in explaining the overall appearance of the Universe today.

There are many curious features about inflation. For a start, it seems to take place faster than the speed of light. Even light takes a little over 3 billionths of a second (3×10^{-9} sec) to cross a single metre, but inflation expands a region many times smaller than a proton to become a sphere 10 centimetres across in only about 10^{-32} sec. This is possible because nothing is moving through space – space itself is stretching, like a stretching rubber sheet, and taking matter along for the ride.

This rapid expansion predicts many features that are seen in the real Universe, notably its extreme uniformity. The Universe is, in spite of the presence of galaxies and clusters of galaxies, a remarkably uniform place, and this is most clearly seen by looking at the background radiation, which tells us what the Universe was like 300,000 years after the Big Bang. Remember that the average temperature of the background radiation is 2.7 Kelvin. COBE found that there are tiny variations in the temperature of this radiation coming from different parts of the sky, amounting to fluctuations of about thirty-millionths of a degree. That is an indication of just how smooth and uniform the Universe was at that time; the irregularities were no bigger than one part in a hundred thousand, or 0.001 per cent (and, incidentally, those fluctuations are just big enough to have grown into clusters of galaxies in the time available).

This uniformity in the early Universe is explained because everything we can see today has come from such a tiny seed, a quantum fluctuation so small that there was no room inside it for any irregularities. Even better, the ripples in the background radiation revealed by COBE have exactly the right structure to be explained as coming from further quantum fluctuations that occurred during the era of inflation, that got frozen in and stretched hugely by the inflation process, but originally occurred when what is now the entire visible Universe was something like 10^{-25} centimetres across – 100 million times bigger than the Planck length. All the irregularity in the Universe today (and that includes us) has, on this picture, grown from these tiny quantum ripples.

Inflation can also explain another remarkable feature of the Universe, the fact that it sits very close to the dividing line between eternal expansion and eventual recollapse. The analogy with the rocket being fired upward from the surface of the Earth comes in useful once again here. Inflation accelerated the expansion of the Universe, but when inflation stopped the expansion began to coast, slowing down under the tug of gravity. In much the same way, a rocket accelerates upward until all its fuel is gone, and then coasts, slowing as it is tugged back by gravity. If the rocket is going fast enough when it runs out of fuel, it will escape from the Earth and go out into space. But if it has less than this critical escape velocity when it stops accelerating, gravity will eventually halt its rise and then bring the rocket crashing down to Earth.

The Universe faces a similar pair of possibilities. If it is expanding fast enough, then gravity can never halt the expansion, which will continue for ever. If it is expanding at less than the critical speed, gravity will one day halt the expansion, then reverse it, eventually crushing everything back into a state like the Big Bang from which the Universe emerged – a Big Crunch, which might conceivably 'bounce' into a new Big Bang. And if the Universe is expanding at exactly the critical speed, gravity will just be able to halt the expansion, but will take for ever to do so.

Which fate the Universe faces depends on only two things – how fast it is expanding (which can be measured from the redshift) and how much matter there is in the Universe trying to pull itself together by gravity. If the Universe will expand for ever, it is said to be 'open'; if it will one day recollapse, it is said to be 'closed'. And if it sits exactly on the dividing line between being open and being closed it is said to be 'flat'. The names come from the way space itself is curved by gravity in the different scenarios. A closed universe is the three-dimensional equivalent of the closed surface of a sphere, like the surface of the Earth. An open universe extends for ever, curving outward like the open surface of a mountain pass, or a saddle. And a flat universe is the three-dimensional equivalent of the flat surface of a piece of paper.

Since we know how fast the Universe is expanding, the only thing we need to measure to determine its fate is how much mass it contains. Fortunately, because the Universe is so uniform, we don't actually have to add up all the mass, but just find the density in a representative large volume of space (large enough, that is, to include several clusters of galaxies). The critical density needed to make the Universe flat can be calculated with great precision – all that is needed is somewhere between 10^{-29} and 2×10^{-32} grams per cubic centimetre, averaged over the entire Universe. Since a single hydrogen atom weighs 1.7×10^{-24} grams, this means that on average, for the Universe to be flat, it must contain a single hydrogen atom in every hundred thousand cubic centimetres of space, or ten hydrogen atoms in every cubic metre. If all the bright stuff in all the stars and galaxies we can see were smeared out evenly through the Universe, it would contribute only about a hundredth of this critical density – but that is not the whole story.

The density of the Universe is usually described in terms of a parameter called omega, in such a way that if omega is 1 the Universe is flat, if omega is less than 1 the Universe is open, and if omega is greater than 1 the Universe is closed. It is difficult to measure omega precisely, mainly because we cannot see all of the matter in the Universe. Obviously, as well as the bright stars and galaxies there must be some dark stuff, but how much? To some extent, we can estimate how much dark stuff there is by studying the way galaxies move. In a cluster of galaxies, the spread of redshifts tells us how quickly the galaxies are moving relative to one another. The only thing that can hold such a cluster together and stop it flying apart is gravity, and the faster the galaxies are moving the stronger the gravitational pull needed to hold the swarm together – which means more dark matter in the cluster to provide the gravity. These studies show that there is at least ten times as much dark matter in large clusters of galaxies as there is bright stuff; what we can see is only the tip of the proverbial iceberg.

So there is no doubt that the Universe contains at least 10 per cent of the critical density of matter needed to make it flat, but even allowing for the possibility of more dark matter that has not yet been detected it seems extremely unlikely that it contains more than the critical density. At first sight, this looks like one of those ropy cosmological estimates – an uncertainty of a factor of 10 in the measurement of a key cosmological number! Even worse than the uncertainty of a factor of 2 in estimates of the age of the Universe. But, like those age estimates, on closer inspection it turns out that this is a very significant discovery.

Unless you can think of some good reason otherwise, it would seem that the Universe could have emerged from the Big Bang with any expansion velocity, and there would then be no reason for the density of the Universe today to be anywhere near the crticial value – which is the only cosmological density that has any special significance. It could have been one-thousandth, or one-millionth of the critical value – or a million times as big.

You can see just how truly remarkable the actual measured density of the Universe is by looking at how the relationship between density and expansion rate changes as the Universe expands. Imagine an open universe emerging from the Big Bang with nearly the critical density appropriate at that time. An open universe expands relatively rapidly, at more than the critical velocity, so it thins quickly, and the density drops rapidly, reducing the effectiveness of gravity in slowing the expansion and increasing the discrepancy between the density needed to close the universe and its expansion rate. As the universe expands and the density decreases, at succeeding epochs the density will be further and further away from the critical value appropriate at those epochs. The same thing happens in the opposite direction if the universe starts out from the Big Bang with even a little more than the critical density. Gravity slows the expansion of the universe rapidly, so that even though the density decreases as the universe expands, the expansion rate decreases more, and the grip of gravity is relatively stronger in succeeding epochs, so the universe becomes more and more obviously closed.

So if the density of the real Universe today is within a factor of 10 of the critical value, even though the Universe has been expanding for some 15 billion years, further back in time (closer to the Big Bang) it must have been closer to the critical value. How close? If you carry the calculation through accurately, you find that at the end of the era of inflation, at the beginning of the Big Bang the Universe must have been flat to a precision of 1 part in 10^{60}. Far from the present measurements of the density parameter, to an accuracy of a factor of 10, being an embarrassment to cosmologists, this means that the value of the density parameter in the Big Bang is actually the most accurate observationally determined number in the whole of science!

Because the critical density itself is the only density that has any special significance, while 10 per cent of the critical density certainly does not have any special significance, this remarkable fact encourages many cosmologists to speculate that the Universe does indeed have precisely the critical density, and is indeed flat.

This idea is saved from being mere speculation by inflation. One of the side effects of inflation is that whatever the curvature of space you start out with, you end up with a very nearly flat universe. Imagine starting out with something like the shrivelled, wrinkly surface of a prune. When a prune is placed in water, it swells up, and all the wrinkles are smoothed out to make a round surface – but still one that is definitely closed, in the sense used by cosmologists. But now imagine doubling the size of that prune a hundred times or more, the equivalent of the inflation that happened in the very early Universe. A hundred doublings would take a sphere a couple of centimetres across and blow it up to a diameter of more than a thousand billion light years, roughly a hundred times the size of the visible Universe. You would still have a surface that was technically closed, forming a sphere; but it would be so huge that any creatures living on the surface of the sphere would be unaware of the curvature, and every test they could devise would show that the surface was flat. Inflation theory suggests that our Universe is like that. It may actually be just closed (or, perhaps, just open), but the actual value of the density parameter omega is so close to 1 that no human observations will ever be able to measure the difference.

Because there is still no direct evidence for the presence of all the dark matter that would be needed to make the Universe flat, some cunning cosmologists have devised variations on the inflationary theme that would allow a universe to emerge from inflation with slightly less than the critical density. Although the ingenuity of these ideas is admirable, the wise money today is betting on the likelihood that the Universe really is flat. And this has led to a wave of experimental activity and new links between the cosmologists and the particle physicists, as they join forces to search for the dark matter that makes up the bulk of the Universe.

The bright stuff that we can see in stars and galaxies makes up only about 1 per cent of the critical density. The way galaxies move in clusters shows that there is at least ten times as much dark stuff, but even this still only adds up to about 10 per cent of the critical density. For the Universe to be flat, there must be ten times more dark matter, and there is independent evidence for this from the way whole clusters of galaxies are seen to be streaming across space, tugged on by some invisible mass. All this means that all the bright stuff we see in stars and galaxies is outweighed by dark matter 100 to 1. The reason why the particle physicists are excited by this possibility is that our understanding of the Big Bang tells us that most of this dark matter cannot be in the same form as the stuff that stars, galaxies, planets and people are made of.

One of the great triumphs of the standard Big Bang model, dating from the 1960s and resting on the secure foundation of everyday physics involving no conditions more extreme than those of nuclear matter today, is that it predicts the mixture of materials emerging from the Big Bang to form the first stars – roughly 75 per cent hydrogen, 25 per cent helium, and the merest smattering of other light elements such as deuterium. These calculations were first carried out approximately by George Gamow and his colleagues in the 1940s, and with great accuracy by Fred Hoyle and his colleagues in the 1960s. The agreement between what the theory predicts and what observers see in old stars, which are presumably made of primordial material, is so striking that there can be no doubt that the Big Bang is a good description of what went on in the Universe from about 0.0001 sec after time zero to about 4 minutes after time zero (of course, the agreement between observation and theory is not perfect, but the differences suggest that no more than fine-tuning is needed to make it better).

But there is another implication of all this. The calculations depend on the rate at which nuclear reactions were going on in the Big Bang, chiefly converting hydrogen into helium. This depended on the rate at which the Universe was expanding and cooling (which we know from winding back the observed expansion, and from the temperature of the background radiation today), the temperature, and the density of the material taking part in those nuclear reactions. Nuclei are made of protons and neutrons, and protons and neutrons are members of a family of particles called baryons, so nuclear matter (and, by extension, everyday matter including the stuff you and I are made of, the

Earth, Sun and everything we can see in the Universe) is called baryonic matter. The calculations of how nuclear reactions went on in the Big Bang, which agree so well with observations of the composition of the oldest stars, say that the density of baryonic matter emerging from the Big Bang was no more than enough to provide a few per cent of the critical density needed to make the Universe closed today. Even by pushing all the numbers to the limit, the amount of baryonic matter in the Universe today cannot be more than 10 per cent of the critical density. Five per cent is regarded by most astronomers as a much more realistic upper limit.

Because we are made of baryons, for many years astronomers were influenced by a kind of unconscious baryon chauvinism into assuming that this meant that the *total* density of the Universe could not be more than a few per cent of the critical density. It was only when studies of the way clusters of galaxies move showed the influence of large amounts of dark matter in the Universe, and inflation suggested that the Universe must be extremely flat, that, in the 1980s, the penny dropped, and cosmologists began to investigate the possibility that there might be other kinds of matter in the Universe, non-baryonic dark stuff which did not participate in those crucial nuclear reactions during the Big Bang.

As soon as they took on board the idea of non-baryonic dark matter, astronomers realized that it could help to solve one of the great puzzles of the Universe – how galaxies formed. Although the dark stuff (or at least most of it) had to be non-baryonic, it would still interact with other matter by gravity. In the expanding Universe, if the density today really were only 10 per cent of the critical density, it would be hard (indeed, impossible) to see how structures as large as galaxies and clusters of galaxies could have formed from primordial fluctuations, by tugging clouds of gas together gravitationally, even in the 15 billion years that have elasped since the Big Bang. But adding in ten times as much non-baryonic dark matter provides just the right amount of extra gravitational pull to do the job.

The way galaxies would have formed under these circumstances can be simulated in a computer, and the simulations look very like the real Universe. Again, as with the match between the composition of the oldest stars and the calculations of the mix of baryons that emerged from the Big Bang, the agreement between calculation and observation is not perfect. But, again, the discrepancies are so small as to suggest that only fine-tuning is needed to make the agreement better.

In order to make their discussions as general as possible, the cosmologists usually make no assumptions about just what the dark matter might be, but refer to it in descriptive terms. There are two forms that the dark matter might take, assuming that it is made up of particles produced in the Big Bang and spread more or less evenly through the Universe. Hot dark matter (HDM) would consist of very light particles, much lighter even than an electron, which stream through the Universe at high speeds, close to the speed of light. Cold dark matter (CDM) would consist of more massive particles, each perhaps even more massive than a proton, which travel through the Universe at low speeds. Together, both kinds of dark matter are sometimes referred to as WIMPs, a rather tortuous acronym for weakly interacting massive particles, a name intended to indicate the key properties of the particles, that they have mass (and therefore interact with other matter gravitationally) but scarcely interact in any other way at all.

All of this was great news for the particle physicists, because those same grand unified theories that indicate the possibility of inflation also predict that there must be as yet unidentified varieties of non-baryonic particles in the Universe – both CDM and HDM. Once again, both cosmology, the study of the Universe on the largest scale, and particle physics, the study of the world of the very small, are suggesting the same thing about the Universe – in this case, that dark matter, in the form of WIMPs, should exist.

The physicists already knew about one kind of particle that could contribute to the non-baryonic dark matter. They are called neutrinos, and they are involved in nuclear reactions, so their presence is allowed for in calculations of the reactions that took place in the Big Bang. But it was originally thought that neutrinos had zero mass, so although the Universe was known to have been full of them, it had been thought that they had no gravitational influence, and could not contribute to slowing the expansion of the Universe.

Neutrinos are extremely reluctant to interact with baryonic matter, even though they are produced in profusion in nuclear reactions. Their existence was first predicted by theorists in the early 1930s, but they are so difficult to detect that it wasn't until the mid-1950s, a quarter of a century later, that they were first identified, pouring out from a nuclear reactor at the Savannah River site in the United States. We now know that the Universe is filled with neutrinos, and a great flood of them washes through us from the Sun, which is, of course, supported by the energy released by nuclear reactions going on in its heart. But they will do you no harm; neutrinos pass through a human body, or even the solid Earth, more easily than light passes through a pane of clear glass. If a beam of neutrinos like those produced inside the Sun were to travel through solid lead for a distance of a thousand parsecs (more than 3,000 light years), only half of them would be captured by the nuclei of lead atoms along the way.

This reluctance of neutrinos to interact explains why even in the 1980s nobody could be quite sure whether or not they have a tiny mass. The electron is the lightest component of ordinary atomic matter, and weighs in with half of one-thousandth of the mass of a proton – so light that its gravitational influence on the Universe is usually lumped in with the protons and neutrons. If neutrinos do have mass, experiments show that it could be no more than about one-hundredth of 1 per cent of the mass of the electron, which for most purposes can indeed be regarded as zero. But there are a *lot* of neutrinos in the Universe, several billion for every baryon, left over from the Big Bang. So many, in fact, that, as astronomers realized in the 1980s, even if each one has only a tiny mass, their overall gravitational influence could greatly exceed the influence of all the baryons put together (but don't imagine that the neutrinos pouring out from stars like the Sun are adding to the density of the Universe; those neutrinos are made out of the mass energy of the stars themselves, helping to compensate for the loss in mass of the stars as mc^2 is converted into E).

Neutrinos are the archetypal form of hot dark matter, zipping through the Universe (including right through stars, planets and people) at close to the speed of light. But computer simulations show that, if all the dark matter were in the form of neutrinos (or any kind of HDM), galaxies and clusters of galaxies like the ones we see in the real Universe could not form, because the fast-moving particles would tend to blow structures apart as they started to form, like a cannonball demolishing a wall made of loosely piled bricks. This is not a problem today, because baryonic matter is spread fairly thinly across the Universe, and is almost transparent to neutrinos; but it would have been a problem during the first few seconds of the Big Bang, when the density of the Universe was very high (greater than the density inside a star today), and the neutrinos would have smoothed out any irregularities imprinted by inflation.

The computer simulations show that the best representation of the pattern of galaxies and clusters of galaxies seen in the real Universe comes from calculations in which there is a mixture of roughly one-third hot dark matter, two-thirds cold dark matter, and a smattering (a few per cent) of baryonic matter. Slow-moving, massive CDM particles tended to clump together gravitationally very early in the life of the Universe, producing gravitational 'pot-holes' which attract baryonic matter. The baryonic matter (mainly hydrogen and helium) falls into the pot-holes under the influence of gravity, and eventually forms galaxies. But if all the dark matter were in the form of CDM, this process would be too efficient – the resulting pattern of galaxies and clusters of galaxies would be more concentrated than we see in the real Universe (of course, the computer simulations do not reproduce the actual pattern of clusters seen today, but a general pattern in which it is possible to measure features such as the numbers of clusters of different sizes, and their separation from one another, and compare these with the equivalent features of the pattern of galaxies in the real Universe). So the favoured model today is mixed dark matter, or MDM.

The dramatic implication of all this is that roughly two-thirds of all the matter in the Universe is not just dark, but is in the form of varieties of particles (perhaps just one kind of particle, perhaps several) that have never been detected on Earth, but which are predicted to exist (and were predicted even before astronomers realized the need for dark matter in the Universe) by particle physics theory. The particle physicists have no qualms about describing the properties of these hypothetical particles in detail, and giving them names, such as axions and gravitinos.

The main problem is that different versions of the grand unified theories predict different varieties of dark matter particles, so there are more candidates than we need to do the job of flattening the Universe. But the positive side of this is that, if some of these particles can be identified and their properties measured, that will tell us which versions of the GUTs are correct, and will eliminate the other possibilities.

Catching a CDM WIMP is not easy, because, like neutrinos, they are reluctant to interact with everyday matter. But, because they have much more mass than a neutrino, and fill the Universe, it may not be all that difficult, either. One kind of possible CDM particle would have a mass comparable to that of a proton, and on average there would be one such particle in every 5 cubic centimetres of space, if the Universe is flat. I don't just mean every 5 cubic centimetres of 'empty' space, but every 5 cubic centimetres in the Universe, including inside the Sun, and passing through the room you are sitting in and through your body as you read these words. Each litre of air that you breathe contains a few hundred WIMPs, on this picture.

The way to detect such a WIMP is to monitor the occasional collision between the CDM particle and an ordinary atom – strictly speaking, the nucleus of an atom. A WIMP detector (and there are several now operating around the world) consists of a lump of material, a small crystal cooled to a temperature of a few Kelvin (about the temperature of the background radiation), which is monitored for any sudden rise in temperature caused by the impact of a WIMP, converting the energy of motion of the WIMP into heat. The impact of the kind of CDM WIMP I have described will raise the temperature of the crystal by a few thousandths of a degree.

Nobody has yet reported the detection of such an event, but it could happen any time in the next few years. Physicists interested in finding the two-thirds of the Universe that has not yet been seen are even now busily searching for it, not with the aid of giant telescopes peering outward into space, but with the aid of small, supercooled crystals being monitored in underground laboratories, far from any potential source of interference.

And there is another way to search for dark matter. The distribution of matter in the very early Universe, the fireball of the Big Bang itself, must have left an imprint on the cosmic microwave background which still fills the Universe today. The detailed structure of these ripples in the background radiation depends on how much matter there was in the Universe at that time (and therefore, of course, on how much matter there is in the Universe still). This structure is on a finer scale than the instruments on the COBE satellite could detect, but its structure can be predicted by different versions of cosmological theory, with different amounts, and different kinds, of dark matter. The next generation of satellites designed to probe the background radiation will be launched in the early years of the twenty-first century, and should soon be able to measure the density of the Universe to an accuracy of 1 per cent. By the year 2010, we will know, for sure, exactly how much dark matter there is, and what proportion of it could only be accounted for by the presence of WIMPs. There is a very real race on today between the astronomers searching for traces of WIMPs, and the particle physicists searching for WIMPs themselves.

Those next-generation satellites will also be able to measure the Hubble Constant to an equivalent accuracy, providing the answers to questions that cosmologists have worried over for decades. Within twenty years, it might seem as if cosmology, as envisaged in the 1960s and 1970s, had been completed, with every *i* dotted and every *t* crossed. But don't think that this will be the end of this branch of science. Already, a few informed speculators are laying down markers for the way things may develop further into the twenty-first century. The most intriguing of these ideas comes from Lee Smolin, who has developed the concept of baby universes, being 'born' (or budded off) from their parents through black holes, to suggest that a form of Darwinian evolution may be at work as this process unfolds. He suggests that there may be slight variations in the laws of physics from one generation of universes to the next, mutations which allow universes to compete with one another for the opportunity to expand and grow, and to make more baby universes, in the immensity of multi-dimensional spacetime.

This idea, a marriage between the Einsteinian theory of relativity and the Darwinian theory of natural selection, is far from being widely accepted, and causes irritation to many cosmologists. It may turn out to be wrong. But it is likely to provide a paradigm which will encourage astronomers to think up new tests and ways to probe the Universe, and even by proving it wrong, those tests would undoubtedly give new insights into how the Universe works. If they proved it right, it would be the biggest revolution in science since Copernicus displaced the Earth from the centre of the Universe.

This is the cutting edge of cosmology today, where informed speculation combines with observation and experiment to improve our understanding of the Universe. But I don't want to leave you with speculation, no matter how respectable. Instead, I want to leave you with solidly established fact, the standard model of the Big Bang, which describes the evolution of the Universe from a time one-hundred-thousandth of a second after time zero. There is nothing speculative in the summary that follows, describing the first 300,000 years in the life of the Universe – that is, the epoch immediately *after* the first ten-thousandth of a second. The science behind this understanding of the early stages in the life of the Universe is arguably the greatest achievement of the human intellect, and it is almost as remarkable that it can be summed up in a few hundred words. As Albert Einstein once said, 'the eternal mystery of the world is its comprehensibility . . . the fact that it is comprehensible is a miracle'.

The Great Achievement

The standard model of the Big Bang tells the story of everything that has happened since 0.0001 (10^{-4}) of a second after the moment of creation. At that time, the temperature of the Universe was 10^{12}K (1,000 billion degrees) and the density was the density of nuclear matter, 10^{14} grams per cubic centimetre (1 gram per cubic centimetre is the density of water).

Under these conditions, the photons (particles of light) of the 'background' radiation carry so much energy that they are interchangeable with particles, in line with Einstein's equation $E = mc^2$. Photons create pairs of particles and antiparticles, such as electron–positron pairs, proton– antiproton pairs, and neutron–antineutron pairs, and these pairs annihilate one another to make energetic photons in a constant interchange of energy. There were also many neutrinos present in the fireball. Because of a tiny asymmetry in the way the fundamental interactions work, slightly more particles were produced than antiparticles – about a billion and one particles for every billion antiparticles.

When the Universe cooled to the point where photons no longer had the energy to make protons and neutrons, all the paired particles and antiparticles annihilated, and the one in a billion particles left over settled down as stable matter.

One-hundredth of a second after time zero, with the temperature down to 100 billion K (10^{11} K), only the lighter electron–positron pairs still interacted in the dance with radiation. Protons and neutrons had settled out of the maelstrom. At that time, there were as many neutrons as protons, but as time passed interactions with energetic electrons and positrons shifted the balance steadily in favour of protons. One-tenth of a second after time zero, the temperature was down to 30 billion K, and there were only thirty-eight neutrons for every sixty-two protons. About a third of a second after time zero, neutrinos ceased to interact with ordinary matter, except through gravity and the ordinary kinetic effect of collisions.

By the time the Universe had cooled to 10^{10} K (10 billion K), 1.1 seconds after time zero, its density was down to just 380,000 times the density of water, and the balance between protons and neutrons had shifted further, with twenty-four neutrons for every seventy-six protons. By the time the Universe had cooled to 3 billion K, 13.8 seconds after time zero, nuclei of deuterium, each containing one proton and one neutron, began to form, but were soon knocked apart by collisions with other particles. Only 17 per cent of the nuclear particles (nucleons) were now left in the form of neutrons.

Three minutes and two seconds after time zero, the Universe had cooled to 1 billion K, only seventy times hotter than the centre of the Sun is today. The proportion of neutrons was down to 14 per cent, but they were saved from disappearing entirely from the scene because the temperature had at last fallen to the point where nuclei of deuterium and helium could be formed and stick together in spite of collisions with other particles.

It was at this epoch, during the fourth minute after time zero, that the reactions outlined by Gamow and his colleagues in the 1940s, and refined by Fred Hoyle and others in the 1960s, took place, locking up the remaining neutrons in helium nuclei. The proportion of the total mass of nucleons converted into helium is twice the abundance of neutrons at the time, because each nucleus of helium (helium-4) contains two protons as well as two neutrons. Four minutes after time zero, the process was complete, with just under 25 per cent of the nuclear material converted into helium, and the rest left behind as lone protons – hydrogen nuclei.

A little more than half an hour after time zero, all of the positrons in the Universe had annihilated with almost all of the electrons – again with one in a billion left over, matching the number of protons – to produce the background radiation proper. The temperature was down to 300 million K, and the density was only 10 per cent of that of water. But the Universe was still too hot for stable atoms to form; as soon as a nucleus latches on to an electron under those conditions, the electron is knocked away by an energetic photon of the background radiation.

This interaction between electrons and photons continued for 300,000 years, until the Universe had cooled to 6,000 K (roughly the temperature at the surface of the Sun) and the photons were becoming too weak to knock electrons off atoms. At this point (actually, over the next few hundred thousand years) the background radiation decoupled, and had no more significant interaction with matter. But by this time the gravitational influence of all the matter in the Universe had built on the tiny irregularities present from the early stages of the Big Bang, tugging the hydrogen and helium into great clouds that left their imprint on the background radiation, and which would one day collapse to form clusters of galaxies. The Big Bang was over, and the Universe was left to expand relatively quietly, cooling as it does so, and expanding ever more slowly as gravity tries to pull it back together.

2 Religion

FELIPE FERNÁNDEZ-ARMESTO

Introduction

'All the old religions are discredited' in the fourth millennium, as Arthur C. Clarke imagines it. Instead, there are immortals of 'pure-energy' who preside over our descendants' world from another, unseen universe. Divinity, it seems, is hard to get rid of and, while religions come and go, religious tics are ineradicable. God is dead: long live the gods!

It used to be fashionable to predict the end of religion. It would be replaced by earth-bound realism, perhaps, critical reason, practical utility, dialectical materialism, scientific humanism or unsentimental science. Nietzsche thought faith was a pathological aberration of which willpower would cure us, Lenin that it could be tolerated as a doomed anachronism. H. G. Wells assumed it would be superseded by progress, like earlier, cruder forms of superstition and magic. Bertrand Russell thought 'as near as possible to certainty' that it was false.

So far, however, ancient faiths have outfaced all proposed successors. In each of the last five centuries the critics of old religions have ended up inventing new ones. Almost all the 'atheists' deplored by divines in the sixteenth and seventeenth centuries turn out, on close examination, to have been something else – usually deists or fideists, sometimes pantheists or merely heretics. More recent attempts to break out of religion have slightly shifted its confines. The eighteenth-century escape-route led to the cult of the Supreme Being, erected alongside the guillotine as a memorial of perverted reason. Modern pragmatists sometimes think they have a non-religious answer to fundamental questions like 'What is truth?' and 'What is right?' – but William James, the most effective spokesman for pragmatism, used it to justify a feeble form of Christianity. Other refugees from faith have turned their disbelief into religion of another sort. Humanists made a god of man. Communists replaced God with equally potent, equally transcendent History. Scientists substituted god-like evolution for discarded providence. Most predictions are no longer of a religionless world, merely of a world with new religions. Religions come and go – but, mostly, they come and stay, changing all the time but never transforming religion itself out of existence.

We want to know now whether traditionally recognizable religions can go on resisting erosion and attack and how, meanwhile, the process will change them. By religion I mean a system of belief, shared in a framework of social relationships, which must include what Schleiermacher, the 'father of modern Protestantism', called 'a sense of and taste for the infinite and eternal'. For purposes of the present essay, and for reasons which will be explained in a moment, I exclude what I call quasi-religions and para-religions, including many influential superstitions, cults and movements, because, despite religious pretensions, they do not nourish a sense of transcendence which genuinely reaches for the infinite and eternal.

To religion in this traditional sense, there are four sources of threat. Secularism could still win the cosmic struggle: science might yet gut the wonder out of creation, and human yearning could be glutted by the material satisfactions of life. Further or alternatively, religion could starve in the barren mental landscape constructed by' postmodern diffidence. Meanwhile, religious revival favours para-religious sects and cults or individual obsessions more than mainstream religion: this raises the fear that religious traditions will fragment into something unrecognizable, retreat into mental ghettos or dematerialize in cyberspace. Finally, new forms of syncretism could transmute religion into a kind of secular therapy, or a range of designer-label faiths, or a form of fantasy for the intellectually challenged: some 'Next Church' movements and 'prosperity gospels', for instance, are so immersed in worldliness as to be unrecognizable as religions. On some current trends, therefore, the chances are that religion will wither or atrophy or merge with the world or become a freakish fringe.

This essay is a short attempt to dismiss those dangers and to predict and explain the inexhaustible appeal of religion in any kind of realistically imaginable future. Religions are their own worst enemies. They have more to fear from each other than, say, from science. They are threatened less by secular rivals than by their own infidelity to their proper objectives. Society, fortunately for them, is changing in their favour.

The Apes of Faith

It is Sunday afternoon and the anthropologist from another galaxy is hovering over Earth.

He would have got here this morning if the complexities of space–time had allowed. For his aim is to test a colleague's earlier fieldwork by replicating, as nearly as possible, its exact conditions. While observing earthlings at worship, he hopes to discover how accurately their religion has been reported or how it has changed since the last observations were made.

He heads for Madrid, where, his files tell him, people are sure to be going to church in large numbers. He has no difficulty in identifying a vast, open-air basilica, thronged by thousands of pilgrims who wear the white-and-purple stoles which, his sources confirm, are part of the standard ritual garb. The congregation gathers in self-induced ecstasy, swaying in unison, singing out repetitive incantations. The priests arrive – two teams of priests, each in an obviously symbolic colour: the white of celestial purity, the red of blood-sacrifice and mephitic fire. This is obviously a dualist religion.

The psychomachia – the symbolic struggle of good and evil – is enacted in a grassy sanctuary in the middle of the basilica. A symbol which roughly reproduces the form of the planet is made to descry lines, arcs and curves across the sanctuary, and to oscillate wildly between the zones of earth and heaven, in apparently simultaneous mimesis of the cosmic and moral courses of the world. From time to time it seems to be engulfed in a net that resembles the maw of some divine creature with the power to destroy creation; but it is always mercifully regurgitated. The world is spared, disgorged, and the symbolic struggle is resumed.

The ball which represents the world is so sacred that not even the priests can normally touch it with their hands, except for two pontiffs of the highest order, who guard the extremities of the holy sward and wear garb of distinctive colours. The only exception admitted is when the ball becomes defiled by bouncing or flying outside the boundaries of the inner enclosure. A priest then reconsecrates it by lifting it above his head and flinging it into the cosmic fray with a gesture evocative of a thunderbolt. Another priest in black, who seems to represent the interventions of chaos, blows a shrill note on a tiny pipe at random intervals and causes the earth-symbol to be shifted from place to place, patternlessly, around the inner temple.

At first the anthropologist is puzzled by the freedom with which the priests use their feet to touch the ball and direct its motions. He knows that the feet are not much revered by earthlings, compared with their heads, which are also allowed to touch the ball (and which they usually treat with vanity unjustified by their ugliness). The obvious interpretation suddenly strikes him. The status of feet is a function of their closeness to the earth, for in locomotion, as the earthlings oddly practise it, the feet are always in contact with the surface of the planet. This is a telluric religion and only the most privileged limbs can touch the earth-symbol.

In 1967, José Luis Sampedro, one of the best Spanish writers of recent times, imagined this device of football-as-rite (which I have adapted with modifications) to satirize secularism and to lampoon academic anthropology. It discloses or suggests a deeper truth: secular life imitates religion. The similarities in football's case have surely not been consciously aped. There are, however, secular ideologies and institutions which adopt rituals, vaunt transcendent explanations, make moral claims, focus loyalties, mobilize identities and create quasi-priesthoods. Some are billed as alternatives or successors to religion.

Marxism and Nazism have been incandescent recent cases, now burnt out. Both were presented by their adherents as 'scientific' prescriptions which made religion dispensable. Yet both were quasi-religions which borrowed heavily from religious tradition. They were alike in many other respects, as rival extremisms always are – as close as the ends of a horseshoe. Along one dimension, there was a long way between them, yet they almost touched. They were united against religion and united in imitation of it.

They replaced God with history but both saw the course of the world as charted by an impersonal, dynamic force, of which individual lives are the plaything. They offered human sacrifices to history, speeding her purposes by immolating profane races and classes. They adopted the framework and imagery of Christian millenarianism, promising the fulfilment of history in a 'classless society' or a 'thousand-year Reich', after a kind of armageddon. They had their well-orchestrated liturgies, their shrines and sanctuaries, their icons and saints, their processions and ecstasies, their hymns and chants. Both demanded irrational assent from their followers – submission to the infallibility of the Führer or to the scriptures of Marx. Both had their theological squabbles, as Internationals splintered like sects and heretics of the Strasser front were purged. Mikhail Tukhaveski, best of the generals of the first Red Army, dreamed of 'returning to our Slav gods'. Nazis fantasized about restoring ancient folk-paganism and turned *Heimschutz* into a mystic quest, leading through stone circles to Wewelsburg Castle, where, Himmler believed, ley-lines met at the centre of Germany and the world.

Marxism and Nazism were crude, looking-glass images of religion. Real religion has seen both off. But we still live in societies with worldly priorities, daunting anxieties, susceptibility to charisma and hunger for 'final solutions'. Some popular secular ideologies already seem to be practising in front of the mirror. Environmentalism sidles into earth-worship. On its sillier edge, feminism erects the mother of all idols and advocates the idiocies of 'Goddess-consciousness'. Mad capitalists celebrate their own millennium: the 'end of history' in a universal triumph of Chicago-style libertarianism. There is a kind of militant atheism which is religious in its fervour. There are scientists who worship Science, replace providence with the selfish gene and venerate Darwin as their prophet. All these threaten to be the post-religions of the future. If past form is anything to go by, as with Marxism and Nazism, real religion will outlive them.

A book on the future of religion might embrace these movements and the weaker imitations which you can see competing with religion today. The cults of celebrities, for instance, generate worship-like hysteria, commerce in icons and the imitation of unsuitable saints. Veneration of historic communities has, for those who belong to them, some of the attractions of life in a sect, nourishing the exclusive identity of chosen people. Rites of business turn corporations into communions and, especially in the context of campaigns to 'motivate' sales, copy the conventions and aspire to the atmosphere of evangelical revivalism.

The difference between religion and business is sometimes hard to define. The 'Church' of Scientology claims to be a religion and has some of the trappings of one, but the law in some countries classes it as a business on the grounds that its purpose is to sell the works and gimcrack inventions of its founder. Is 'Exegesis' – a seminar-network devoted to the 'business of transformation and the transformation of business' by therapies which target the spirit – a business or a religion? The cult founded by the Baghwan Shree Rajneesh and made familiar by its adherents' orange robes offers 'Awareness courses' to those it calls 'clients' as well as rituals for believers.

This essay, however, is about the future of religion as traditionally defined, and the quasi-religions have an important place in it only in two respects: as reminders of the continuing power of real faith to attract imitators, and as rivals which – in some people's hopes or fears – will sap its appeal.

For similar reasons, renascent and newly contrived superstitions – for all their importance nowadays – have to be confined to the same margin as quasi-religions, even when they acquire sophisticated organizations. By superstitions, I mean irrational beliefs which represent defences against hostile nature rather than a religious commitment to the infinite and eternal, though they may add what some other imitations of religion lack: a celebration of the rationally imperceptible. Astrology, for instance, invests astral influences with the powers of providence. Flying-saucer freaks and corn-circle cranks are seeking 'encounters' with the kind of controlling intelligence which real religions leave to God. From elves to 'aliens', all the commonest delusions of superstition are emanations from a species afraid to be alone in the universe.

Nowadays there is almost no such thing as harmless superstition. Instant communications make every nerd a potential neophyte. For most dabblers, astrology and tarot are parlour pranks; but the scale on which they are trusted and the money they make suggest their potential social influence is enormous. The same was true of 'table-turning' in the past and the history of

Spiritualism is a useful object-lesson. It started in a middle-class household in small-town, upstate New York, in 1848, where two young sisters heard rappings which their mother interpreted as messages from the spirit of a murder victim. More mediums, most of whom were women of otherwise unmarketable talents, discovered similar gifts. There was a time – not certainly over until the 1930s – when Spiritualism threatened to become one of the routine rituals of polite society in the West, perhaps because it responded to trivial anxieties which crowd great questions out of most people's minds. For Spiritualists favoured simpletons as mediums – partly as proof against charges of charlatanism. In consequence, messages from the other side were dominated by humdrum news of the loved ones' health and hobbies and petty friendships and jealousies.

This example is worrying for anyone who wants reasonable religion to survive today's weird fashions in belief. If Spiritualism could enjoy such a triumph how much more are equivalent forms of modern silliness likely to thrive, with information micro-technology at their command. Astrology is the starting-point of the 'New Age' movement, which seems lightly organized, if at all, but which is united by a common focus, a common literature and a certain wild consistency. The 'dawn of Aquarius' irradiates all its maunderings: the doctrine that the astral prominence of the constellation of Pisces is gradually being replaced, after about 2,000 years. New Age expectations defy critical intelligence. The movement is a sump into which every kind of fashionable superstition drains. It is hard to credit many people with belief in much of it – but even a little is brain-rotting. It taints the respectably suprarational by contagion and puts coins in the charlatans' slots. Its success is an index of spiritual malaise: it responds to a craving for wonder and fervour which religion ought to be able to supply. Superstition and secular quasi-religions have no part in an essay on the future of religion; but they may leave religion with no role in life.

Yet profane movements' habits of self-sacralization help to make some students of the subject suspect that religion is an inescapable part of being human. We can claim to reject it as individuals but in societies we really seem unable to do without it. At least, so it is often said, none of our human societies has managed so far. The ocean of collective experience is unnavigable without mast and sail and flag, which religion seems satisfactorily – perhaps uniquely – able to provide. Religions are ways of encoding inherited wisdom, without which the species would not be truly itself. Religious behaviour is part of the skeleton of culture which cannot be filleted without collapse.

This argument is useless except, perhaps, to doom religions to the fall which follows complacency. For, if religion were really necessary, what would make it so? It cannot be instinct, because there are some people who are genuinely irreligious. It cannot be social evolution, for that would be logically unsatisfactory – it would imply a stage or state of society prior to the need for religion. The view that religion is inescapable or in some sense natural is based on the fallacy that it is universal. On the contrary, it seems to me, religion properly understood – in terms which encompass belief and an active, lively sense of human responsibilities that transcend this world – is a relatively rare state of man. There never was an 'age of faith'. Most people, for most of history, have been indifferent to transcendence, unmindful of the eternal, neglectful of the infinite and content or obliged to wallow in worldly priorities. Quasi-religions ape only external habits that arise from a life of faith. If – for one reason above all others – it is unconvincing to suppose that religion is over, it is because, so far, we have seen so little of it.

This does not mean that religion, understood as sociologists of religion commonly understand it – as a social phenomenon or as part of the adhesive of culture – can be ignored. On the contrary (as I shall argue), nothing claimed to be religious can properly be counted as such unless it happens between people, not just inside individuals. But it does mean that we have a criterion for distinguishing real religions from secular imitations. This criterion has, however, to be applied by way of the study of religion as a social phenomenon, because only along that route are there useful points of comparison in other, non-religious ways of organizing life.

The Social Trap

Your religion is not only what you believe but how you behave. It lives more, thrives better in the web of relationships than in the circuits of the mind. In practice, religions are communities, not so much of the like-minded as of the similarly inclined, by taste, values, scale of companionability and all the drag and drift of the cultures which surround them. Cicero represented an intellectual's prejudice when he derived the word *religio* from a root common to 'lecture' and 'election'; it is more likely to come from the root of 'ligature', 'league', and 'legal'. For most practitioners, it is about ties that bind you into a society, rather than thoughts you have in your head. The future of religion depends, therefore, not so much on the progress of science or the rise of scepticism or the corrosion of doubt as on how society goes on changing.

Catholics are not Catholics, for example, because they believe all or any of the forty dogmas of the faith. Most are unable to remember them, if they were ever taught them in the first place. But they hunger and thirst for the sacraments – the rites by which divine grace is mediated. Most Orthodox could not tell you the difference between the Procession of the Holy Spirit and the Consubstantiality of the Son if these delicacies were served up with watercress. But they love the sense of belonging to a communion of numinous worship, universal claims and reassuring antiquity. Early Protestants were fired by the experience of vernacular services and congregational participation. Their rebellion against Rome was not defined, as so many historians define it, doctrinally: by Luther's belief in man's helplessness to contribute to his own salvation in competition with God. This doctrine of 'justification by faith' was part of Catholic tradition anyway.

All but a few traditional Christian Churches share a creed which states that 'no man can be saved' unless he believes that 'three incomprehensibles are not three incomprehensibles but one incomprehensible'. The effect of this clause in the creed of St Athanasius is to take belief, in most normal senses of the word, out of the act of Christian commitment altogether. In the context, 'belief' in such a nebulous formula can only mean willingness to say it, without being able to grasp it intellectually. It is an act rather than a belief that is demanded – an act of submission to higher wisdom and of conformity to a community. Christianity obeys the sociology of the Spanish proverb: 'Tell me whom you walk with and I will tell you who you are.' So do most religions.

Judaism, Islam and Buddhism, with Christianity, are the religions whose adherents are most likely to repudiate this suggestion. All of them were founded in reaction against religions of ritual – the superstitions of pagans who thought their relationships with transcendent beings depended on acts of appeasement and divine payola. Jews, Christians, Muslims and Buddhists, by contrast, emphasized the prior necessity of the right state of mind. All these faiths have been prolific in formulating rival orthodoxies and minatory demands for 'correct belief'. Yet all slide back into the temptation to judge people by outward signs – the gestures, speech-arts, cringings, abasements, ablutions, body language, parades and displays by which members of a community recognize each other.

Judaism seems to have more to do with how you are identified than what you believe. Conversions can happen but Jews generally admit each other to shared identity by birth-right, which has nothing to do with belief. They exclude each other from their rival sects according to criteria of ritual observance and way of life. Their religion can be defined as reverence for a particular body of tradition – the 'Law and the Prophets' – which prescribes a practical civil code and a programme of rites. It includes what might be classified as a matter of belief: adherence to the ancient Hebrew concept of a supreme being as a universal creator who made everything from nothing, a stern judge of mankind according to the criterion of righteousness, a tribal god of a 'chosen people' and a cosmic provider with an elusive plan for the whole of creation. Now, however, other religions have pillaged this concept: it has become part of the booty of the ravaged Temple. It no longer distinguishes Jews, whose sense of Jewishness is forged instead by the terrible memory of a unique 'sacred history' of common suffering and fellow feeling.

Islam was proclaimed by its founder as a state of life, not just a system of belief. That is what 'Islam' means – literally, resignation or self-surrender. In contrast with Christ, whose social prescriptions seemed defiantly unpractical, Muhammad devised a blueprint for an invincibly efficient society. He discarded the tribal model, which had kept Arabs divided, and substituted allegiance to the person of the Prophet and his successors. Today that loyalty has become problematic. No convincing successor exists and submission is transferred to pretenders or diffused among the 'community of the faithful'. In the early days, however, when the 'commander of the faithful' really was a general in a holy war, Muslim unity resembled military discipline. Once mobilized, Islam could not be stopped until, less than a hundred years after the Prophet's death, it had reached out of the remote corner of Arabia where it began, to the walls of Constantinople and the ramparts of the Cantabrian mountains.

Muhammad enjoined a realistic marriage code – up to four wives, easy divorce. By the standards of the time, this represented a demanding level of continence but it seems relaxed compared with Christ's requirement of lifelong monogamy, with celibacy as the only alternative. The Prophet also called for a socially useful, individually beneficial routine of fasting, alms-giving and prayer. He specified tough regulations for dealing with enemies or criminals and benign practices for slaves, orphans, widows and the weak and oppressed. Rites were distinctive enough to declare a new dispensation yet conformable to the religious traditions of the region: pagans would recognize the veneration of the black rock of Mecca; Jews would sympathize with circumcision as an initiation procedure; Christians would notice the scriptural resonances in recitations of the Quran. The formula Muslims repeat as a proclamation of Islamic identity is a statement of belief in no god but God and Muhammad as his Prophet. But its utterance is a ritual. What defines the Muslim as Muslim is the ritual act, not his private opinion of its content.

Buddhism has a creed which all adherents are supposed to accept. The beliefs it specifies, however, amount to confidence in a programme of conduct – pain obliterated by the annihilation of craving. All other tracks in the 'right path' reduce to aspects of behaviour: speech, action, way of life, effort, consistency, concentration. Indeed, Buddhism is so weak in beliefs that some people, including Buddhists, want to deny that it is a religion at all. According to tradition, Buddha refused to commit himself, in dialogue with disciples, on questions generally considered fundamental to a religious understanding of the cosmos, such as whether God exists, whether heaven exists, whether the universe was created, whether the soul is separable from the body and whether there are other worlds than ours.

Religious behaviour differs from secular behaviour not because it involves belief but because it is linked with committed attitudes to transcendence. But, if such an attitude is a defining characteristic of religion, we should not be surprised if, like many defining characteristics, it gets left out of account, marginalized or forgotten. No one who draws a line on a page or paints one on a billboard or a pitch allows himself to be influenced by the definition of a line as length without magnitude. No one calculates metres in awareness of the stick in Paris that defines their dimensions. Lovers do not trouble about the definition of love, if there is one; nor artists about that of art, except when their inspiration withers. Religious people usually go through their observances without sparing much thought for God. Those whose religion is residual or distracted by worldly priorities, often remember their basic attitude only on the brink of death, like Lord Marchmain, resisting religion and defying extinction with the same tenacity, but summoning his last strength to make the sign of the cross.

The sense of transcendence distinguishes the sacred from the profane. But we should not expect religions to be unaware of the world. The sense of transcendence is an addition to a worldly perspective, not a substitute for it. If heaven exists, the world is enclosed by it. If there are other universes than ours, ours forms part of the array of them. The here-and-now is part of the universal and everlasting. The future of religion, if there is one, will happen in the world we know. The problem is one of balance. When religions become absorbed with the world, they cease to be religions. When they ignore it, they cease to be effective.

The Glutinous World

It is hard for this world to compete with others. We know it too well. When we imagine a better one, we start with the defects of the world we already have.

As a result, religions tend to acquire an other-worldly look. Their objectives seem focused on an afterlife or a kind of parallel universe called heaven. They proclaim standards of perfection unattainable in the confines of the flesh and the realm of the devil. Seekers after an earthly paradise are not considered religious in the same sense; we call them social utopians, for instance, or Marxists or Nazis or some such name. When the clergy want religious inspiration to be employed to make our world better, politicians accuse them of interfering outside their sphere.

Yet matter and spirit, for most people, for most of the time, have been mutually charged, thoroughly interpenetrated or inseparably fused. States and faiths have always corrupted each other. The pretence of religion has been politically exploited, to justify wars and terrorism, to impose social ethics, to bolster elites or legitimate revolutions, to sanctify authority or subvert it. Most ways of life which their adherents represented as religion have been this-worldly, more concerned with satisfaction or survival in this world than with salvation in the next. Rites directed to the afterlife are normally postponed in favour of the more urgent demands of the next rains or floods or harvest.

Even in a religion of fairly recent origin, like Christianity, which is hardly 2,000 years old, and which might therefore be supposed to be relatively sophisticated, godly elites have had to make continual concessions to the earthy, earthly priorities of under-evangelized masses. Common people's prayers are for good weather or good hunting and good cheer – things you need well in advance of the next world. In nominally Christian countrysides, the sacrament is abused as a talisman against hostile nature – drought, say, or plagues of insects – and the feasts of saints are treated as acts of propitiation to influence the weather or hold pestilence at bay. Worldliness has made durable intrusions in the Christian calendar. Urban churches, where congregations are well protected by modern technology from failures of the harvest elsewhere, still have their harvest festivals, when altars are laden with marrows from the supermarket or with 'home' produce cooked up out of shop-bought ingredients. Christmas, Epiphany, Easter and Lent are all survivals from the ritual calendars of paganism, determined by the rhythm of the seasons and the vital cycle of the sunshine.

Considered from one point of view, the movements we call the 'Reformation' and the 'Counter-Reformation' were a common war of divines against popular culture, an attempt to wean on to a spiritual diet lives permanently threatened by natural disaster. Trials of rats and exorcisms of locusts, appeals to folk-healers and wise-women, vows to saints for worldly purposes, charms to master nature and spells to conjure the occult – these were the shared enemies whom the clergy of all Christian traditions strove to control or curtail. The clergy set out to make the rough places plain but most of the familiar, irrational bumps in the rural landscape survived the epoch of reform.

Religion stayed where it had always been – in the community rather than the Church. Everywhere, devotion ticked away to the time-scale of the countryside, with feasts and fasts adjusted to the oscillations of dearth and glut. Industrialization and urbanization have shifted religious priorities out of the furrows and penfolds, but not out of this world. Every week I hear the bidding prayers of ordinary people. When they mention peace, it is peace in Bosnia or Ulster or some other earth-bound place. When they speak of health, it is usually of the body. They pray for graces rather than grace, succour or solace for the victims of modern life – the homeless, the elderly, the poor, the prey and perpetrators of crime, the work-stressed and the examination candidates. Except in cases of bereavement, heaven hardly gets mentioned. When I have finished hearing the voices of the faithful, I read the views of Christian intellectuals. Their weeklies are full of social Christianity. They spend far more time suggesting improvements to this world than making provision for the next. Up to a point, this all seems appropriate. Christianity is trapped in anxieties for the earth by the veneration of a god who chose to live in it.

In my favourite painting of Christ, Murillo makes him a naughty boy. The infant Jesus is treating a pet bird badly, gripping it tightly, waggling it aloft to tease the family dog. Mary and Joseph interfere with the typical resolve of parents: reproofs tempered by indulgence. According to Catholic orthodoxy, the human Christ was 'a man like us in all things but sin' and the painting escapes the charge of heresy only because the naughtiness of a child can be considered unsinful. It is engaging, however, precisely because it is so perilous, edging round heresy by a delicate margin. The idea of a god so human that his parents have to teach him to be good heightens the convincing paradox of the faith. Murillo's mischievous *gamin* makes an invigorating change from the anodyne Christ-child commonly depicted – so good that he seems inhuman, so untouched by temptation that he seems detached from the world. Unless invested with the kind of sympathetic humanity Murillo gives him, he might as well have stayed in heaven.

The freedom to be naughty is part of the fallibility we ought to expect of a human god. The fallibility of his suffering – of his despair, of his powerlessness on earth, of his broken, bleeding body on the cross – is incomplete without it. Without evidence of his frailty, it is impossible to believe in the tears he weeps for the death of a friend whom he knows he can raise, or in the prayers he utters to escape his duty of submission to sacrifice, when his divine self knows he will rise again. The naughty boy grew up into the teenager who reprimanded his mother and the adult who tormented the Pharisees, teased the Samaritan woman, lost his temper with the moneylenders and recommended meekness as a way of 'heaping coals of fire' on an enemy's head.

A god brought down to earth is an avowal, by anyone who claims to believe in him, that religion is worldly. I am suspicious of the Christian commitment of all the fellow travellers of the Church who show how little faith they have in the human god by expressing outrage at depictions of his humanity. Outrage of this sort is usually prompted by speculations about Christ's sexual desires. A film which shows him attracted by Mary of Magdala or by the woman – if it was a different woman – who dried his feet with her long hair draws demonstrators to the edges of the cinema queue. A poem which makes him the prey or promise of gay temptations incites accusations of blasphemy. But, without sexuality, could Christ be truly human?

Artists rarely show him satisfying physical needs. I know of no work in which he urinates or defecates or even blows his nose, though there are plenty of artists who do not feel constrained in other respects by the gospel-writers' priorities. He is often shown at table – at the Last Supper, the meeting at Emmaus, the feast at the House of Levi – but food is a kind of matter invested with transcendence in Christendom by the doctrine of the eucharist. On the high altar of the Charterhouse of Miraflores, just outside Burgos, he sits down to a Last Supper of roast suckling pig – a cruel joke of the sculptor's at the expense of the monks, who were forbidden meat. But that kind of earthy, humanizing subtlety is rare. A variety of excessive delicacy keeps screening Christ from the world he chose to live in, with a veil of sanctity. I often think the gospel-writer had this in mind when he wrote, 'He came into the world and the world did not know him.' Those in his day who failed to recognize his divinity were not much further from understanding him than the followers ever since who have hesitated to celebrate his humanity.

The difficulty of balancing Christ's two natures, human and divine, worldly and other-worldly, was already acute in the first documented era of the Church. The gospels are full of evidence that Christ's vocation was a constant struggle between love for the world and resistance to its corruptions. Satan tempted him in the wilderness by spreading the whole earth before him: Satan knew what Christ loved. The words with which Christ repelled him – 'Away with you, Satan!' – he repeated when Peter wanted him to elude suffering and death. To glory in the world and to escape from it were both diabolic temptations. Early Christian writers lived the same tensions. On the one hand they had to fend off zealots, who assumed that the master's kingdom would be of this world and who therefore disqualified Christ from messiahship; and on the other they had to repel gnostics, who wanted to purify him of all earthly grossness – to make him unpolluted spirit, whose body was an illusion and whose suffering was a pretence or a con-trick. In a gnostic rewrite of the passion, Simon of Cyrene dies in Christ's place and God laughs to have cheated the devil. The difficulty of reconciling love of the world with revulsion from its excesses has never spared Christians. My body is so full of fat and gore and bile and pus and spunk and spittle that I shall be glad to be rid of it when the time comes. But the early creed-writers promised or threatened its resurrection. They seem to have read God's mind consistently, since he hallowed the world by creating it and the flesh by his incarnation.

Christ's claims to divinity enfleshed make this ambivalence peculiarly acute in Christendom. But all religions are caught in a similar dilemma. All are embedded in this world and yet all yearn for another. Some, like Judaism and Islam, entail codes of conduct for civil society which look strikingly like secular laws. Others, like Hinduism and some forms of Christianity, rewrite the chaos of the world as a mirror of divine order. Some, like Christianity and Buddhism, impose on their followers ethical constraints to make relationships tolerable and society sustainable. All get entangled in social engineering, politics and war. People now think of Tibetan lamaism as a beacon of peace. But between periods of political unity, from the fourteenth century to the seventeenth, monasteries were rivals for power. They maintained their private armies and fought internecine wars. For most disciples, nirvana is always a long way off and the best you can hope for meanwhile is a series of reincarnations – each returning you, in one shape or another, to the folds of flesh on a familiar planet.

So, just as secular life imitates religion, religions ape the world. Their leaders get distracted from other-worldly objectives by their sense of mission to this world and their desire to be 'relevant'. They start judging their own 'performance' by worldly standards of 'success': bums on seats, return on portfolios, influence on government policies. They have to 'work'. They have to take the friction out of the nitty-gritty of life. They have to compete with the state and with secular institutions or take up the slack they leave dangling – the human unhappiness state welfare cannot touch, the incurables medicine cannot help, the social problems for which society has no stomach. Religions are organized to comfort the afflicted and the bereaved, help the widow and orphan, consecrate physical love, help families stay together, keep neighbours from blows. They often operate hospitals and schools. People who are not religious reproach them for serving gods who permit human suffering; as if in an attempt to compensate, they represent themselves as organizations to alleviate it.

The Corrupting Consequences

Worldliness sometimes girds to go too far. The shadow it casts in pilgrimage begins to blot out visions of heaven. This is how that sense of transcendence, which distinguishes religion from politics, gets overlooked. Faiths turn into theocracies, prosperity-gospels, political lobbies, terrorist cells, ersatz families, welfare organizations, alternative health-care agencies, entertainment centres and consumer-communities. In Iran an ayatollah can direct the fortunes of a state. In South Korea Dr Yonggi Cho invites catechumens into his 'Full Gospel' Church with a promise of bounding riches and bouncing bodies. In Japan Soko Gakkai can develop an equally abominable prosperity-cult from a Buddhist starting-point, acquire millions of members, found a political party and spread to other consumerist societies in America and Europe. In Latin America, liberation theology carries its bias to the poor to the point of forgetfulness of God. In Newport, California, 'Mariners Southcoast Church' organizes therapy sessions that undercut the shrinks. All the vices of worldly contamination speckle the great radical Christian movement of contemporary America of which Mariners forms part: the Next Church movement, in which some forecasters perceive a model for the future of religion.

The Next Church is a concept selected for marketability and developed on lines straight out of business school. In an urbanized, motorized society, churches do not have to be local, neighbourhood-scale buildings. People can drive in. The parish is dead. The Next Church church is more like a stadium. By cramming in big numbers – and the Next Church works with congregations of thousands rather than hundreds – pastors can make economies of scale. Some of them talk about the models of the shopping mall and the multi-screen cinema. The pastor of America's biggest congregation – 15,000 strong in Illinois – speaks of 'increasing our market share'. When Next Church congregations found new communities or colonize new premises, it is like a franchising operation. The worshipper is a customer; the services, support groups and 'fellowship opportunities' are product lines. The anthropologist from outer space, who mistook football for religion, might take a Next Church service for a development in the entertainment industry. He might be right.

Where holiness puts an altarpiece, worldliness substitutes the cinema screen for overhead projection, subtitles and video clips. Where a traditional service might have a scholarly explication of the scripture of the day, the Next Church will probably have a multi-media performance. Everything is designed to be instantly recognizable to the first-time worshipper, who needs to be made to feel at home. So the beauty of holiness is swept away in favour of the bricolage of a middle-class lifestyle: the casual-chic clothes, the synthesized muzak, the electronic gadgetry, the cappuccino-party in the narthex or yard, the 'car-repair ministry', the optional class in 'discovering divorce dynamics'. There may be discussion groups about television soap operas as well as Bible-study classes. Instead of striving to imitate heaven, the Church sinks to imitate the world outside. Instead of summoning worshippers to conversion, it prolongs their existing, trivial lives. This is Christianity as the devil might have designed it, a triumph of the prince of this world.

Rich men's heresies and sophisticates' sins are responsible for some of Christendom's fastest-growing, newest-looking congregations, polluted by consumerism, materialism and hedonism. Some of them live a gospel of worldly success, others of bodily health, others of sexual antinomianism. Preachers of the 'gospel of prosperity' are common in the United States. In Orange County, California, which became a byword for the free-enterprise magic of instant riches in the 1980s, the Reverend Robert Schuller – the Pastor Wavelaar *de nos jours* – has built a 'crystal cathedral' of glass and chrome, capable of housing thousands of worshippers who regard business success as a mark of divine election. There are tele-evangelists who carry the prosperity-gospel to unscrupulous lengths, hosting phone-ins from grateful adherents whose public confessions are of confidence in the divine origin of their business windfalls. Commonly, such profits are represented as returns on the value of donations. Despite the Christian rhetoric, this sort of religion seems more readily classifiable as a form of commodity-fetishism. It has its folk-religion equivalent in the banknote-baptisms practised by Blacks in the southern Cauca valley in Colombia: by palming a banknote during the baptism ceremony, godparents divert the sacrament from the child to the bill, which is then expected continually to return from circulation to its owner, bringing interest with it.

These world-obsessed corruptions of religion are all syncretic growths – the cargo-cults of civilization, which mix faith with worldliness the way voodoo mixes magic with paganism. This may seem a paradoxical claim, since syncretic religion is usually identified with 'primitive' cultures, recently emerged from paganism or retarded by impoverished education systems. Yet the rich man has to struggle, like a camel through the eye of a needle, to get into the kingdom of heaven. Paganism and superstition are as rife in modern, developed societies as ever in the past. The culture the unchurched take with them into first-time worship in Burbank, California, is as glutinous as that of the mission-folk of the Capuchin parishes in New Guinea, where the priests vest in grass skirts for mass.

The compromises made by the Next Church and the prosperity-gospel look modern. But religions rarely attract big followings without responding to demand. Religions usually 'take off' only if they fit a social context, find a constituency and supply a want felt here and now. They have to be culturally indigenous, or capable of becoming so. The originator of the modern missionary textbook-tradition was Ramon Llull, the Majorcan mystic and Franciscan lay brother of the late thirteenth and early fourteenth centuries, who laid down the rule acknowledged as essential ever since: to evangelize in the field, you have to penetrate the culture and learn the language. In the modern West, the culture is consumerism and the language is demotic. The priority is me, now. The hereafter only ever comes next.

To protect traditional religion from adulteration by new forms of syncretism, we need religious leaders who can defy worldly vanities and who are prepared to risk worldly failure for God. If they stake the success of their message on its claim to be true, rather than on its cultural appeal, they will deserve respect and may win adherents. When the pontificate of John Paul II began, popes were supposed to have forfeited their power to a new democratic – or, at least, conciliar – spirit in the Church. But a pope's authority has always depended less on its institutional framework than on the responses of Catholics to the initiatives he takes. John Paul has shown that a pope can still guide the Church according to his own vision and inspiration against political, social and economic trends of apparently irresistible power. It is hard to elude this preacher's spell. He is uncompromisingly committed to holiness against worldliness. His defiance of communism seemed derisory when it started – 'How many divisions has the Pope?' the worldly said. His criticisms of unrestrained capitalism may be equally prophetic. He has promoted modernization when it has meant harnessing lay power for the Church and embracing non-Catholics in shared causes; he has resisted it when it has meant concessions to secular fashions. His programme of 'loving our age and saving it' shines through with impressive sincerity. 'Get thee behind me, Satan,' said Christ to Peter when John Paul's first predecessor succumbed to worldly temptations. This Pope will surely never hear that rebuke from his God.

There ought to be similar cases of resistance in Islam today. But hatred of the West is not the same as holiness and to be un-Western is not necessarily to be unworldly. The revulsion I feel from the memory of the Ayatollah Khomeini is tempered with admiration. Like Pope John Paul, the Ayatollah deserved some of the same praise for withstanding worldly values. He was a master of the microphone and the airwaves but he hated almost every other kind of modernization. In a country where it could be said that the best way to kill a mullah was to invite him to over-eat, Khomeini was austere and incorruptible. On the other hand, his call to faith was seriously flawed by worldly contamination. Instead of escaping worldly influence, he reflected it, as if in a distorting mirror. He packaged his message in a political programme of magnetic naivety: he divided the world into 'oppressors' and 'oppressed'. He borrowed the traditional oversimplifications of prophetic critics of injustice. Yet the Islamic Republic he envisaged was a contrivance of our times, a welfare state which would enrich all its faithful and in which the necessities of life would be free. The model came from the detested West. Khomeini found it in the social-welfare programme of oil-states in the Arabian peninsula, which he professed to abhor as realms of darkness. He was seduced by another modern heresy: nationalism. The foreign policy he wanted was nakedly xenophobic, but hardly more so than that of the secular nationalism which was already well established in Iran. Still, for all his impurities, Khomeini did represent a kind of religious reaction against worldliness. Perhaps, if you try to build the kingdom of God on earth, you are bound to get spattered with its mud.

The extreme form of revulsion from the world is the desire to destroy it. Just as we can expect more and more religions of worldly compromise – more syncretic abominations, more prosperity-cults, more theocracies – so we can expect more of the opposite: movements of withdrawal from the world, of self-isolation in introspective ghettos and, ultimately, more fanatics resolved to precipitate armageddon. Contemporary millenarianism demands to be examined for two reasons. First, we want to know whether it is a permanent phenomenon, or one merely excited by the approach of the year 2000 and likely to come to an end with its passing. Secondly, we can test the presumption that religious revival towards the end of the present millennium is a *fin de siècle* twitch in a long-term trend away from religion or whether long-term predictions of the triumph of secularism are being proved false.

Dissolving the Glue

A lot can happen while we are waiting for entropy. We might blow ourselves up or destroy our habitats. We might get replaced by evolution or survive in savagery – for the history of civilizations is a path picked across ruins. There is nothing irrational or improbable about expecting the apocalypse. The perversity of hoping for it seems pardonable if you take a dispassionately critical view of mankind's achievements so far.

Millenarianism ought to be respectable. Plenty of decent religions with clever, unthreatening believers started as end-is-nigh cults, including Mormonism, Adventism, Shi'ism and good old Christianity. When I got to know some Mormon historians, who were attending a conference of their kind at my college in Oxford, I was surprised to find that such admirably rational people were prepared to profess what seemed to me the obvious nonsense of Mormonism: the angelic revelation to Joseph Smith, the lost tablets of gold, Christ's sojourn in America, the self-consciousness of 'latter-day saints'. They replied that these claims were tainted by their novelty. Give them 2,000 years, they said, and they will seem quaint, at worst. Millenarianism matures gracefully.

Yet when we meet modern millenarians we regard them as mad and suspect them as dangerous. Their beliefs are not much more irrational than our fears. More murders, suicides and terrorism happen outside millenarian movements than within them. So what are we really afraid of?

Thoughts on the subject have been concentrated by well-publicized cases of lethally mad millenarianism in the 1990s. In 1993 the self-appointed 'sinful messiah' David Koresh was immolated with eighty followers in Waco. Between 1994 and 1997 almost as many members of the chalet-chic 'Solar Temple Cult' perished in mass murders and suicides, ostensibly 'to escape a fate of destruction now awaiting the whole wicked world in a matter of months, if not weeks'. In 1995 followers of a supposedly Buddhist cult-leader in Japan tried to stir up collective nirvana with a poison-gas attack on Tokyo's deepest subway station. But none of these seems necessarily related to the year 2000. It is hard to find any millenarian group which seriously or consistently attaches special significance to a date with three zeros in it. At the time of writing, the only exception I know of is the bizarre suicide pact called Heaven's Gate. In March 1997, thirty-nine sad, ageing, 'zoned-out' computer-freaks in a villa in California poisoned themselves in anticipation of the end. They had every New Age trait except optimism. Wrapped up in a nerdish world of web-surfing, they thought – according to their own 'exit videos' – that a UFO would transport them in the trail of a comet before 'heaven's gate' closed. They even posted a 'Red Alert' on the Internet, warning, 'Planet about to be recycled'. The leader's rambling last message emphasized the millennium's end as the cut-off point for intending fugitives.

The year 2000 will mark a thousand years since nothing-in-particular. It is quite close to the 2,000th anniversary of the incarnation of Christ but – owing to an error of computation by the monk who devised the system – misses it by a few years. Even among millenarian Christians, the incarnation has only occasionally figured as a key date from which to calculate the end of the world. Most movements have expected armageddon in years not divisible – in our system of reckoning – by 1,000, or even 100. No evidence supports the myth, peddled in trashy history books, that the end of the world was widely expected in 1000 AD. Rather, 1260 was the year which aroused most apocalyptic excitement in the Middle Ages in Europe. Various prophets staked their reputations on dates in the 1670s. The early Adventists experienced their Great Disappointment in 1844.

People are silly enough to expect or demand change at the turn of decades or centuries, and the emotions they invest sometimes generate the force of self-fulfilling prophecies. But predictions of the end of the world have rarely coincided with such moods. Enthusiasm for apocalypse now has, I suspect, to do less with the approach of 2000 than with the increasing, disorientating pace of change. People who find change unbearable expect it to become uncontainable. We can expect millenarianism to continue after 2000.

The current religious revival, at least in Christendom, does, however, have something to do with the calendar; but only because most Churches are taking the opportunity to concentrate their celebrations of roughly 2,000 years of Christianity. An evangelizing mood has been aroused. Some Churches announced as the decade began that the 1990s would be 'a decade of evangelization'. The Pope has proposed to Catholics a programme of deepening awareness of the faith in the years up to and including 2000. The effectiveness of these initiatives is doubtful, however. Religious revival is stronger outside the mainstream Churches than within them, stronger on the frontiers of Christendom than in its heartlands. It is strong, too, in some religions which have nothing to celebrate in 2000, on any reasonable calculation; and, in any case, it has been going on for longer than reference to the millennium's end can explain. In the West, the low-point for numbers of adherents to religions came in the 1960s, and numbers of respondents to surveys who identify themselves as religious have been increasing ever since. In the same period, the explosion of 'new religions' all over the world and the multiplication of numbers of faithful in traditional communions in Asia and Africa have been too swift to monitor accurately.

Meanwhile, odious Protestants on the extreme right are destroying cultures and backing dictatorships in their anxiety to prepare the Third World for the Second Coming. Susceptible Catholics are being duped and frightened by phoney visionaries. Anti-Semitism is being cunningly masked as New Age babble. Pseudo-Churches sell 'ringside seats for the death-throes of civilization'. Aum Shinrikyo lookalikes dream of precipitating the end with spectacular feats of chemical and biological terrorism. Groups withdraw into self-nourishing communities of fear and nurse each other's fantasies on the Internet.

The Authoritarian Genie

The new *Kulturkampf* is usually said to be between liberalism and the 'moral majority'. In the global village, secular liberalism is a tool of survival. Without it, its advocates feel, the multicultural, pluralistic societies, to which history consigns us, will dissolve in bloodshed. Its critics reply in either of two ways. A society characterized by secular liberalism is, some say, not worth preserving anyway. According to others, including me, it cannot survive in any case because it is programmed for self-destruction. Enfeebled by its inconsistencies, it seems bound to be wishy-washed away. Abortion and euthanasia are the slashed prices of life cheapened by glut. Their liberal advocates have deprived themselves of the right to defend the inviolability of other unwanted lives – of criminals, say, the socially subversive, the genetically undesirable, the surplus poor and sick. In secular hands, liberal principles become the forerunners of death camps and eugenics.

Multicultural policies, meanwhile, merely bank the blood of future massacres. Lifestyle-tolerance has faced us with the unforeseeable consequences of families on new patterns, composed of step-relations and 'single parents', instead of the traditional 'nucleus'. Thanks to academic freedom, the pioneers of artificial intelligence and genetic engineering in this generation are poised to become the Frankensteins of the next. Cultural relativism, the precious touchstone of a richly diverse world, has equivocal implications: how can you invoke it on behalf, say, of polygamy or arranged marriage or incest while excluding cannibalism or female circumcision or 'child abuse'? The heirs to our liberalism in my children's generation are going to have to defend cultural relativism while protecting us from the worst of its effects. They will also have to find ways of protecting freedom from itself. Free speech and free association favour the incubation of parties which want to abolish them. Free societies are disarmed against terrorists.

By way of a reaction against the deficiencies of societies forged by liberalism, religions will be increasingly popular as a way of sanctifying moral absolutism, social conformity and uniformity of mind. Christian hierarchs today are often in league with liberalism, because a society based on the Christian principles of charity should, in principle, resemble the society of tolerance which liberals want. It cannot be denied, however, that Christianity and liberalism have a long history of divergence and could revert to a sort of natural hostility in new culture wars. Islam, too, has had its domesticated liberals. The justification of pluralism is precious to some Islamic thinkers today, especially in South-east Asia, where the ethnic and religious *mélange* is as thoroughly mixed as any region of the world. I want the alliance of religion and liberalism to continue; it will only have a chance of doing so if we are aware of its fragility and defend it against its foes.

Societies in recoil from pluralism will demand uniformity, and sceptics and dissenters will probably be the victims of new witch-hunts and burnings. We are creating an environment propitious for a new, religious form of fascism. Academic experts have reclaimed 'fascism' as the name of a syndrome of features common to specific European political movements in the period between the First and Second World Wars. Yet even then the movements' defining characteristics were hard to specify. 'There are too many programmes,' said Mussolini, refusing to commit himself to another. Fascism was an agile insect, never still for long enough to swat. Today's fascisms can be equally elusive. We must be flexible, too, and adjust our aim as the target dodges and flits. We should identify fascism not only by its conformity to a checklist of past examples, but also by the effects you can feel: the sweat of the fear of it, the stamp of its heel. The colour of its shirtings may change or fade. The form of its rites may be altered or discarded. Its models of society may differ. Still, you can always know it by its works. The pace of change forced by breakneck technology is unsettling to most people and bewildering to many. In this state of mind, electors reach for 'men of destiny' and prophets of order. In increasingly complex societies – struggling to cope with rising expectations, gigantic collective projects, baffling demographic imbalances and alarming external threats – order and social control come to be more highly valued than freedom and human rights. Perceptions of society undermined by moral irresponsibility, sexual permissiveness, an alienated under-class, terrorism and rising crime are the fuel of fascist revanche.

Islamic fundamentalism represents this kind of menace, intol-erant of pluralism, terrifying to dissenters, bloody in its enforce-ment of moral conformity. It has escaped classification as fascism on the grounds that it is religious, but Franco and Perón escaped largely on the same grounds. A society which exalts war as virtuous is likely to be a danger to the rest of the world, whether or not it calls war 'holy'. The fact that fascism was once secular does not mean that it can never be religious. Some of the most threatening forms of quasi-fascism today are hallowed by ayatol-lahs and tele-presbyters of the 'moral majority', who insist on the unique credentials of a given set of values and want to force them on dissidents. 'Christian fundamentalism' is becoming as much a political term as 'Islamic fundamentalism'. In parts of Latin Amer-ica, radical Protestant sects are already guilty of trying to mobilize congregations in support of military-backed dictatorships and hierarchies of wealth and race. Some religious cults, with their crushing effects on individual identity, their ethic of obedience to charismatic leadership, their paranoid habits and their campaigns against the rest of the world, behave in frightening ways like early fascist cells.

At an extreme even more remote than fundamentalism, danger-ous reactions erect fanatical sects, cults and 'new religions' – communities of prophetic outrage and moral withdrawal. As long as modern society creates internal exiles, they will flee to these alternative homes, where members nourish each other's commit-ment in introspective 'compounds' or in 'cyberspace cells'. Some of the fastest-growing examples, like pantheism, nature-worship and New Age mysticisms, have victim-constituencies among the ecologically anxious and intellectually challenged. Others get their recruits among refugees from examination hells and compet-itive stress; or among middle-aged drop-outs who hanker for the privileges and protectedness of their adolescence in the West in the 1960s; or among youngsters separated from love by a gener-ation-gap. As we know, in the millenarian undergrowth of our *fin de siècle* lurk some of the weirdest cases but almost every religious impulse has the power to spawn a sect or cult.

Schism is like a shivered mirror. The breaks multiply along the lines of the cracks. The images reflected back get smaller as they multiply. Once the Christian Church began to splinter, the sects dwindled as they proliferated, as if in parallel mirrors, to the numbers of legion and the dimensions of specks. Hinduism, as E. M. Forster saw it, looked solid from a distance but friable in close-up, 'riven into sects and clans'. Some forms of other mainstream religions – Shi'ite Islam, Nichiren Buddhism – exhibit similar fissiparous habits. Religion is an infinitely reproducible amoeba and, though some sects perish, most manage to reproduce before they die.

Cults can start independently of existing religious traditions. Inventions from scratch are bound to become more common as people brought up in ignorance of their religious heritage increase the potential constituency of charlatans. A bewildering range of 'mind control' methods, 'human development' seminars and 'spiritual fellowships' have been trumped up in the last thirty years and are available, with web sites, direct debiting and some of the amenities of cult-life.

Usually, however, cults evolve out of sectarian divisions. Sects become cults by displaying a fairly well-defined range of symptoms. They fall under the spell of charismatic leadership, generate their own scriptures, create disciplines of their own to control members' beliefs or behaviour. They adopt distinctive moral values at variance with those of the society around them or the parent-body from which they have seceded. And they try to embody radical forms of self-differentiation – such as withdrawal into communes and isolation of members from families and former friends. Recruitment by love-bombing and enslavement by brainwashing are not defining features of cult behaviour but are often part of the equipment.

The path from sect to cult can be matched by a pilgrimage in the other direction. When it started in 1968, the movement called 'The Family' or the 'Children of God' had all the cult-beast's spots and horns. Its founder, who called himself 'Moses David', exhibited messianic delusions. His writings were revered as holy and were regarded by his followers as equal in authority to the Epistles of St Paul. He enjoined withdrawal from the world, except for purposes of proselytization, and moved his followers into communes. The early years were notorious for lurid sexual antinomianism: apostolic sharing extended to sexual partners; proselytization was by 'hookers for Jesus'; and there were accusations of child abuse. Court cases in the mid-1990s, however, seemed to reveal communes which had opened their doors to the world, reintroduced conventional morals and moved closer to more traditional forms of radical Protestantism. It may be too soon to affirm that the Children of God have graduated to respectability; but this phenomenon of self-domestication by cults is actually quite common in history. It is happening today in other cases. The strangest, perhaps, is that of Bwiti, which started late in the last century among the Fang of Gabon as a syncretist cult of seances, drug-induced visions and rites of witchcraft-avoidance. Christianity at first contributed only a mythic framework. Now Christian theology seems to be taking the movement over and turning it into something like a regular Church.

Current conditions favour cults, in some respects, more than traditional religion. Deracinated, spiritually uneducated constituencies are waiting in the streets. Instantly erected ghettos are easily contrived with a modem and the dole. Societies diffident about truth and unassertive of morality encourage value-systems extemporized in rejection of tradition. Meanwhile, the urbanizing and unurbanized worlds are hives of excited expectations, awaiting colonization by syncretist cults that can magic bewilderment into consolation. These pullulate and perish with astonishing rapidity but it is impossible to imagine a less-then-uniform world without them. The oddest, paradoxically, seem the most representative. Cao-Dai was founded in 1919 by Spiritualists who claimed to be in touch with the 'Chinese Homer' of the Tang dynasty; its litany of saints includes the Jade Emperor, St Bernard, La Rochefoucauld and Victor Hugo. By promising to fuse benefits of Eastern and Western wisdom, it attracted two million adherents in Vietnam under the French occupation and put armies of thousands into the field in the wars of the 1950s and 1960s. The 'Vailala madness' first struck Papua in the year Cao-Dai was founded, when ancestor-spirits prophesied a paradoxical paradise: wealth in shiploads of European cargo for those who rejected

Western ways. A similar cargo-cult on Vanuatu, the 'Jon Frum' movement, first appeared in the 1930s and periodically resurfaces to this day, exciting expectations of the return of the messianic Jon Frum to distribute cargo, drive out the whites and restore a religion of orgiastic excess.

Braving the stagnation of mainstream religions in the developed world, religious leaders try to reassure us with reports of exponential growth in Africa and East Asia. Much of the missionary field in those regions, however, is in the hands of radical sects or incompetent evangelists who bulldoze traditional culture and expose confused congregations to syncretic temptations. In these breeding-grounds of the bizarre, only a tentative welcome can be given to the spread of Islam and Christianity. The Catholic Church has had to disown some wayward offshoots, like the Maria Legio in Kenya with its sinister exorcism-rites and orgiastic worship, or the healing ministry of Emmanuel Milingo in Zambia, which turned into a personality cult, or Deima in the Ivory Coast, which repudiates the Bible and is led by a female 'pope'. Among offshoots of Protestantism, of course, discipline is laxer and syncretic divergences more weird and, sometimes, bloody. The often trailed prospect of a secular Europe, one day re-evangelized from what we now call the Third World, is appealing and credible; but it depends on a more disciplined growth in volatile societies than is going on at present.

Nor are the missionaries of this imagined future likely to be confronted by secularism. If mainstream religion disappears in the developed West, inveterate paganism may survive it. Folk and local religions are widely supposed to be threatened with extinction by modern trends, but they show amazing powers of endurance. They have survived centuries of pressure. The history of the last 500 years of Christianity could be characterized as that of an unsuccessful struggle by the godly to purge local traditions, eliminate popular superstitions and promote universal cults. Similar compromises with folk beliefs are made today by science and medicine, which find they have to work alongside ineradicable popular prejudices and preferences. Modern Japan is a land of hi-tech Shinto where computers are infested by spirits and where a plate-glass office-block might be topped off with a shrine to the fox-god Inari. Pharmacists have to contend with or exploit the patent remedies which inspire the superstitious brand-loyalty of their customers. Conventional practitioners have to share common rooms with psychotherapists and herbalists whom they privately regard as quacks.

Some doctors now collaborate with faith-healers. This seems equally offensive to science, properly understood, and religion, properly understood. At one level, faith-healing is a relic of pre-scientific diagnostics, which saw sickness as the wages of sin. At another it remains, like prayers for the sick, as a touching submission to God's omnipotence out of the mouths of babes and sucklings – the charming, innocent folly of holy fools. In the healing ministry of Maurice Cerullo, it is big business. In the world of holy hucksters depicted in the film *Golden Child* it is a sad scam, occasionally redeemed by real conversions. All these abiding features of modern life have the characteristics of folk religion as I understand it: they invest nature with purpose; they behold it with reverence; and they practise to control or influence it by magic or to procure miracles by manipulative rites.

Folk religion – despite its association in most people's minds with primitive rusticity – will outlive urbanization and the refinements of a post-industrial economy. Old animism is not yet dead and a new animism is abroad. People believe in material angels and demons who, inseparable from nature, patronize or imperil mankind with their daunting powers. Japanese adherents of New Sect Shinto, maintaining in a technologically managed environment their traditional mental picture of nature teeming with gods, are surely typical. In Hindu tradition, which assigns man top place as the last resort of reincarnations, human supremacy is only tentatively asserted. Non-human forms of life are reverently handled in a spirit similar to what we now call 'deep ecology': not just conserving the environment or refraining from irresponsible exploitation of it, but treating it as sacred. In E. M. Forster's *A Passage to India*, where the missionary conceded that monkeys could enjoy 'their collateral share of bliss,' 'what', asked the Brahmins, 'about insects, oranges, crystals and mud?' Scientists who think life may have originated in a chemical accident ought not to blench at the inclusion of crystals.

To the predicted survival of folk religion, there is one important exception. Ironically, while folk religions survive in the urban jungle, they seem doomed to extermination in their traditional, 'natural' habitats. Sequestered savagery is obsolete. Tribal ways of life, which survive in ice-worlds and jungles, deserts and caves, are shrinking from the saw-mills and oil-drills, the missions and the massacres. They are condemned by 'progress'. Like endangered species and redundant churches, the planet's most isolated peoples have become objects of conservationist campaigns – a sure sign of impending extinction. If they escape the viruses carried by anthropologists and missionaries, they are likely to succumb to cultural contagion. The twentieth-century privilege of studying an extensive range of human societies, with peoples arrested at different stages of change, will be unrepeatable. We live in a uniquely comprehensive laboratory of mankind, which worldwide cultural exchange is destroying.

The Demons of Affluence

While, outside the ranks of doomed peoples, folk religion survives as it always does, it is the 'great faiths' that face the gravest menace from today's hostile trends. The paganism of prosperity and longevity lures some people from worship; others are deflected by the delusion that science can supersede religion. Truth and faith both tend to get submerged by scepticism, relativism and anomie. These sources of menace have to be looked at in turn.

First, the problems of prosperity are worth contemplating for a moment since, on present trends, though 'wealth gaps' are widening, most people in the world are getting steadily more prosperous and the religion of the future will have to find ways of appealing to the affluent. The masses will be able to afford more effective opiates, if that is what they want. The commonplace that prosperity is an enemy of faith is supported by Christ's analogy with the camel and the eye of a needle: the rich can buy happiness in this life – so why should they bother with the next? Poverty, however, seems even more corrosive of piety. Belly-rumblings make finer sensibilities inaudible. To think about the afterlife, you need to be able to buy a little leisure for reflection. Once your place and future in this world are assured, you can spare the effort to contemplate the next.

Though the nobility of poverty was praised in medieval Christendom and every Dives prayed to Lazarus at his death, the statistics of sainthood seem to show a divine bias to the rich. Alexander Murray has compiled them: out of a hundred cases between 900 and 1500 AD, only ten at most can be classified as 'born into a family undistinguished by exceptional wealth or social position'. Even some of these are equivocal: Catherine of Siena was the daughter of a dyer – a minor capitalist occupation.

Peter Damian worked as a swineherd – but this was as a penance, not a livelihood. Early hagiographers claimed that Vincent Ferrer was noble. Wulfric of Haselbury, who died in 1154, went hunting in his youth, had silver coins to give to a beggar and kept a boy servant even when he was living as a hermit.

Admittedly, the signs of our own times are less encouraging. The leisure conferred by prosperity in the modern West is more likely to be spent in trash-entertainments, mindless self-indulgence and festeringly slobbish indolence than in serious meditation about life, death and the cosmos. In the pockets of most people, money buys a life of sensation, not of thought. Most people who do think about transcendence fall prey to modern superstitions or contemptible sects and cults. Still, a big increase in prosperity must buy at least a small increase in thinking and some of that will nourish real piety.

Prosperity really threatens religion when it becomes a quasi-religion itself – a new form of paganism. It happens when shopping replaces worship as a family rite, when mail-order catalogues replace scriptures as family reading, when consumer products are revered on the television screen and the glossy page, when the television or music stack occupies in the home the shrine's traditional pride of place, when zeal is deflected into money-making and charity into spending on the self.

Longevity is another two-faced god. It is a depressingly predictable fact about people that they tend to get religious when they are near death. By postponing death, modern society keeps them secular-minded for longer. Yet the elderly are a reliable constituency for God. Their increasing numbers must favour the growth of congregations. Again, longevity is a real threat when it becomes an object of worship. The unholy folly of preferring this world to the next tempts new idolaters into obscene acts: cannibalizing the organs of the dying, freezing them for future resuscitation and reconstructing their bodies out of phoney parts, like Swift's whore, who, going to bed, strips herself of every borrowed appendage to unmask her real self: a repulsive crone, toothless, wrinkled and with withered dugs.

Scepticism and relativism can also have equivocal effects, promoting religion by way of reaction. Religion was most threatened for a brief period in the West in the eighteenth and nineteenth centuries, when science purported to make God an 'unnecessary hypothesis'. Now that new or resurgent forms of scepticism have made all claims incredible – including those of science and secular rationalism – belief is relicensed and all things, visible and invisible, herded together into the corral of uncertainty. We inhabit a civilization of crumbling confidence, in which it is hard to be sure of anything. The vast scientific counter-revolution of the twentieth century has overthrown the ordered model of the universe we inherited from the past and substituted the chaotic, contradictory model we live with today, of incoherent data, imperfectly resolved into partial images, like a Cubist painting. Philosophy gradually lost confidence in everything that had once seemed sure. Logic, once a guarantor of truth, was reclassified as an imperfect system. Language, once a guarantor of meaning, was reduced to a 'means of misinterpretation'. Existentialism destroyed belief in the object, deconstruction in the subject. Paradoxically, perhaps, this looking-glass world is one in which faith can thrive. Of all traditional sources of certainty, faith is, perhaps, the only one which is immune from its annihilating viruses. The most striking demonstration can be achieved by peering into the camp of some of religion's most tenacious enemies: scientific materialists.

The Complicity of Science

God is easy to fit around the cosmos. The problem for religion is where to fit man inside it. The expectation that religion will wither has been based on a false reading of history, according to which religion belongs to an anthropocentric vision of the universe. A religious outlook, according to this line of thought, derives from the notion that everything was made for us and that human beings have a privileged rank in divine order. Science, this theory tells us, makes such a cosmos incredible. Therefore religion is purposeless.

The process is said to have begun with Copernicus, who displaced the planet we live on from its central place; every subsequent revelation of astronomy has reduced the relative dimensions of our dwelling-place and ground its apparent significance into tinier fragments. Even on earth, human beings look ever less special compared with the rest of creation. Our current beliefs about the antiquity of the planet make the period of our occupancy seem despicable – like a scraping off the fingernail – in Stephen Jay Gould's simile – at the end of the king's arm. The arrogance which formerly sustained mankind's struggle against nature has vanished, now that we see ours as a partner-species in frail ecosystems. We have expelled ourselves from every Eden of our own construction.

Where once we loved to warp nature to our own purposes we now defer to her again, seeing her as we think our remote ancestors saw her: a venerable mother to be honoured, cosseted and conserved, to whom we are no more important than her other children. We have discovered the random effects of chaos in systems we once thought predictable. We have lit a few brands with which to peer into corners of the universe – and they seem to have put out the cosmic watchmaker's eyes. In a purposeless world there is no place for providence. A puny, short-lived species, on a fragment of rock in the unstable, orderless immensity of everything, deserves the care of no god.

Against this background, expectations of the end of religion are – it seems to me – fundamentally misconceived. Religion is not an inference from the apparent order of the universe, but a reaction against chaos, an act of defiance of muddle. No society has been more committed to the worship of a benevolent deity than that of medieval Christendom. It is true that almost everyone who thought about it then had a geocentric mental image of the relationship of the earth, sun and stars; yet it is a mistake to suppose that the 'medieval mind' was focused on man. The centre of the total composition was God. The world was tiny, puny, compared to heaven. Time was dwarfed by eternity. The part of creation inhabited by men in their lifetimes was a blob in a corner of the image of God at work, painted by the illuminator of a thirteenth-century French Bible. Earth and firmament together were a small disc measured between God's dividers, like a bit of fluff trapped in a pair of tweezers. We are now reverting to a similarly humble self-image: marginal, squeezed. There is a lot of room for God in the rest of the frame.

Only in the compact and intelligible universe formerly favoured by science was God 'an unnecessary hypothesis'. When the universe looked manageable and intelligible, people could hope to manage and understand it. Not any more. By exposing its vastness, recent science has set itself an insuperable challenge. Both ends of creation have become undiscernible to human scrutiny: its magnitude is too vast to grasp; the particles of which it is composed are too small to imagine. All we can get at is a tiny range between the infinite and the infinitesimal. It was always a delusion that cosmic order betrayed God's hand. If he existed, he would surely not be so easily mocked. The apparent purposelessness, which is all we can now discern, is more convincingly godlike. This is how a truly divine mind would create a world: to baffle merely human intelligence.

Far from undermining religion, science strengthens its appeal. The Big Bang theory has turned scientists into creationists by giving time, space, energy and matter a single, common origin. The theory does not necessarily represent an admission of the existence of God or of a purposeful act of creation. The Big Bang is just a way of interpreting the mathematics of some of the observations of modern physics. Even if it were both fully intelligible and true, the idea that the universe began in this way would not support either a metaphysical or a materialist attempt to explain it. But it is an example of how metaphysical speculations and empirical observations seem, in modern science, to be on convergent courses. Particles of a thousandth of a millionth of a millionth of a millionth of a millionth of a cubic centimetre are still part of the material world – or, at least, can legitimately be claimed as such. But to track their movements, physics has to fill the gaps between them with electrostatic behaviour, with charges and waves. Even this does not suffice: particles still seem to turn up in experimentally unpredictable places. The forces postulated by traditional metaphysics – divine will, creative energy, God's omnipotence, demons and spirits – are not, in practice, it seems, very different from those postulated by science, except that they tend to be endowed with purpose or consciousness; yet scientists who deride the soul classify consciousness as a by-product of the chemistry and electricity of the brain. 'Purpose' and 'chaos' come to mean the same thing. Both are metaphors with which we fill the gaps between matter.

Quantum science is not mystical but it does give comfort to mystics. The whirl of electrons is made intelligible to a physicist on a California beach by the sudden realization that it resembles the 'dance of Shiva'. Science has been 're-enchanted' – in David Griffin's phrase – or, at least, 'opened to re-enchantment' by holism and uncertainty, ways of deferring explanation that acknowledge the limitations of clear-cut interpretations of the world. We are used to reliable observations which cannot be objectively checked and valid experiments which cannot be strictly repeated. We are familiar with motions that cannot be measured, events which cannot be tracked, causes which cannot be traced and effects which cannot be predicted. A worldview can now qualify as scientific without being rigidly materialistic. Scientists who deny this sound old-fashioned. The machine has grown a ghost.

The Self-Satisfied Dot

Reverence for metaphysics can resist scientific cross-examination, but this does not guarantee the survival of religion in traditional form. In atomized, rootless societies with little respect for authority and rampantly non-judgemental values, religious movements could get replaced altogether by individual 'personal faith'. Before rejecting this as a deplorable future, we should admit that occasionally great geniuses devise religions for themselves which no one shares but everyone can respect. Two examples which might bear recapitulation are those of Spinoza and Blake.

Spinoza's faith was so odd that Christians and Jews alike regarded him as an apostate, and many of the religious in both traditions as an atheist. His notion of God was so all-encompassing as to seem meaningless to critics. He thought that God and nature were coterminous or, rather, that they were names for comprehensive infinity, in which everything perceived as particular is comprised. The immortality of the soul was a valid doctrine, only inasmuch as individual souls are aspects or particularizations of the infinite. The infinite, he said in effect, is inelastic. There can be nothing other than what is, so there can be no free will, no 'possible worlds'. All that befalls is part of a great web. Evil is the illusion of beings incapable of seeing the whole of which they are part. It is 'silence implying sound'. Time is a similar illusion. In the eternity filled by God, there are no successive moments, just one moment which lasts for ever. Spinoza believed, he said, in a God of love; but, since all things severally were part of him, there was nothing for God to love except himself. This way of putting it could not commend itself to conventional Christians.

Blake had a similar, holistic way of looking at reality but he devised for himself a religion so peculiar that no one else could understand it. It is still impossible to find an explanation in the work of Blake's critics which makes sense without seeming to sacrifice the writer's intention. As an artist, he had terrible clarity of vision but he began his spiritual pilgrimage with a muddled mind. His brilliance was undulled, his thought unprejudiced by formal education, so that he could achieve originality with ease. He inherited some doctrines from a fringe sect of radical Protestants who proclaimed God's withdrawal from the world, outlawed worship and ascribed reason to the devil. He was spellbound by Swedenborg, another crafter of personal religion, who had visions and talked with spirits. The mixture, however, into which Blake eventually stirred all the insights which wide reading and vivid imagination gave him was his own. He understood the visible world so well that he was convinced of its incompleteness without spirit. He worshipped an indwelling God in every man and sensed the unity of divinized humanity. He often called this widespread divine principle 'Jesus'. When asked who Jesus was, he replied, 'The Son of God . . . but so is every man.' His unique insight was to see God as art and imagination or 'poetic genius'. The act by which God created the world was similar to Blake's own in creating a poem or picture.

He revered and hated all religions equally but followed only his own. Usually, this is an egotist's faith and makes an idol of the self. In Blake, however, the result was beatific. It gave him integrity he never compromised, austerity he never betrayed and charity which glowed in all his work. That charity failed only when it contemplated political tyranny, pedantic intellectualism, social injustice and institutionalized religion. Some of his battiest notions generated some of his greatest art. The belief that England was the original homeland of the Jews produced *Jerusalem*. The creation of Adam by the Elohim became a grand picture. The four mysterious 'life principles' Blake detected were the subject-matter of a sublime mythology of his own invention.

It is hard to suppress respect for genius like Blake's or Spinoza's and some people must be allowed the power and right to invent worthwhile religions of their own. Most 'personal' religions, however, are not really religions at all; to call them so is to mask self-indulgence. The 'religion' of divinized humanity is usually narcissism masquerading as generosity of soul. Worship on one's own, without the discipline of sharing, is lightly ritualized arrogance. Personal religions are usually a pretence: if intelligible, they can be shared; if unintelligible, they are probably nonsense. At best, those who claim to have them do so out of laziness – unwillingness to devise rites or refine doctrine. Believing what you like is a variant on doing what you like, the selfishness of the slob throughout the ages.

We face a future in which increasing numbers of ungifted and self-indulgent people will credit themselves with their own religions and think themselves wiser than the saints, deeper than the doctors. Three hundred years of subjectivism in the West have puffed individuals up with unjustified pride. The contemporary culture of the self makes self-gratification prized and turns self-esteem, which ought to be condemned as vicious, into a lofty good. One of the dearest objects of modern counselling, therapy and teaching techniques is to suppress all the instincts that make us good: self-loathing and guilt, the repression of desire, the will to suffer, resignation to pain, self-abasement, self-abnegation and deference to the interests of others. The highest happiness this way of life leaves its victims is the inert contentment of a well-fed beast. True happiness, by contrast, is a restless state of soaring imperfection, which can only come of a strenuous dialogue with duty. Practitioners of personal religion make a devil's pact to suit themselves at the cost of higher striving.

Most 'personal' religion is rubbish – and never more so than now, when idiocy is sanctified by the postmodernist doctrine that everyone's opinion is as good as everyone else's. People who tell you they believe in God but do not believe what established religions teach are rarely able to give you a coherent account of their faith. They are the worst kind of egotists, preferring their own views for no better reason than that they are their own. People who tell you that they never go to collective acts of worship but worship 'in their own way' rarely have any ground for their preference except idleness or caprice.

Prospects of Meltdown

When religions feel strong, they fight each other. When they feel weak, they unite against common enemies. No evidence is clearer for the beleaguered feelings of religious leaders today than their willingness to 'put aside their differences' and emphasize the 'common ground'. The attempt to pool religiosity in order to swamp secularism started when the challenge from scientific materialism was at its most threatening. The first meeting of the World's Parliament of Religions in Chicago in 1893 was convened in an evacuated temple of consumerism: the site of the Quincentennial World Fair. Its aims were to demonstrate the resilience of faith in an age of scientific derision and to defend God-centred morals and cosmology by establishing a framework of co-operation against humanism and materialism. Swami Vivekananda stole the show with the message of his own guru, that all religions worship the same God under a different name. The same conclusion had already been reached by Blake from a Christian starting-point, by the Baha'i faith from within a Shi'ite form of Islam and even by a thirteenth-century Mongol emperor whose own religious heritage was shamanism but who kept Muslim, Christian and Buddhist clergy in his service. Khan Mongke's own image for the unity of all faiths was particularly striking. Religions, he said, are like the fingers of a single hand.

Co-operation between religions does have the advantage of mobilizing extra clout for shared programmes of political morality. Catholics and Muslims have made common cause in favour of legislative disciplines to control abortion, and to remit Third World debt. Baptists and Catholics collaborate in the United States to lobby for the inviolability of life and the defence of the traditional family. The danger of founding such programmes on a pretence of theological convergence is twofold. First, it is dishonest and therefore self-undermining. Secondly, it only shifts hostility into new channels. The sense in which God as Christian tradition conceives him is 'the same' as that of Muslims or Jews – much less Hindus and Buddhists – is so weak as to be not worth mentioning. If the destination of all religions is really the same, how could we reach it without shedding the differences along the way? If, in the end, they all boil down to the same ingredients, why not shed the rest of the menu? If they are all good, why choose one rather than another or why not discard them all and devise a less encumbered means to the supposed common end? If the grounds of differentiation are merely cultural, what is the justification for tolerating different cultures? And what in the various religions' current beliefs, as distinct from their supposed goal, can be said to be true? If, in the approach to their shared goal, some religions represent better methods than others, what is to stop the rival methods from inspiring hatreds and violence as intense and destructive as arose in the past from their incompatible claims to truth? If all religions ever were successfully fused, the result would be meltdown.

Within Christendom, the tendency to ignore differences is called ecumenism. Potentially, Christian ecumenism makes sense, as would any movement for reunification of once uniform traditions. It is impossible to contemplate Christian history objectively without seeing that most of its schisms have been the result of misprision and myopia and that continuing obstacles to unity are the result of prejudice, arrogance, indiscipline and unclear thinking. Yet it would be naive to expect ecumenical momentum to be sustained. The movement has already lost appeal for some of those with most to gain from it. Some Catholics are anxious that ecumenism has gone too far – diluting truth and easing the pressure on Protestants to reconsider their own attitudes. Protestant traditionalists suspect that hallowed customs and hard-won beliefs are being trampled in a panic induced by falling numbers. Traditions, traced to saints and apostles and defended for so long at the cost of so much blood and anguish, seem threatened with immersion in a postmodern mishmash which needs no further stirring.

The present situation is abnormal. Religions are naturally each other's enemies. Conflict between them has happened wherever they have shared the same turf, for two inescapable reasons. First, each represents a claim to privileged access to truth. Every difference is therefore the occasion of a lie, waiting to be demonstrated. Secondly, as social phenomena, religions are expressions of identity and, to judge from their willingness to fight for it, nothing is so precious to people as their credentials for belonging to the group they identify with.

Meanwhile, religions go on threatening each other and hatreds incubate under the shell of collaborative programmes. While they confront common enemies, the world's major faiths are convulsed by new evangelism, retrenching against each other in worldwide competition for allegiance. The most alarming, violent and potentially violent cases divide Muslims from Christians, Hindus from Muslims, Sikhs from Hindus, Catholics from Protestants, Shia from Sunni. Religion continues to play a big part in forging and preserving political frontiers, inspiring the sense of historic community, and refreshing the sense of self-differentiation from the other on which historic identities depend. Prospects of new religious wars have to be faced. Indeed, we have never been without them and there is no good reason to hope we ever shall.

In Europe, toleration is commonly supposed to have made religious warfare obsolete by the end of the seventeenth century. Yet no earlier religious war was more savage than those of the eighteenth century, waged to extirpate the Protestants of the Cevennes. In Poland, toleration was more characteristic of the seventeenth century than the eighteenth: government-sponsored violence against Protestants began in 1724. In 1725 Catholic and Protestant alliances were formed by European powers, each expressly for the defence of its religion against the other. In the 1730s the exile of Protestants from Lorraine and Salzburg inspired a vivid literature of exodus. The eschatological dreams of exiled Huguenots helped to excite the 'enthusiasm' which eighteenth-century churchmen considered excessive. Early in the second half of the century, Protestants in many parts of Europe experienced a 'great fear' of an imminent war of annihilation to be unleashed by Catholics. The American War of Independence was at least in part a war of religion, and as late as the 1840s religion was the main issue in the Swiss civil war. The Christian genius seemed at least as well adapted to trench-digging as to bridge-building.

'Know-nothing' bigotry in the United States and Bismarck's *Kulturkampf* in Germany stopped only a little short of violent persecution of the Catholic communion. Wars of religion have an almost continuous history: it would be rash to suppose it was over.

The persistence of religious warfare says a lot about the power of religion in a supposedly secular world. It may be power to do harm rather than good; it may reflect the imperfect understanding of their religions by adherents who seem incapable of absorbing lessons of charity, peacemaking, resignation or social co-operation, but it does show the strength of religious affiliations as a source of identity. This makes ethnic and religious conflict inseparable in some cases. A lot of twentieth-century warfare has both characters. The Irish troubles pit Catholics against Protestants. Religious war rent newly independent India and religion is still rumbling in conflicts in the region. Some Balkan wars have involved tripartite confrontations between Catholics, Orthodox and Muslims; the parties in the civil wars of Lebanon are identified by religious labels as Christian, Sunni, Shia and Druze. There was a religious element, exploited by secessionist rhetoric, in the Nigerian civil war. Wars between Greeks and Turks are complicated by religious divisions, as are those between Armenians and Azeri, Russians and Chechen, Indonesians and East Timorese. Those of Jews and Arabs are also to a large extent wars of Jews and Muslims. Afghan resistance to Russian invaders took on the character of *jihad*. There are movements of resistance by Muslim minorities waging war in Thailand, the Philippines and incipiently in Xinjiang. The Sikh search for Kalistan is ever on the brink of becoming a holy war. Impressive cases have been made out for religious motivation as a factor in the 'new Zapatista' rebellion in Mexico and the Guatemalan civil war. Religions which renounce the right of self-defence, like Baha'i in modern Iran, do not prevent war: they merely expedite their own adherents' massacre.

The Resurrection of Tradition

To judge from short-term trends, the future of religion lies with marginal sects and cults, which thrive on the carrion of the world, and with the Next Church movement that is so good at cashing in on the anxieties and opportunities of 'late capitalism'. There will, no doubt, always be short-lived movements of these kinds which will be able to stay flexible enough to keep up with a rapidly changing social environment, and we should expect to have to live with them for a while yet.

Current trends, however, are usually deceptive in the long run. The short term is always short. In predicting the future, we should look rather at trends discernible over a long period and at the needs which 'winners' among religions will have to meet. On the basis of long-term observation, five main reasons for faith in the future of faith can be discerned. Their total effect, I think, will be to strengthen some forms of traditional religion at the expense of the new movements which are lurching across history at the moment.

1. *The unintelligible cosmos disclosed by postmodern science and philosophy will drive people back to the comforting certainties of suprarational faiths*. Many who lapse from traditional religions today are victims of their own ignorance. They think the doubts suggested by modern science and postmodern philosophy are new and that no traditional solutions are available. Yet traditional religions have been fortified by long survival in a world where similar doubts are always being recycled in new mouths and languages. New religions and crackpot sects and cults are too shallow intellectually to be satisfying, except for a limited constituency. They can only accommodate followers whose revulsion from bewilderment is genuinely unreflective. People who want to be equipped for a dialogue with doubt – not just to duck it – will

need the immense treasury of reflection built up by religious philosophers over the last 3,000 years, or at least to know that all the arguments have been rehearsed before and that rational belief in God has survived doubts like ours before.

2. *In a morally deprived world societies will need moral dogma to survive and individuals will want peremptory guidance to relieve their bewilderment.* Traditional religions, which have a lot of experience in making societies work, will be more appealing than secular solutions, which are riven with contradictions and lack the power to command assent. Terrible temptations to a kind of religious fascism will be posed by fundamentalist programmes and anyone who wants a decent society – whether they think of it as a society of liberalism or of love – will have to be alarmed with vigilance and armed with arguments. We need two kinds of alliance: between mainstream religious leaders and liberal politicians in defence of freedom and pluralism; and between religions to restrain the state – especially in guarding the most basic freedom of all, the inviolability of human life.

3. *Apocalyptic forebodings aroused by the pace of change and the vulnerability of a small world will concentrate minds on eternity.* If I am right, the approach of the millennium has little to do either with the current religious revival or specifically with millenarianism. But the 'future shock' effect of rapid winds sends the crew of our ship of fools reaching for the windlass. The assumption that change has to go on getting faster and stormier may be false. For most of human history, change has been painfully slow and the uniformity of its accelerations has been exaggerated. When contemplated from a greater distance than is accessible to us, its pattern may resemble punctuated equilibrium. We may revert to our normal near-inertia. Cataclysm could stop us short or we may learn self-restraint of the kind recommended by arguments for no-growth economics. For the foreseeable future, however, future shock is going to keep most of the world in its grip. In particular, deracinated societies created by rapid urbanization and de-urbanization will nourish longing for roots. No condition could be more favourable for religions to revive and grow.

4. *Demographic trends in the developed world will favour traditional religion.* The conservative nirvana of a world dominated by the elderly will increase demand for the sort of religion old people

like. A lot of the character of nasty new churches in the Next Church movement can be explained by recent demographic blips: they are religions of 'boomers' and 'busters'. The real next churches – the communions which will have most appeal in the new millennium – will be religions of Darby and Joan.

5. *We face what can be called a 'holiness gap': religions that get distracted by worldly objectives will not be likely to do secular jobs well.* The world ought to be a religious place and religious people should not be too eager to abandon it to its own devices. If it was good enough for God to create, it is good enough for his worshippers to work in. Society has, in particular, to be saved from the worst effects of secularism. Righting the world, however, is not what religion does best and people will still want heaven, even if they get close to building their earthly paradise. The most urgent need that faces religious organizations today is to prise themselves out of worldly priorities in favour of reflection on the transcendent, infinite and eternal.

There has – it is worth repeating – never been an age of faith and only a prophet crazed by hope could suppose that one was coming. I am writing these lines on the Day of the Resurrection, amid signs of hell harrowed and the Church resurgent with a streaming flag. Yet insistent suspicions make me wonder whether another empty tomb has not been prepared for the interment of religion. On the table before me are the latest statistics about my own communion in Europe. In some respects the picture they offer is bleak. The numbers of Catholic baptisms barely keep pace with population. In countries where the clergy have a progressive reputation, numbers relative to population are falling. Although the crisis in religious vocations is palliated by the strong appeal of the priesthood in ex-communist countries, some of the most developed countries, which are regarded as blueprints for the future, are suffering terrible losses – over 30 per cent in Holland and Belgium from 1978 to 1994, with levels around 20 per cent in France, Austria and Germany. The most depressing outlook is in religious vocations for women. In the era of feminism, it looks as if Europe will have to manage almost without those giants of prayer and parish-work, the nuns.

Moreover, while almost all Catholics seem to have their children baptized, large numbers of them now spend long periods of their lives almost without seeking the other sacraments. Religion is getting pushed to the extremities of life in childhood and old age. There are peculiar reasons why this happens to Catholics: the sexually active tend to secede from a Church with an uncompromising discipline of the sexual life, unsupported by society at large. But the same trend is obvious to some degree in all mainstream religions, even those which condone, in various measures, birth control and the remarriage of divorcees.

This seems no reason to repine. Tradition upheld and magisterium respected is a more reliable indicator of success in the long term than bums on seats. The strategy of John Paul II eschews short-termism but could be a model for traditional confessions to follow. He has responded to social change by mobilizing lay talent and manpower while re-endowing the Church with her ancient strengths. Where it is unsupported by society, or done in defiance of prevailing values, worship counts for more than when it is an almost inescapable routine. If religious observance gets crowded out of some phases of people's lives or relocated in particular phases of them, religious feelings do not necessarily wane or roots wither. The graces with which people temporarily defect to secularism can still be galvanized to make this world better and the next accessible for them. The enduring need for faith should ensure the strength of religion in the next millennium. Religions which lose out – which vanish or get marginalized – will include some of today's rapid growths: the freakish sects, the syncretic cults, the shallow enthusiasms. What the future most needs is contact with the past; those most in demand will be the best-tried ways of keeping in touch with God. And the religions truest to their traditions will be best able to respond.

3 Warfare

FRANÇOIS HEISBOURG

Introduction: War as a Social Activity

In attempting to predict the future of warfare, one needs to concentrate on why and by whom wars will be fought, and what kinds of wars they will be. The way technology is integrated into future conflicts will largely depend on the objectives of wars to come. Taking a comparison from society as a whole, it was easy twenty years ago to describe what fax machines and personal computers were supposed to do technically and how; but it was considerably more difficult – and much more important – to forecast their immense social impact. Similarly, a distinction must be made between the existence of technologies for warfare and their actual integration into combat.

We are witnessing a simultaneous transformation of the reasons for war and the means of war. The death of the totalitarian ideologies which accompanied the Industrial Revolution; the disappearance of the Soviet Empire; the undermining of the traditional role of the nation-state as the sole coiner of currency and organizer of military force; the emergence of a broad range of transnational centres of power and influence, from global financial markets to international criminal groups; the rebirth of tribal warfare, not least in the ex-communist states – all these are transforming the nature of warfare.

As for the tools of war, these are diversifying in striking ways which are already made obvious by what we see on our television screens. At one extreme, the Gulf War of 1990–1 highlighted video-arcade technology. At the other, primitive machetes killed more people in Liberia and Rwanda than smart munitions ever did in the Gulf. Low-tech landmines kill and maim thousands of civilians long after their military utility has disappeared. But even in such cases modern technology is exploited to maximize the damage inflicted by the simplest weapons: the genocidal civil war in Rwanda was orchestrated by the electronic tom-tom of Radio Mille Collines, which directed the hands of the murderers in the remotest mountain hamlets. This synergy between the old and the new will be enhanced wherever the strategic pressures which weigh upon the Western democracies do not prevail. Limiting damage to innocent bystanders has not exactly been the dominant concern of the warlords in Bosnia of 1992–5, for whom driving out, or exterminating, 'ethnically' alien civilians has been a war aim in itself.

Finally, new technology opens up new battlefields, whose very existence was hardly conceivable only twenty years ago. American defence and intelligence professionals increasingly express their fears of an electronic 'Pearl Harbor', meaning a sneak attack against their computer networks by foes whose offensive capabilities in this domain have been direly underestimated. The first skirmishes of cyberwars waged by a vanguard of computer hackers have already occurred, even as hapless civilians were being chopped to death by age-old weapons in Monrovia or Kigali. Such contrasts will become the norm as universally available technologies are harnessed to vastly different military ends in contrasting social contexts.

From Machetes to Designer-Genes:
The Tools of War

A three-dimensional conventional war rages on a global scale. Cruise missiles rain destruction on a territory the size of the British Home Counties at a rate of more than a hundred a day, killing thousands of civilians; ballistic missiles crash into centuries-old cities. Battleships are sunk with unerring aim by a tiny number of aircraft launching guided air-to-surface missiles. Strategic bombers penetrate into the heart of enemy territory, drawing in turn fire from jet aircraft and radar-equipped night-fighters. Submarines range under the oceans, attacking the enemy without ever having to emerge out of the waters; equipped with ballistic missiles, they can wreak terror in their adversary's heartland. Robot tracked vehicles attack enemy lines or clear the way through uncharted minefields. Night-sight devices make round-the-clock military operations possible. Modern electronics give military commanders the ability to detect their adversaries and orchestrate their own actions in real time, that is without the slightest delay between a decision and its implementation.

Déjà Vu All Over Again

This is not a capsule description of the Gulf War, and its whizz-bang technology, but a schematic reminder of the closing stages of the Second World War. More than 32,000 cruise missiles (German V-1s) were manufactured, of which 9,200 were launched during a period of four months in 1944 against the UK, where they killed close to 5,000 civilians. Some 4,300 ballistic V-2s (comparable to today's Scud missiles) were launched by Germany over an eight-month period. Radio-controlled 'I 400 FX' air-launched missiles destroyed, *inter alia*, the Italian battleship *Roma* in 1943. US and British long-range bombers ravaged Germany, opposed by its Messerschmitt Me-262 jet aircraft and radar-guided night-fighters. Long-range German snorkel submarines were deployed at the end of the war, which also witnessed initial development work on underwater-launched ballistic missiles. Remotely guided unmanned Goliath mini-tanks were used by the Germans during the last two years of the war. The first infra-red devices were used against Soviet tanks during night-time operations in January 1945. The strategic and tactical use of radio communications and the decisive use of radar during the Second World War, not least in the Battle of Britain, are familiar to all.

Even such a bare-bones description highlights one of the paradoxes of the current situation. Much of what passes today for hi-tech is a straightforward extrapolation of long-standing developments. Furthermore, 'new' technology can take many years to reach its full potential as an effective part of an operational force structure. Thus it took several decades to move from the invention of battle tanks (1915) to their effective use in the *Blitzkrieg* (1939–40). This viscosity in introducing new technology is increased by the long lifetimes of the tools of war, when they are not expended in battle. Aircraft and warships can serve for decades provided they are periodically retrofitted with the latest electronic kit and upgraded with new armaments. For example, the B-52 strategic bomber entered service during the 1950s; the US Air Force plans to keep a substantial number operational until 2040.

The Revolution in Military Affairs

What meets the eye is not necessarily the most important. A number of fundamental but initially unspectacular technological breakthroughs have taken place in recent years, leading to increasingly revolutionary applications.

At the top of the list, because it lies at the technical and organizational heart of the current revolution in military affairs, is the invention of the semiconductor, with its first and, by today's standards, primitive manifestation as the transistor in 1948. Followed by the first integrated circuits (1958) and microprocessors (1971), it has benefited from continuous quantitative improvement, with the processing capability for a given surface of silicium multiplying more than fivefold every five years. This means that, in the forty years which have elapsed since the first integrated circuits, capacity has increased by close to nine powers of five, or more than a millionfold, on the basis of unchanged cost and size. If such a trend had prevailed in the automobile industry, an ordinary car would cost around £4 and would run 100,000 kilometres on a litre of petrol.

In practical terms, this makes it possible to transform the 'silliest' of munitions – such as 500lb iron bombs which have hitherto relied on the laws of gravity and air resistance for determining their landing point after being dropped from their aircraft – into a 'brilliant' weapon. Such a bomb can have an ever cheaper guidance package strapped on, which will help steer it towards its target.

These trends are set to last well into the new century. Eventually, physical barriers will be met in microelectronics, with the size of individual atoms possibly setting those limits, but this point is still far from being reached. If today's laptop computer has more computing power than the world's largest room-sized computer had in the mid-1950s, in the near future the power of that PC will fit into a single chip. For the human user, the limiting factor to miniaturization will be the size of the display screen. This will not be a consideration on board inanimate weapons systems into which ever greater amounts of processing power will be crammed.

Alongside the military consequences of the electronics and information revolution several technical breakthroughs are occurring, with more or less portentous consequences, in the fields of stealth, lasers and biotechnology.

Stealth, the art of making weapons almost invisible to the enemy, is the most recent and hi-tech version of camouflage and concealment. Metal and traditional forms and structures are abandoned in favour of 'low observable' paints, composite materials, shapes and structures. A two-metre missile can be given the radar cross-section of a playground marble. In contradistinction to modern electronics and software, where progress is driven by the general requirements of society, stealth is a purely military technology: civilian air-traffic controllers are interested in making airliners more, rather than less, visible. Stealth is expensive when it is applied to large and complex objects such as combat aircraft: it has cost the United States $45 billion since its inception to develop and produce twenty stealth B-2 strategic bombers. However, it becomes more generally affordable when applied to smaller devices such as missiles.

When the principle of lasers, using light (or other wavelengths, such as infra-red or ultra-violet) for projecting and directing energy, was discovered in 1958, it was thought that they might play the role of 'death rays' *à la* Flash Gordon. Lasers have captured imaginations – as in the cinematic *Star Wars* trilogy – and research budgets. Indeed, they have already proved to be of military importance in non-lethal applications, for communications, guidance, range-finding and gun-laying purposes. Although much American money and effort has been put, and continues to be put, into research for lasers which can shoot down rockets from the ground or the air, no such systems have yet reached the battlefield. This may change, but problems remain. To be militarily effective, lasers must shoot off large amounts of energy at their targets in short bursts. This entails access to a bulky and potentially vulnerable power-plant. Lasers also have great trouble coping with the normal turbulence of the atmosphere. Further progress in electronics, with computing power compensating in real time for some of these effects, may be part of the answer.

Biotechnology may become a major factor in the military arena. No doubt biological and chemical weapons are as old as war itself: poisoning wells, or polluting besieged towns with the carcasses of diseased animals were biblical or medieval forerunners of the widespread use of chemical weapons during the First World War or the Iran–Iraq War of 1980–8. Although their battlefield effects were unpleasant, chemical weapons did not determine the outcome of these conflicts. However, the accidental death of 6,954 people caused by the leakage of an American chemical plant in Bhopal, India, in 1984 is an indication of the destructive potential of some modern chemicals, even in the absence of any military intent. A Japanese religious sect, Aum Shinrikyo, was able to produce nerve gas and to proceed with field tests in both Australia and Japan without being detected. In March 1995, this gas was used against travellers in the Tokyo area mass transit system, killing twelve and injuring more than 5,000. The same sect had also initiated research into biological weapons.

The future picture is particularly grim in the area of biological weapons. Since the 1980s, Iraq has produced large quantities of particularly noxious microbes, which were thankfully not used during the Gulf War. Iraqi-produced botulism, aflatoxin and anthrax could have produced serious casualties among coalition soldiers. The military threat was real enough, since we now know that by the time of the Gulf War some 165 bombs containing such germs had been produced for delivery by Iraqi aircraft, as well as twenty-five Scud warheads.

Even more ominously, biotechnology has now opened up the prospect of modifying the genes of micro-organisms in order to create new strains of disease or to produce poisons against which there exists no vaccine or antidote. This is the hideous face of techniques which have been harnessed to produce life-saving substances such as interferon or insulin. Unfortunately, this is a realm which will be extraordinarily difficult to control. Although the technology implies specialized know-how and equipment in the medical and biological fields, it does not require a broad and diversified industrial base; nor is it immensely expensive. Fairly small facilities can suffice, and their products can be transported in containers which cannot be readily detected.

There have also been improvements of existing technologies. Satellites for military purposes and smart weapons offer dramatic examples of this. Every part of the Earth can be observed by spy satellites, picking up levels of detail sufficiently small to target a weapon at the right-hand window of a house rather than at the left-hand one. Not only is this within the technical reach of the United States and the erstwhile Soviet Union; France and Israel have also joined the game, as will others. Costs too, which used to be considerable in this area – billions of dollars for US Keyhole satellites which can see objects less than a few dozen centimetres across – are beginning to come down, thanks to the overall progress of information technology. By the end of the decade, spy satellites will be available for a few dozen million dollars, well within the grasp of small states and large corporations; these satellites will be to Keyhole what a Citroën 2cv is to a Rolls Royce.

But just as a Citroën 2cv will get one from A to B, cheap spy satellites can have the same high resolution as some of their costlier cousins. The information gathered by these devices can be factored at ever lower costs into the 'intelligence' of 'brilliant weapons'; smart weapons will be assigned their targets in close to real time thanks to data acquired by satellites and other sources of intelligence.

The development of cheap and accurate equipment for locating oneself and one's target is of similar strategic importance. In less than ten years, the US Global Positioning System (GPS), consisting of twenty-four satellites, has made it possible to navigate with an accuracy of a few metres to several dozen metres. This system is complemented by a similar Russian network, GLONASS. GPS is rapidly becoming indispensable for society as a whole: it is, for instance, beginning to replace traditional air-traffic control as a means of regulating the movements of airliners. Thus the US or Russia won't have the option of simply shutting off their satellites in case of war. The practical consequence is that any country acquiring even rudimentary cruise missiles can give them pin-point accuracy for a ridiculously low cost. Can one imagine the military effect of German V-1 'buzz bombs' in 1944 having better than ten-metre precision rather than the erratic ten-kilometre inaccuracy they actually possessed? In such a contingency, the Allies would have been compelled to evacuate the D-Day landing beaches in Normandy.

Smart weapons – highly accurate, low-cost weapons tied into lower-cost, higher-quality intelligence-gathering and command-and-control arrangements – are characteristic of the cutting edge of war tomorrow. The technology is advancing fast and is, in turn, being pushed forward by strategic pressures. Now that the Soviet Empire is gone, NATO's countries are no longer threatened by territorial invasion, which means that whatever military activity they engage in will usually be about strategic rather than life-or-death interests. The Gulf War and the Bosnian conflict are examples of this.

Under such circumstances, a high premium will be given to reduction of losses, whether they be our own or those of the innocent bystanders of the theatres in which we intervene. This calls for the ability to launch unmanned weapons from afar –

what is called 'stand-off' capability – such as long-range cruise missiles. In the same spirit, new systems will operate against an enemy without direct human intervention, including 'arsenal ships' containing up to several hundred ready-to-launch cruise missiles, pilotless aircraft or, on the battlefield, driverless vehicles whose sensors and computing power allow them to find their own way. In some cases, such robot devices will be barely visible to the naked eye, thanks to the progress of 'nano-engines', the marriage of microelectronics with mechanics. Smart weapons will be endowed with great discrimination and accuracy in dealing with their chosen targets, the product of excellent real-time intelligence and high-precision terminal guidance, in order to avoid what is euphemistically described as 'collateral damage' – in plainer language, the unintended butchering of civilians or the gratuitous destruction of militarily irrelevant assets.

The thrust of this revolution in military affairs is reinforced by budgetary pressures. Unmanned missiles or satellites packed with electronics escape what has been called Augustine's Law, popularized by Norman Augustine, the redoubtable defence official and businessman who heads the world's largest defence contractor, Lockheed Martin. In essence, this states that the cost of major weapon platforms – combat aircraft, main battle tanks, aircraft carriers and the like – doubles with each change of generation. Thus the point has been reached where certain weapon platforms have simply become too costly to purchase. When Augustine's law was coined during the Cold War, the forecast outcome was that by 2021 the US Air Force would be able to purchase only one state-of-the-art manned combat aircraft a year. Given post-Cold War budget cuts, this stage may be reached rather earlier. In addition, when a single platform costs as much as it does – for instance, more than $2 billion for a single American B-2 bomber, more than $10 billion for a fully equipped nuclear-powered French aircraft carrier – the consequences of losing it act as a major incentive to keep it out of harm's way, which rather reduces its military utility.

Hence, the structure of the armed forces will have to change. The force structures inherited from the Cold War are those of a muscle-bound athlete: too strong to cope with contingencies calling for nimbleness in contests where the issue is not national survival. In a limited but real shooting war, the weapons of choice will not be extraordinarily costly platforms, but stand-off systems, such as cruise missiles or pilotless aircraft. In turn, stand-off weapons can be launched from fairly low-cost platforms kept well to the rear: arsenal ships at sea, retrofitted old combat aircraft, or even militarized airliners.

Budget pressure also increases the emphasis on electronics and computing power brought from the general economy, where the discipline of flat-out competition in the marketplace promotes cost reduction along with excellence of performance. The defence sector will rely less and less on so-called military specifications, which imply custom-built and therefore costly components and subsystems. This is in contrast to the previous decades of the century, in which military requirements tended to generate spin-off towards the general economy. The first jet aircraft, the first computers and the ancestor of the Internet were all developed to meet military needs. Internet, initially called ARPAnet – after the name of the American Defense Advanced Research Projects Agency – was set up by the Pentagon in 1969. It was to serve not only as a modern means of communication between scientists and engineers working on military contracts, but also as part of an effort to maintain connections between US research establishments even after a Soviet nuclear attack would have destroyed traditional communication links. But if the Internet was a child of the Cold War, the hyperactive civilian adolescent it has since become will, in turn, spawn military applications in future command and information systems.

This new reliance of defence on the civilian sector has major strategic consequences, since anyone with a minimum of financial means and technical expertise at their disposal will have access to the fruits of the process. The days when it could be said, as in the era of colonial conquest, that the Western countries would prevail because 'we have the Maxim gun and they do not' are rapidly passing and the old industrial countries will find that their technical advance in military affairs is a wasting asset.

Video-Clip Wars

Technology will also change war as it is fought out through the media. War being a battle of wills, its propaganda and information dimension has always been important, as is made clear in the first recorded accounts of conflict in the Bible Lands, Ancient Greece or the China of the Warring Kingdoms. Technology which offers the instantaneous relay of breaking news – and, just as important, the expectation of instant coverage – has now become a reality.

Live or close-to-real-time TV coverage offers extraordinary opportunities for contenders in the battle of the wills. The crude bomb that exploded during the 1996 Olympic Games in Atlanta enjoyed a degree of international coverage out of all proportion to its casualties or political significance. The visual from the Atlanta open-air entertainment park – which drove out coverage of the unexplained mid-air explosion of flight TWA 800 off the US coast a few days earlier – was a vivid example of the inflationary impact of pent-up demand among journalists and viewers for news that seemed in short supply. Instant access and demand for it will become more widespread in the coming decades, as cheaper and more convenient satellite transmission from camera in the field to television set in the living room becomes available and as the use of on-line computer networks spreads.

Spectacular changes indeed, but to what extent will they really transform the manner in which wars are fought, notably by open democracies? A first key lies in the fact that real-time and almost universal media coverage does not necessarily entail the disappearance of censorship or manipulation. Indeed, the opposite may be the case: in a civilization which becomes accustomed to quick access to news, what will count for the broadcaster is the existence of immediately available images as opposed to access to higher-grade but less spectacular and less rapidly available information. The probing war correspondents who bedevilled the lives of field commanders from Balaclava (1854) to the fall of Saigon (1975) are not nearly as valuable to the shareholders of the modern broadcasting media as exciting live imagery hyped up by talking heads.

This reality has been rapidly seized upon by the military and their political masters, since it provides the opportunity for exercising new forms of control on the flow of news from battlefield to living room. The Gulf War showed what could be done, following the smaller-scale experiment conducted by the US military during the invasion of Grenada in 1983. In the Gulf, journalists were cooped up in rear-echelon hotels, occasionally taken on brief, highly regimented tours of the forces well clear of the front lines, and fed with whatever could produce good television. Militarily trivial but otherwise lively information was pumped through the system: video-game images from smart bombs; fireworks as incoming Scuds were met by Patriot surface-to-air missiles; Multiple-Launch Rocket Systems (MLRS) generating plumes of smoke as they blasted away towards Iraqi lines beyond the horizon ... There was hardly any access to the front itself. Not a single dead Allied soldier was ever shown during the war itself.

The pace of coverage has now become that of the video-clip: staccato reporting, in a context where one item of news immediately chases away the previous one, and where the presentation of information becomes an element of audience entertainment in competition with other forms of entertainment. Under those circumstances, coverage of military intervention in conflicts of less than vital importance has to be self-contained – in effect, a story with a beginning and an end – and it has to be dramatic, as well as positive, since only those characteristics will sustain both audience interest and political support. The Gulf War had to be short in its 'active' phase, even if its build-up could be slow, since the preparatory phase could be dealt with as the deliberate setting of the stage for the ensuing drama.

This means that two types of war not involving vital interests will be sustainable in a modern society: on the one hand, short and apparently decisive conflicts with a high media profile; on the other, long-drawn-out affairs provided they retain a low degree of media interest, which in turn implies an absence of casualties or other unpleasantness. US forces could remain in Beirut for fourteen months from September 1982 because nobody really noticed, once the hoopla surrounding the initial deployment had died down. As soon as spectacular casualties occurred – the truck-bombing of the US headquarters in Beirut in November 1983 – the cue for the exit was given.

With the development of access to the media – we can call it mediatization – these effects will become ever more pervasive. Iran, Saudi Arabia or China seek in vain to suppress satellite dishes for private use; and yet these are prominent fixtures compared with the unobtrusive means of access to the Internet or to the global direct satellite mobile telephone networks which will proliferate during the coming decade. This extreme mediatization of conflict will play into the hands of groups conducting terrorist operations or countries undertaking a high-prestige *coup de main*: either the targeted party will have to resolve the conflict in its favour immediately, or it will have to give in.

This comes with a caveat: the logic of mediatization can go into reverse when the challenged entity considers that its vital interests are at stake. As we have noted, if damage is inflicted against forces or assets engaged in the defence of peripheral interests, the media pressure will tend to play against continuing a military operation. This is what happened to the Americans in Beirut in 1983. But if a given society feels that its essential interests – territorial integrity, political freedom, national sovereignty and the like – are being threatened, the media can help sustain patriotic fervour for the long haul. In such situations, even bad news – the Japanese attack on the US fleet at Pearl Harbor, for instance – will become part of the process of mass mobilization.

The Devil's Playground

During the Cold War, the opposition between the Soviet Empire and the West was, with few exceptions, the shaping force of the world's military conflicts. Admittedly, most wars had their own unique origins: it didn't take a KGB plot or a CIA conspiracy to set Arabs and Israelis at each other's throats. But scarcely any conflict, including the Arab–Israeli wars, evolved independently of superpower intervention. On the one hand, each of the superpowers was prone to provoking, fuelling or exploiting conflict to its own ends, if only for fear that its rival would seize an advantage. This increased the number and lethality of conflicts which otherwise would either not have happened or would at least have remained of a lower order of intensity. The wars in Korea and Vietnam are cases in point. On the other hand, after the Cuban Missile Crisis of 1962, neither of the superpowers wished to put to the ultimate test the limits of their mutual nuclear deterrence. So-called regional conflicts were not allowed to get out of hand. The October 1973 war pitting Israel against Egypt and Syria was an example of this mixture of superpower 'arson' (in the form of massive airlifts of weaponry by the US and the USSR to their respective allies) and 'fire-fighting' (the same superpowers imposing a ceasefire).

The Cold War, with its emphasis on security, helped create a sense of willing discipline among the democracies; and among other states it provided an excuse for repressive political systems. In the field of warfare, as in others, the disciplines of the Cold War system have disappeared. This is often for the good. The removal of the threat of a nuclear holocaust as a result of a superpower confrontation is not a small blessing. There is also a lot to be said for the disappearance of conflicts which relied heavily on superpower and other outside support – the return to peace in Southern Africa, in Ethiopia–Eritrea, in Indo-China, in Central America, owes a lot to the passing of the Cold War. But the end of the ideological and power contest between the USSR and the USA has also opened new opportunities for warfare. Liberation from Soviet oppression and from the threat of a third world war has produced many beneficiaries, some worthy, some much less so. War has also been freed, from the particular rules and occasional limits set by the realities of the Cold War. Former 'no-go areas' have been opened to warfare, from the Balkans to Tajikistan. Formerly important allies or assets have ceased to be regarded as worth having. State power has been allowed to break down in areas considered to be marginal to global prosperity, such as Africa. Unrestrained violence has occurred as a result, notably producing disintegration in Somalia and Liberia.

The age when the West and the East had to some extent to see every conflict through the prism of the superpower confrontation has given way to a period of stand-alone rationales for warfare. During the next twenty-five years we may in effect witness four broad categories of warfare. First, there will be 'rogue state' wars, undertaken by virulently anti-Western dictatorships gaining access to weapons of mass destruction. This type of conflict is most likely to occur in the 'crescent of crisis' extending from North Africa to Afghanistan. Although a source of widespread anxiety, this may not prove to be the most difficult challenge to cope with. The second category will be wars of secession by subgroups seeking power for themselves within previously existing states, as in the former Yugoslavia. The Indian subcontinent and subSaharan Africa, as well as the Balkans and parts of the former Soviet Union, are likely theatres of such conflicts, which may be characterized by extremes of hatred and violence. Third will be wars of disruption directed by foreign and domestic groups against the functioning of existing societies, with means as different as the terror of extreme violence or the 'virtual destruction' of cyberwar. The industrialized countries will be particularly vulnerable to this type of warfare. Finally, there will be 'classical' Clausewitzian wars, where nineteenth-century goals will be sought with twenty-first century tools, East Asia being particularly at risk. If much of the world has been witnessing a reduction of the role of the nation-state as the prime actor in foreign affairs and as the monopoly wielder of the power to make war, these changes have not occurred in East Asia. There, traditional state-based power relations are the norm. On the basis of current trends, in 2014 East Asia may bear an uncanny resemblance to 1914 Europe.

These categories of warfare will rarely be encountered in a 'pure' form – for instance, the Gulf War fits into at least three of these categories – and they can be waged with widely varying degrees of violence. But, for the purpose of highlighting the stakes and the risks involved, we will illustrate these various types of war with capsule scenarios with a mix of regional conflicts and confrontations involving the remaining superpower, the United States; these scenarios also assume high levels of force, thus putting into play an array of tools in keeping with the nature of the conflict described.

Rogue State: How Libya Returned to the Stone Age

In 2012, Colonel Muammar Gadaffi celebrated his seventieth birthday with a great military parade and a grand display of fireworks on the Tripoli waterfront. Although invitations had been sent to the heads of state in countries belonging to what used to be called the Third World, only two of his peers stood at his side on the reviewing stand: Fidel Castro (age eighty-five) of Cuba and Saddam Hussein (age seventy-five) of Iraq. His other anti-imperialist friends had died away or been overthrown. Gadaffi knew that he was himself a dying man, his personal physician having diagnosed the onset of Creutzfeldt-Jakob disease.

Despite its oil exports, Colonel Gadaffi's police-state was a wreck of a country, after forty years of economic mismanagement. Neighbouring Tunisia, a fraction of the size of Libya, had meanwhile become the first of the 'Lions' – African and Arab states which had followed in the footsteps of the Asian Tiger economies. But Gadaffi had something that his neighbours didn't. After many years of frustrating efforts, Libya had assembled a handful of missile-launched nuclear warheads and weaponized nerve gas and biotoxins.

In 2012, the day after the birthday parade, the Libyans used the old trick of staging manoeuvres as a cover for the invasion of Tunisia. After claims that there had been Tunisian armed provocations, Libyan ground forces crossed the border. Radio Tripoli called for an immediate Tunisian capitulation, otherwise 'special weapons' would be used. Conversely, Tunisian acquiescence would bring about the merger of the two states. Although Tunisian forces were unprepared, they managed to hold their ground a hundred kilometres or so to the rear of the border along the Mareth Line of Second World War fame. Washington and Paris had immediately declared their readiness to provide full political and military support, an offer snapped up by Tunis. Forty-eight hours after the Libyans had entered Tunisia, the conflict was internationalized.

Libya took the first step in changing the nature of a war which had started out as a remake of El Alamein rather than of *Star Wars*. Colonel Gadaffi loosed a barrage of eighteen Scud missiles against Tunis and Bizerte. Many of these antiquated devices broke up in flight and crashed harmlessly into the neighbouring waters or on to farmland. However, five chemical and three biological warheads scored bull's-eyes and successfully dispersed their deadly cargo in heavily populated central Tunis. Fifty thousand inhabitants were killed by nerve gas. Within days several hundred thousand more were in the terminal throes of lethal anthrax.

The Western Allies' military intervention was at once thrown into high gear. Within minutes of the Libyan Scud strike, swarms of precision-guided bombs and cruise missiles destroyed the bulk of Libya's military communication and command networks, along with most of the air-defence and logistics infrastructure. The Allies succeeded in doing what the Gulf War coalition had signally failed to do in 1991 despite their overwhelming airpower: to detect and destroy mobile Scud launchers. Within twenty-four hours, Libya was shorn of most of the means of waging an organized war, whether offensive or defensive. A US Marine brigade and a French combat helicopter regiment were deployed alongside their Tunisian allies in the next few days.

Each Allied infantry soldier was equipped with a glove-back computer screen allowing him (or her) to visualize any chosen aspect of the battle, providing instant 'battlefield awareness'. Hand-held keyboards enabled soldiers to call in support, exchange information or keep in touch with battlefield 'crawlies' – miniature robots operating behind Libyan lines, providing data or wreaking electronic havoc. Head-up displays mounted on goggles no more obtrusive than ordinary spectacles made it possible to 'see' in the infra-red and ultra-violet parts of the spectrum – a useful capability for operating at night or for detecting camouflaged sources of heat such as tank engines or bivouacs.

This select force, operating against ten times its own number, reached and breached the Libyan border within hours of its deployment. However, when it approached the outskirts of Tripoli, Colonel Gadaffi played his last card, issuing an ultimatum: either the foreign forces returned from where they came, or else Libyan nuclear weapons would be detonated. Relayed by the Libyan leader himself during an interview by Oriana Fallaci on CNN, the threat could not be disregarded. Gadaffi was helped by the elements. A major thunderstorm, preceded by a sandstorm, struck in the Tripoli area. Smothered by the sand, soaked by the rain, the Allies forces were temporarily pinned down, their precision-guided weapons blinded by the elements while the electrical storm played havoc with their computer links. For a time, combat conditions were brought back to those of an earlier age.

Allied forces were ordered by their political leaders to cease fire and stop their advance, while Gadaffi was put on notice that any use of weapons of mass destruction against the Allies would be punished in kind, and disproportionately so.

Had Gadaffi been a healthy and sane dictator, mutual deterrence of sorts could have taken hold. He would have avoided running the mortal risk of putting Allied determination to the test, and would thus have remained in power, albeit in charge of a shattered country partly occupied by the enemy. As an already condemned man, he decided otherwise. His remaining mobile missile launchers were wheeled out and fired at the main US and French staging-point. The four Scuds and six surface-to-surface cruise missiles were intercepted by American missile defences. Two nuclear warheads, however, made it through the defences. The bombs wrought less damage than the previous chemical and biological attacks against Tunisia, because the Allied forces were well spread out in the desert: immediate casualties were in the low thousands. But the Allies did not wait to count the bodies. Retaliation was massive. Within minutes, two multiple-warhead Trident II D-5 missiles were launched by the submarine USS

Tennessee and the French shot ten ASMP-*Plus* nuclear cruise missiles from their Corsica-based *Rafale* fighter-bombers. The combined twenty-six warheads erased Tripoli and Benghazi from the face of the earth and destroyed Libya's hitherto untouched petroleum industry. Along with its dictator, Libya had ceased to exist as a nation.

Secession: The Break-Up of India

By 2010, successful economic reform had transformed a hitherto slow-growing Indian Union into the new Asian powerhouse: ten years of 10 per cent growth a year had turned India with its then 1.1 billion inhabitants into the equivalent of what China had become in the mid-1990s. However, and unlike the Chinese heartland with its fairly homogeneous population, India was composed of a disparate patchwork of ethnic, linguistic and religious groups and castes. Over time, unequal economic growth created unbearable strains between the successful states of the Union – from the flourishing agro-business of Punjab to the world's software capital in Bangalore via the booming financial centre of Bombay – and those which were left behind – the teeming unemployed and destitute masses of states such as Uttar Pradesh and Bihar. The richer states became increasingly resentful of the financial demands of the All-Union authorities in favour of the underprivileged, who were increasingly being mobilized by a national-populist surge of militant Hindu xenophobia.

After the electoral victory of the Hindu nationalists at the Union level, Karnataka's 60 million inhabitants issued a unilateral declaration of independence, followed by Maharashtra (100 million) and Bengal (90 million). Comparatively small but economically powerful Punjab split into a three-way civil war between Sikh separatists, central government forces and local Hindu authorities. In major Indian cities, lynch mobs attacked those belonging to the 'wrong' group. Organized warfare erupted between federal forces and local militias initially equipped through the seizure of isolated garrisons, arms depots and deserting Union units. The conflict rapidly escalated as the arms industries in the hands of the secessionists were made to operate at maximum capacity; modern combat aircraft, missiles, main-battle tanks and artillery were fielded by all sides. The software wizards of Bangalore wrought electronic havoc in the Union forces' command-and-control system.

The ethnic fragility of the Union was paralleled by the geographical and political dispersal of territorially unconnected but individually powerful secessionist areas, making for a particularly violent conflict, reminiscent – albeit on a vastly larger scale – of the American Civil War of 1861–5 or the Spanish Civil War of 1936–9. The strategic stakes could not be ignored by China, Russia and the United States, but the general tendency of the outside powers was to keep their distance from a conflict with an unpredictable outcome. Although sorely tempted to seize Kashmir from a beleaguered Delhi government, Pakistan too stayed out of the conflict.

The most vulnerable secessionist state, Maharashtra, escalated the conflict by using biologically produced neurotoxins against the federal forces. Flying columns of Maharashtra and Bengali soldiers then converged on New Delhi. As a last resort, the Union threatened the use of nuclear weapons. Maharashtra, having seized weapons-grade plutonium from the atomic reprocessing facility in Trombay, threatened retaliation in kind. Stalemate and a ceasefire appeared to be within grasp. But the progress of a particularly effective computer virus created a panic among Union authorities, who feared the rapid crippling of their capability to exercise effective command and control of their nuclear weapons. Faced with a 'use them or lose them' dilemma, the federal government fired a salvo of nuclear-tipped Prithvi ballistic missiles against secessionist targets.

The nuclear exchange destroyed key cities and infrastructure in the former Indian Union, killing millions. But a third world war did not take place, because outside powers stood aloof from the internecine massacre. Nor did this crossing of the nuclear threshold lead to a 'nuclear-winter', plunging the planet into a new Ice Age: after all, the quantity of nuclear weapons actually used remained significantly smaller than the dozens of much more powerful nuclear tests which had been conducted in the atmosphere each year by the superpowers in the early 1960s. However, the world economy was precipitated into a devastating economic but brief depression as the nuclear scare paralysed consumers and investors everywhere.

On the ground nothing was resolved in the short run, large scale military operations being impossible to conduct under such conditions: anarchy prevailed for the better part of the decade.

War in Cyberspace: An Electronic Pearl Harbor

As the end of the millennium approached, new sects and fringe groups emerged in a United States more than ever characterized by religious revivalism and extreme individualism. Among such organizations, the Brigade of Luddites Against State Terror (BLAST) was to acquire a particular notoriety for having unleashed what the then serving American President was to call a 'micro-second that will live in infamy'. BLAST had recruited a phalanx of science students from prestigious universities, building on the organizational expertise of some of the most skilled people in the death-and-terror business. The creed of the group was simple: the world would come to an end on 1 January 2000. Only the select few would gain redemption, having actively helped the Lord bring about the end of a World of Evil exemplified by the oppressive federal American state.

The battle plan of the sect consisted in the injection of an unobtrusive dormant computer virus into the software of the main ground-based US telecommunication nodes. The virus would be activated as soon as the digits 00 had replaced the digits 99, a threshold which would be crossed at midnight on 31 December 1999 upon the arrival of the new millennium. Once set in motion in cyberspace, the virus would comprehensively destroy the software of all digital telephone switching equipment. Its effectiveness would be enhanced by the frailness of computer systems which would have trouble enough coping with the normal passage from 1999 to 2000.

At 00:00 on 1 January 2000, North America's main telecommunications networks went dead; voice and data links were interrupted. The Millennium Virus brought the US economy to an instant halt, as all externally networked organizations, from financial markets to mail-order firms, were prevented from communicating. CB operators, ham radio buffs and subscribers to the first satellite systems offering direct communications links were among the select groups which could still talk, albeit only with others similarly equipped. A number of defence facilities with their inward-focused networks, strong electronic 'firewalls' and dedicated communication links could still function normally. But these were the exceptions.

Across the country, airports closed – indeed two airliners collided in mid-air, killing hundreds, as a result of air-traffic-control failure. Hospitals with their computers down were operating in battlefield conditions. A cataclysm was only narrowly averted when an overflow of liquefied natural gas occurred in Boston Harbor because of the electronic failure of valve-control equipment during transshipment operations.

Fortunately the US was not at war; and the economy would hardly have been functioning anyway on 1 January 2000. The great American talent for organization helped limit the initial catastrophe; indeed, after a few months of economic collapse and its toll on the standard of living, a new boom began, led by firms specializing in hardened software, in 'firewall' technology protecting computer networks, and in satellite-based voice and data links. Constellations of satellites entirely obviating the need for earth-based relays and switches spread like wildfire.

Unlike the Japanese during the surprise attack on Pearl Harbor, the cyberterrorists remained undetected after their misdeed. Soon they were busily working on the algorithms for Satellite Array Destruction, which became known as the SAD Virus, to be used on the 150th anniversary of the death of Ada Byron in 1851. Ada Byron, a daughter of Lord Byron, could be described as the first computer programmer, who had provided the software for Babbage's mechanical calculator, the forerunner of the digital revolution.

Wars of Value Projection, or How the US Navy Was Sunk

Before the post-Cold War era had entered its second decade, hopes of establishing a 'new world order' had been reduced to proportions rather more modest than those expressed by President Bush during the Gulf crisis of 1990–1. In Iraq as in Bosnia, the incumbents had survived foreign intervention. Yet these countries had been the theatre of successful operations.

For fear of losing casualties, the United States had become increasingly wary of military interventions involving ground forces. Military operations had to aim for zero casualties. However, such stand-off interventions had fairly narrow limits against a determined foe: despite forty days of unrelenting air strikes, ground forces had to be used to secure the liberation of Kuwait in February 1991. Furthermore, these limits were to narrow further, as the corresponding technology, when available to both sides, tended to make things easier for the defender than for the intervener. This asymmetry was greatly enhanced if the intervener was aiming for a speedy and low-casualty conclusion. This is not a constraint usually experienced by the country which is being intervened against.

The US Navy was to discover this at its expense in the Battle of the Pescadores in the spring of 2007. After the reincorporation of Hong Kong into China on 1 July 1997, the leadership in Beijing sought the conquest of Taiwan. A costly but successful landing operation had captured the Taiwanese islands of Quemoy and Matsu in late 2006. A tight blockade by the Chinese air and naval forces was hampering the foreign trade on which Taiwan's economy was entirely dependent: harbours and territorial waters were mined and Taiwanese ships were sunk. However, China was careful not to attack foreign shipping on the high seas, since freedom of navigation is a vital interest of sea-faring nations, including the United States. The next step for China was to seize the Pescadore Islands, which would serve as the springboard for the final invasion of Taiwan proper, less than thirty miles distant.

Under pressure from US public opinion and the Congress, the American government decided to send a naval task force to defend the principle of self-determination in the face of military coercion. The Americans had not forgotten how Beijing had previously destroyed Hong Kong's freedom. The task force despatched to protect the Pescadores was built around the carriers *Harry S Truman* and *Dwight D. Eisenhower*, fielding a total of twenty-four F-14 and forty-two F-18 combat aircraft, along with eighty other aeroplanes and twenty-four helicopters, as well as enough Harpoon missiles to sink most of China's fleet. China was given due warning that the US force had rules of engagement which would in effect prevent Chinese forces from landing on the Pescadores. It was also pointed out to Beijing that using combat radars (by 'illuminating' prospective targets) would be considered a hostile act. This constraint was readily circumvented by the Chinese, who used their radar-surveillance satellites and their air-traffic-control radars to keep track of the US task force.

For several weeks, little happened. The Chinese fleet, after some careful probing which drew convincing American counter-moves, refrained from any behaviour which could have been construed as a threat. Indeed, it slipped away for routine repair and overhaul in Fuzhou and Amoy. Rhetoric in Beijing about 'liberation by 1 July' was all but dropped. Even the giant 'countdown-meter' which displayed the number of hours remaining before the symbolic date of 1 July was removed from Tiananmen Square. The US relaxed, while normal trade-flows with Taiwan were resumed in the wake of large and unimpeded minesweeping operations.

At twilight on May Day, the officers on watch in the *Dwight D. Eisenhower*'s combat centre were intrigued by the somewhat unusual flight pattern of the regular Fuzhou–Hong Kong civilian air service, provided by a Boeing 747. Mindful of disaster caused in 1988 when the USS *Vincennes* shot down a civilian Iranian Airbus, killing 290 passengers, the task force did not respond immediately. The Americans were also hampered by the knowledge that Beijing had indicated that it also would consider the use of combat radars as a hostile act.

When US surveillance radars finally picked up the several dozen objects released by the Boeing 747, it was too late for the American fleet to mount a convincing response; a second 'civilian' Boeing 747 flying in the first one's shadow had already followed suit. Guided by GPS as well as by infra-red and radar seekers, the swarm of cruise missiles swamped American defences. Surface-to-air missiles, Phalanx rapid-fire machine guns, decoys and smoke managed to destroy or divert up to three-quarters of the incoming rockets: but one out of four got through. The *Dwight D. Eisenhower* and the *Harry S. Truman* both took at least ten hits of armour-penetrating 800-kilo warheads. This was only the first wave; within seconds more than 200 ground-launched sea-skimming missiles followed the initial salvo. When the sun had set, the two

US flagships were sinking, along with several Aegis air-defence and anti-missile cruisers, not to mention other craft. Not a single Chinese ship or combat aircraft had been damaged. Beijing sent a message through the 'hot line' to the White House that any military reprisal against Chinese territory would draw a nuclear response. To bring home the message, the doors of Chinese missile silos in Sinkiang were opened, for US spy satellites to contemplate. At the same time, China recalled that it did not consider itself to be in a state of war with the US, whose ships had no business attempting to prevent 'the settlement of a domestic Chinese matter'.

Following the Battle of the Pescadores, the United States Navy speeded up its arsenal-ship programme, which had reached prototype stage during the previous year. These barge-like ships were capable of shooting several hundred long-range cruise missiles without getting into harm's way.

Clausewitz in Asia: A 2020 Vision

The flashpoints for the 2020 War, as it later became known, were the oil and gas fields under the waters of the South China Sea. The quest for fossil fuels had become desperate for the energy-guzzling industrialized states in the region. At the same time, these countries were seeking a geopolitical role in keeping with their recently acquired strength.

China, which had overtaken the United States economy by 2017, needed oil imports of more than 7 million barrels a day – as much as Western Europe or North America. China was also rivalling the United States in the scale of its military spending. Indonesia, with its quarter-billion population, had an economy and a military as big as Japan's. Korean reunification had reproduced the erstwhile German economic miracle. Thailand, with a population of 60 million-plus, was the economic equivalent of France. Malaysia had completed its '2020 development plan' launched in the early 1990s, and had overtaken Australia econ-omically. All of the Asian countries were net oil importers, even Indonesia, which had been a founding member of OPEC, the Organization of Petroleum Exporting Countries.

In the late 1990s people believed that crisis had been avoided when the South-east Asian states and China had peacefully settled claims for the ownership of the Spratly Islands in the South China Sea, thought to be rich in oil. China had acquired possession of most of these tiny low-lying islands, and an international consortium had been set up between the nations of the region to share out the hydrocarbon resources. The agreement was deemed a historic breakthrough, because the matter had brought the region to the brink of war several times. Alas, it gradually transpired that the area was practically barren of oil.

Meanwhile, Indonesia struck pay dirt by discovering giant oil fields in the Natuna Island region, which had already been producing gas and oil in the early 1990s. Jakarta might have been able to benefit unhindered from the windfall: its title was strong, and its armed forces should have been capable of defending the area. But a tight-fisted Finance Ministry had prevented the establishment of a solid, in-depth defence of the oil and gas installations.

War became inevitable as the consequence of a power vacuum in Indonesia. After inconclusive election results, a coalition of opponents attempted to overthrow the government. Turmoil ensued, marked by widespread anti-Chinese pogroms in Java which inflamed emotion in Beijing. China sealed a secret alliance with Malaysia, and together they challenged the historical basis of Indonesia's possession of Natuna. Not entirely by coincidence, Chinese historians stated that the Ming Dynasty traveller and explorer Zheng He had set up an outpost in Natuna in 1433. Malaysia in turn recalled that the islands had been a favourite haunt of the pirate-princes of Sarawak. Diplomatic pressure and military moves short of war unfolded over a period of several months.

A last-ditch diplomatic conference was set up in the suitably neutral Spanish city of Algeciras to attempt to devise a solution. *En route*, the head of the Chinese delegation was assassinated by a terrorist group of the Aceh–North Sumatra Liberation Army. Beijing issued an ultimatum to the Indonesian government. The answer was considered unsatisfactory and Beijing's naval forces seized key Natuna oil installations. Most were destroyed in the process, unleashing an ecological catastrophe exceeding that created by the torching of the Kuwaiti oil wells in 1991. The modern blue-water navy which China had built up over the previous decades performed creditably in the military task of taking over the archipelago, although a number of ships were sunk by Indonesian air-launched stand-off weapons.

The 2020 War spiralled out of control as extremists took over in Malaysia. The reincorporation of Singapore into the Malaysian Federation (from which it had seceded in 1965) was a key item on their agenda but the city-state put up a robust resistance. Australia provided economic support to Indonesia. Thailand struck at Malaysia, in order to seize Kedah, Kelantan, Perlis and Terengganu, the sultanates which had been under its suzerainty before 1909 and which it had annexed for four years during the Second World War. Oil-starved Korea and Japan sought American protection.

Beijing had a relatively free hand in dealing with its southern adversaries, because the US remained studiously neutral as long as China did not attack America's interests or the territory of its allies. But fear of Russian, Japanese and Korean military involvement restrained it from committing more naval and land forces to the south than strictly necessary for achieving its limited objective of seizing and holding Natuna.

The war did not trigger the use of nuclear weapons. Beijing's nuclear arsenal deterred any strike against Chinese territory. Korea, Japan and Australia, thanks to their American alliance, had the US nuclear umbrella to shield their homelands. However, the infrastructure of all the South-east Asian states was shattered by the intensive use of air- and sea-launched stand-off missiles during the six-week war. Direct civilian casualties remained limited, since weapons of mass destruction were not used and because the geography of the area lent itself to air and naval operations rather than to the deployment of mass armies.

Indirect losses in the region were phenomenal, as starvation gripped essentially urban populations deprived of the key elements of their physical and electronic infrastructure. It would have required something like the Marshall Plan of 1947–8 to build the region to its previous dynamism and prosperity. No such plan was forthcoming. The United States of 2020 did not occupy the commanding economic position it had held at the end of the

Second World War. Although Chinese, Japanese and Korean cities remained unscathed, the ecomomic disruption caused by the demise of South-East Asia as a source of consumer and investment demand led to a global slump.

Grunts, Geeks and Crazies

Each generation develops its own particular organization of warfare in terms of who directs the fighting or fights the wars. The mercenary bands of the Thirty Years' War (1618–48), of which the Vatican's Swiss Guards are a residual manifestation, are one type of military organization. Armed forces as an amalgam of young noblemen and press-ganged unfortunates in eighteenth-century Europe or the *levée en masse* of the French Revolutionary Wars are other contrasting examples. They show how over fairly short periods of time the human and organizational elements of war can change.

War in the twentieth century had two main sets of actors: conscripts and managers. Only with the draft could states raise sufficient forces to seize and hold territory against similarly organized foes. Universal and compulsory military service had been the consequence of major improvements in the organization of the central state, which made it possible to tally, induct and regiment vast cohorts of young men. This form of military organization was invented, and used with great success at the end of the eighteenth century, by a young French general, Napoleon Bonaparte, who harnessed the growing central power of the French state to new purposes. Supplying conscripts with reasonably effective weapons while providing their units with a sufficiency of long-range firepower – notably in the form of field artillery – became possible with the beginnings of mass production of standardized arms: Napoleonic artillery and musketry were early examples of this.

The other prominent member of the twentieth-century cast of military characters was that of the organizer, the manager of war, in the form of the modern staff officer. Although Napoleonic warfare saw the beginnings of dedicated general staff and quartermaster organizations, these really came into their own after the middle of the nineteenth century. The Prussian General Staff had brought about within a few years of its creation the defeat of Denmark (1864), Austria and the anti-Prussian German states (1866) and France (1870–1). The German General Staff of 1871–1914 inspired other countries to follow suit, while the progress of industry, transportation networks and state organization made it possible to wage total war drawing on all of modern society's human and material resources. Over the decades, military staffs grew as the impedimenta of modern military units became ever more heavy and complex.

By the end of the Cold War, the operational aspects of staff work were playing second fiddle to logistics: in the Gulf War, millions of tonnes of *matériel* had to be moved before the first shot was fired. Any disruption of the logistics flow would have 'deorchestrated' the force build-up and disorganized the conduct of operations. It was most fortunate for the coalition forces that Saddam Hussein did not shoot one or two cruise missiles every day at the staging-points of the build-up in the port of Jubail and the airbase of Dhahran.

If General Norman Schwarzkopf is well known for having successfully directed and conducted the Allied operations in the Gulf, it is his less well-known subordinate in charge of logistics, General 'Gus' Pagonis, who made the operations possible in the first place. But this in turn brings to mind the French comment: *'C'est magnifique, mais ce n'est pas la guerre'* – it was a feat of management, not of strategy, which was accomplished. The forces of inertia such as the sheer bulk of things and people to be moved, the pressure of time, the complexity of the logistics flows, the difficulties of geography and climate: these were the defeated 'enemies'. The forces of the Gulf War coalition came very close to collapsing under their own weight. Yet there will be relatively few circumstances in which an intervention force will be able to build up a massive array without being disturbed by the real enemy.

Once one adds to that observation the political and strategic realities of the post-Cold War era, it should not come as a surprise that a substantial degree of recasting will take place as the theatre of war changes in nature. The era of the 'managers of war', in the form of military staff officers, is coming to a close, as other actors come to the fore. Three archetypes have been chosen here. They are not entirely new, but not all have played such prominent roles hitherto.

Grunts

The footsoldier will remain central to warfare. But instead of the multitudes produced by conscription from the Napoleonic Wars to the rice fields of Vietnam, the infantryman (or woman) will have chosen his (or her) calling. Since professional armies have been around in modern industrialized countries for some time – notably in the United Kingdom and the United States – one already has a fair idea of the kind of human profile such forces tend to have.

In practice, attitudes and background do not greatly depart from what they would be in a conscript force. The percentage of ethnic minorities may be higher (as in the US Army), the proportion of working- or lower-middle-class youths may be greater (as in the British Army), than would be the case with universal military service; but the ethos and the habits are not substantially different from those prevalent in a draft army. With the partial exception of special forces – Rangers or Force Delta in the US, the Special Air Service or Special Boat Service in the UK – these professional armies do not project an image of 'dogs of war'. As for special forces, those too have their counterparts in conscript forces (the French Service Action, not to mention the Foreign Legion; the Spanish Tercio; the former Soviet Spetsnaz, and so on).

Indeed, one of the problems of professional forces in the future may be that they won't have enough of a war-fighting attitude. In modern armies, the concerns of the soldiers may not be substantially different from those of society at large: pay scales, conditions of rotation between garrisons, the state of living quarters, the situation of employed spouses and so forth may take precedence over more martial topics. In societies such as the United States which emphasize the notion of 'zero death' conflict and the need for overwhelming superiority as a prerequisite for military intervention, the notion of risk and sacrifice may become exceedingly hazy. That being said, once a military force, whether conscript or professional, has been put in the presence of a shooting adversary, little time elapses before it functions as a fighting force, if only out of a sense of active self-preservation. Its degree of success in this process will then depend on the nature and extent of prior training, tradecraft and unit cohesion.

The footsoldier – or the 'grunt' as front-line American infantrymen became known in Vietnam – of the next century will possess one major advantage and a no less important liability compared to his forebears. He, or indeed she, will benefit from the greater simplicity and ease of use which modern technology gives to modern weapons (as it does to more mundane appliances). A modern assault rifle, a GPS receiver for accurate navigation, a hand-held or glove-back computer and 'fire and forget' anti-tank missiles are immeasurably more convenient to operate, particularly in the stress of battle, than a wheel-lock musket, a compass-cum-ordnance-survey-map, a first-generation walkie-talkie or a muzzle-loading cannon. Technical sophistication goes hand in hand with simplicity of use: the difficulties of maintenance and repair are shunted towards the rear.

The liability is the immediate corollary of the asset. With such tools being made available to all and sundry, the battlefield of the future will be a particularly demanding one. With night-vision devices, the distinction between night and day will diminish; with man-portable fire-and-forget missiles and rapid-fire individual arms, attacks will occur with little opportunity to counter-fire effectively against a barely revealed foe; drones and other pilotless aircraft or robots will be on a permanent lookout and will fire (or direct fire) at any detected target; instant liaison with longer-range weapons – field artillery, combat helicopters, close-air-support aircraft – will allow the rapid and accurate concentration of heavy fire in any part of the battlefield. These conditions will force each infantry unit to spread out as much as possible in order to avoid exposing a concentration of soldiers as a target, so each individual soldier will be more on his own than ever. The modern battlefield is, in this respect, a very lonely place to be in – and the future battlefield will be even more so.

The demands of continuous high-intensity combat on each individual will be formidable, with each second implying life-or-death decision-making under extreme stress. In a sense, this will recall the round-the-clock violence of trench warfare in 1914–18 France, but on a much broader, more rapidly moving battlefield, and without the possibility of hunkering down in deep shelters during enemy artillery attacks. In the future, these will be vulnerable to all manner of precision-strike stand-off weapons. In other words, infantry clashes will either be brief, or imply the rapid rotation of soldiers in and out of the area of battle. With stand-off weapons and remotely piloted vehicles reaching deep behind the immediate ground battle area, movement in and out may itself become an arduous feat of operations and logistics. The wars of 1956, 1967 and 1973 in the Middle East or the Falklands War may be the relevant model here, with active operations lasting days or weeks rather than months or years.

In effect, short bursts of fighting will be separated by lengthier interludes of longer-range exchange of fire not involving the use of infantry, along the lines of the 1969–71 War of Attrition between Egypt and Israel after the Six Day War. Indeed, the savage character of post-Cold War army operations may make the democracies particularly wary of entering into them, unless the enemy has already had his stuffing kicked out through air and naval operations. The Gulf War offered a preview of this, with the prolonged air offensive preceding the ground attack.

Geeks

The profile of the key players in long-distance, deep-strike warfare will be largely the same as that of the people who invent new software and navigate the Internet: geeks, or nerds, who are often extremely young, libertarian and completely immersed in their world of binary digits. But if their creativeness makes the world economy move forward they will also be developing and orchestrating the most modern means of destruction.

The intelligence which they make use of will be collected by unmanned sensors: optical, radar and eavesdropping satellites, drones, remotely piloted vehicles and miniaturized, remotely operated sensors deployed in enemy-controlled territory. Strikes against fortified or heavily-defended targets will be undertaken by cruise missiles and other stand-off weapons, while area targets, such as airfields or concentrations of vehicles, will be shattered by missiles releasing multiple bomblets. Power grids will be shorted by unmanned aircraft dispensing ribbons of metal. More insidiously, electronic networks will be infected by software-destroying viruses.

The co-ordination and management of this array of weapons will require a technical and organizational expertise somewhat different from what was required of the military staff officers of the First World War or the logisticians of the Second World War and its aftermath. Young men and women, wholly absorbed in the world of computer algorithms, software and networks, will be the essential operators. Their outlook and background will be largely civilian, the military dimension no more than an add-on.

The comparison between video-games and modern warfare is over-simple, but it contains more than a grain of truth. The skills for modern military mission planning are not substantially different from civilian applications, including computer games. Indeed, some of the more popular CD-ROM games are variants of declassified military mission preparation and other simulations of war. In 1996, the public could buy for $20 top-of-the-line war games which in 1993 or 1994 would have been available only to specialized military institutions, such as the US Naval Warfare Center. The world of games is virtual, whereas hi-tech war can be real – but the software and methodology which go into them are sometimes barely distinguishable.

Crazies

'Crazies' have always been among the wielders of violence, insofar as the word applies to individuals who operate outside the mainstream rules and attitudes which prevail in a given society. These 'social suicides', inhabiting fringe groups, use extreme levels of force, while being more or less ready to accept martyrdom, but they have not usually been major actors in large-scale warfare. The *Carbonari* of early nineteenth-century Italy, the radical anarchists of a century ago in Europe, the armed terrorists of the Baby Boom generation (including *Weathermen* in the US, *Brigate Rosse* in Italy, *Rote Armee Fraktion* in Germany, *Action Directe* in France, *Cellules Communistes Combattantes* in Belgium) have all made use of violence, but no one would pretend that it was war in the habitual sense. This may change as several kinds of pressure combine.

First, a comparatively large number of individuals can fit the stereotype description of militant radicalism as their own societies lose their bearings under the strain of internal contradictions and external pressures. For instance, in much of the Islamic world, radical conduct, or rather misconduct, is all the more widespread because the societies involved remain mired in despotism or poverty while being subjected to all that is vacuous or frustrating in Western influence, and yet being denied the West's positive political and economic values. Spawning grounds for extreme radicalism have thus flourished from the Atlas Mountains to the Hindu Kush. Not all the societies involved are poor – Bahrain or Saudi Arabia are nobody's idea of Third World poorhouses – but nearly all are intolerant of political and religious dissent. Indeed, it is the few countries in the region having at least some of the appurtenances of tolerance and democracy which have proved most resistant to the emergence of widespread violent fanaticism: Morocco, Jordan, Egypt.

Second, the power of the 'crazies' to wreak violence on a large scale rises if they are backed up by the logistics of supporting states. Iran, Syria, Libya, Sudan and Iraq have, at one time or another, played this role of the 'sponsor state'. US, Saudi and Pakistani support of the Mujahidin in Soviet-occupied Afghanistan played a similar, if unintended role. 'Afghanis' – up to 15,000 terrorists from various countries trained in the refugee camps of Peshawar in Pakistan – have become a standard fixture in the Islamic world, not least in Algeria, Saudi Arabia, Egypt and even the Philippines. Although the initial US–Saudi programme has since disappeared, the infrastructure remains, with substantial support from private Gulf state sources and from some of the larger radical Islamic movements.

Last, and possibly most important, the means of terror may well become as destructive as the tools of traditional warfare. The hand-held bombs of nineteenth-century anarchists or the Kalashnikovs of the Baader–Meinhof gang (the predecessors of the Rote Armee Fraktion) could kill dozens but not thousands. Conventional explosives in car- and truck-bombs already approach the scale of military operations: 299 US and French servicemen were killed by two truck-bombs in Beirut in November 1983; 168 civilians were killed by an explosive-stuffed van in Oklahoma City in 1995. Bombs in aircraft have on several occasions snuffed out several hundred lives: 329 fatalities in the Air India flight destroyed off Ireland in 1985, and 259 in the Pan Am jet at Lockerbie in 1988. Access to weapons of mass destruction will add one or two orders of magnitude to the terrorists' ability to kill – thousands or dozens of thousands in a single attack. Given the nature of the industrial processes involved, the logistics of transportation and operational ease of use, it is more likely that biological and chemical weapons will be used, rather than nuclear explosive. A nuclear weapon is hardly simple to produce, and if acquired 'off the shelf' – something which may not be possible even in a mafiosi-infested Russia – its transportation and detonation would be complex tasks for a non-state group to conduct. A flask of viruses, toxins or nerve gas is easier to handle and use. In particular, the noisome products of the ex-Soviet Biopreparat organization are a source of concern, at least as much so as the 'loose nukes' of the former Soviet Empire.

If the recent past is any sort of guide, 'crazies' will not be lacking in knowledge or training. Unabomber, a highly skilled mathematician, or the university graduates of the Rote Armee Fraktion typify what will be a common profile. Violent radicalism demonstrates a lack of morality and common sense, but not necessarily a dearth of ability and intelligence.

Some analysts of terrorism entertain the hope that extreme groups will not use weapons of mass destruction, making the point that terrorists are more interested in being talked about than in killing for its own sake. Aside from the fact that mass murder is a sure conversation-grabber, it is more likely than not that it is the lack of capability rather than the lack of intent which has kept the numbers killed by terrorists at levels below those of more conventional warfare. Inducing fear of sudden and brutal death is the purpose of terrorism. To create that fear, the act of killing itself is not always necessary, but it is no doubt the most straightforward way of achieving that purpose.

Civilians

As in previous ages of warfare, the central characters will be playing along with that large supporting cast known as the civilian population. Its involvement has greatly varied through time. Although civilians were traditionally victimized by armies on the move which lived off the land – a practice which was the norm well into the Napoleonic era – states didn't have the organizational ability to field large forces for any length of time. Overall, therefore, the population at large suffered little from war outside the areas lying directly in the path of armies. Particularly savage and long-lasting conflicts with a strong religious or ideological dimension, however, could lead to massive civilian losses: the Thirty Years' War in the seventeenth century destroyed about one-third of Germany's population.

For much of the twentieth century, civilian populations have been the principal victims of conflict, with soldiers often having a greater chance of survival than other members of the population. In 1939–45, some 50 million individuals were killed in Europe, of whom fewer than 20 million were soldiers. This pattern was repeated in many of the subsequent wars, Vietnam and Afghanistan being cases in point.

'Clean' wars, that is conflicts in which the civilian population remains essentially unscathed, have also existed in the twentieth century – most notably the series of Israeli–Arab wars of 1956, 1967 and 1973, the Indo-Pakistan wars of 1948 and 1965, and the Falklands War. It would be a mistake to ascribe the 'clean' nature of these conflicts simply to geographical factors ('there are few civilians in the desert') or to the limited nature of war aims. After all Israel and its Arab neighbours have had the means to strike at each other's population centres, including cities such as Damascus, Cairo or Tel Aviv, but have generally refrained from doing so. Nor was a conflict like the Six Day War limited in terms of its aims, since Israel's very existence was seen to be at stake by all parties at the beginning of that war. Leaving aside the restraint which the fear of reprisals can inspire, the distinction between wars of civilian slaughter and 'clean' wars depends fundamentally on whether or not the destruction or removal of civilians is in itself a war aim. The bloodiest wars are and will be those in which the answer to this question is positive. Ethnic cleansing (as in former Yugoslavia) and terrorism both arise from this wish to victimize civilians.

On the other hand, the move towards high-accuracy, long-range weaponry implies that previously unavoidable civilian (and indeed military) losses can be curtailed to a greater extent than hitherto: 'clean' wars can be made less damaging if the damage is irrelevant to the achievement of the war aims. 'Pinpoint bombing' was more often than not a bad joke during the Second World War, and numerous cities in France (for instance) bear the scars of what was then an oxymoron. Post-war US Air Force operational research came to the conclusion that some 3,000 aircraft, inflicting massive damage in the general area of the aim point, had to be used in order to guarantee the destruction of a given target the size of a football pitch. Conversely, the Gulf War demonstrated that the infrastructure of a capital city such as Baghdad could be destroyed with comparatively little damage to the surrounding people and housing.

There will thus be a greater polarization between wars directed against whole populations – Rwanda or Bosnia are illustrative of this – and wars which will in some ways resemble the fighting of the eighteenth century – military against military, with less direct impact on the population at large than was the case in the Second World War or Vietnam.

Choices

In warfare, as in other human endeavours, the future is not preordained. The shape of conflicts to come will be determined by initiative – individual and collective – not simply by mechanical processes dictated by technology alone. And technology itself does not evolve on its own: its manifestations and uses are the result of human decisions. So the future of war will be decided by specific choices, such as coming to terms with new weaponry, coping with terrorism or curbing the spread of nuclear weapons. In this context, the nations of America, Europe and Asia will bear an essential responsibility.

Coming to Terms with 'Smart Weapons'

There is little doubt about what technological change is bringing to the art of war. We are moving from an era marked by the massive application of indiscriminate firepower – characteristic of the wars of the Industrial Revolution – to an age where firepower can be projected from afar with great selectivity. The strategic, political and indeed moral consequences of such a shift are potentially immense.

But it remains to be seen, particularly in those countries which already possess large and well-entrenched standing armies, whether this potential will be tapped to the fullest possible extent. It may be true that 'Old soldiers never die, they only fade away'; but old armies don't even fade away – they hang on until they are blown away in a moment of truth. This is what happened to the Allied armies in the spring of 1940. High-cost equipment and practices, associated with Cold War military structures, will crowd out the lower-cost paraphernalia of the post-Cold War era. Thus a handful of state-of-the-art combat aircraft cost hundreds of millions of pounds to acquire, whereas the same sum will purchase enough cruise missiles to equip the existing air force of a major country. Most countries cannot afford both, in the same way that in the 1930s France could not afford both to extend the Maginot Line to the North Sea and build up a significant number of armoured divisions; at the end of the day, it had done neither satisfactorily, and the results were all too evident.

Unfortunately, such decisions involve complex trade-offs, the consequences of which often become apparent only in hindsight. Thus it won't be easy to choose between the priority of rapidly transporting troops afar – a reasonable proposition if most American or European wars will be fought far from home – and the priority of striking an enemy accurately with effective stand-off missiles. The first goal is immensely costly, the second much less so, but in a conflict such as the Gulf War it was not possible to do one without the other. In effect, a reduction of strategic ambitions may be the only way to reconcile the terms of such a debate. In practice, this could mean emphasizing the defence of one's own region – Western and Central Europe and its immediate vicinity in the case of the members of the European Union – as opposed to investing in longer-range power projection.

Terrorism as War, War as Terrorism

The dividing line between terrorism and warfare will be increasingly blurred. The notion of terrorism here does not embrace guerrilla warfare, which may use some of the terrorist's tools but whose actors aspire to state power and are organized in consequence. Rather, it includes the work of groups or individuals whose agendas are in complete contradiction to the eventual exercise of state power. Terror is equated in this regard with a form of social suicide. With weapons of mass destruction becoming more readily available, the scope of the destruction which such groups will be able to wreak will become less distinguishable from the destruction of war. Furthermore, since they operate from within a given society, such threats cannot be readily countered by conventional military forces or by nuclear deterrence.

In parallel, interaction between the media and society will make it increasingly appealing for some state, or state-supported, actors to use the psychology and arms of terror. The symbiosis between terrorist groups and sponsoring states (Libya, Iran, Sudan and so on) bears witness to this reality. This may well turn out to be a mistaken calculation by the countries concerned, since they will be vulnerable to the threat of reprisals against their territory and institutions in a way which would be impossible against non-state terrorists. However, much unpleasantness may occur before they are convinced of their mistake.

Prevention of and action against terrorist warfare will as a consequence become much more important than it has tended to be in the area of security and defence policy. Military forces will have to adapt to these new circumstances. Special operations commands and the forces which are subordinated to them will have to play a greater part in fighting terrorism. Specialist units and research into coping with chemical and biological weapons will have to receive a higher priority.

Circumstances certainly push the political rhetoric in such a direction. Whether it will turn into a tangible reality remains to be seen. In military organizations, as in other institutions, the scale of priorities can be measured by looking at the system of career development. The ranks attached to the corresponding special operations commands or specialist units and the career prospects opened to those who enter such forces offer tangible yardsticks of the importance being placed on the military aspects of counter-terrorism. The evidence today does not always point in that direction. This is true also of intelligence services. During the Cold War, the CIA was reputed to give the inside track to those who dealt with technical means rather than to operatives who traded in the uncertainties of 'human intelligence' – which lies at the heart of effective counter-terrorism.

Avoiding the Spread of Nuclear Weapons

The experience of the last quarter-century has demonstrated the possibility of curbing the spread of nuclear weapons beyond the small group of countries which already possess them: the five official nuclear powers (the United States, Russia, Britain, France and China) and the so-called threshold states (India, Israel and Pakistan). The tools for an effective non-proliferation policy certainly exist, and several decades of experience give a fairly clear idea of what can or should be done (or avoided) in the future.

However, things could go wrong, suddenly and dramatically. The acquisition of weapons-grade plutonium or uranium in the former USSR by so-called rogue states or terrorist groups is a possibility. So is a nuclear 'chain reaction' such as: 'North Korea goes nuclear, despite the world's efforts; South Korea follows suit (or, in a variation, a united Korea inherits the North's arsenal); Japan, given its entrenched loathing of Korea, does so in turn.' In another scenario: 'India detonates an H-bomb; Pakistan explodes an atom bomb; Iran, aided by Pakistan, has an increased motivation to become a nuclear power.' Non-proliferation is a sisyphean task, in which, at any given moment, previous progress risks being brought to naught. The good news of South Africa's denuclearization and the removal of nuclear weapons from Kazakhstan and Ukraine could thus be more than negated by subsequent developments elsewhere.

Of all policy objectives which will help avoid mass destruction, non-proliferation is possibly the most important – and this applies not only to nuclear but also to biological and chemical weapons. The international community has actually devised a remarkable treaty banning the production of chemical weapons, with an elaborate and intrusive set of verification measures. This convention came into force in 1997. Unfortunately, it is unlikely that some of the states most likely to produce and use chemical weapons – such as Libya or Iraq – will feel compelled to sign it. Similarly, the effectiveness of the international convention forbidding biological weapons – opened to signature in 1972 – is undermined by a lack of serious verification measures.

America, Europe, Asia

Some defence policy decisions are general in nature – countering terrorism, for instance, is not specific to a single region, even if the United States believed until recently in the immunity of its home ground – but others are directly tied to the strategic circumstances of a given area. America, for its part, has the ability, by virtue of its geography – no enemy state lies close to its borders – its military spending and the force structure inherited from the

Cold War, to pursue several major strategic goals simultaneously, on a global scale. This inheritance, even if somewhat modified during the post-Cold War years, may prove to be a hidden liability as time passes. Under current circumstances there is little incentive for the Pentagon to focus the defence budget and organize the force structure around a small number of clear-cut priorities. Even when the Pentagon wants to reform in this way, the Congress finds reasons to impose upon it unwanted spending such as additional numbers of immensely costly B-2 stealth bombers to the detriment of less expensive post-Cold War priorities. This also applies to funding imposed by the Congress for the defence of the US against intercontinental ballistic missiles, which is arguably not the wisest way to allocate relatively scarce military spending. The armed forces themselves are often prone to over-invest in new *matériel*: it is debatable whether the US needs to simultaneously develop the F-22 combat aircraft, acquire the $200 billion Joint Strike Fighter and upgrade its existing fighter-bombers.

In 1996, the US had some 100,000 military personnel based or home-ported in East Asia and a similar number in Western Europe – a total of 15 per cent of its armed forces. These assets are essential to America's influence in the world. They also greatly facilitate far-flung US military operations, as was the case during the Gulf War. These forces stabilize the strategic situation in the regions in which they are based, reassuring local powers which would otherwise have greater cause to fear the strategic ambitions of their immediate neighbours. A US decision to reduce these overseas forces substantially would amount to an isolationist withdrawal to North America, and would lead to the opening-up of regional rivalries, notably in East Asia. The US could be tempted to carry out such reductions given the attractions of long-range stand-off weapons including strategic aircraft with cruise missiles, based in the US and capable of reaching practically any point of the globe, or arsenal ships home-ported in US waters. Such platforms with associated missiles would provide the US with 'punishment impunity' – the ability to hit anyone anywhere without serious risk to its own territory. The risk is that, as a corollary, the US would reduce its participation in expeditionary operations, such as the Gulf War, which are comparatively more risky because they imply the participation of ground forces. Occasional 'metal-on-metal' strikes by unmanned, long-range cruise missiles against air-defence installations in Iraq, of the sort which occurred in 1996, are no substitute for effective in-depth influence in the affairs of the region.

So in coming decades a US drift away from alliances and coalitions towards a combination of unilateral military action and *de facto* political isolationism is entirely possible.

The challenge of adapting forces to future risks is even greater in Europe. Europe's current defence budgets cannot bear the cost of creating a major force-projection capability. As things stand, it is difficult enough to find a place in existing defence budgets for post-Cold War priorities in the field of intelligence-gathering (spy satellites, battlefield drones) or stand-off weaponry. Europe should concentrate on those areas which give it the greatest strategic return. Investing in intelligence, including spy satellites, is one such domain, since the better the information one has to trade, the better the terms of exchange (not least with the US) will tend to be. Similarly, it is both desirable and feasible to acquire the ability to bring significant and accurate firepower, especially in the form of stand-off weapons, to bear in the vicinity of Western Europe at relatively low cost. Such priorities would require the Europeans to retain a competent, broad-based defence industry, which in turn means that European firms should be similar in size, scope and competitiveness to those in the United States. This is entirely possible, provided European governments favour the restructuring of defence industries as much as the Americans do.

Air transport will remain a weak link in European force arrays, but it is not of the essence in dealing with threats close to home. When push comes to shove a combination of existing European air transport assets, chartering from Russian or Ukrainian airlines and American co-operation will enable contingencies further afield to be dealt with. But this is not an ideal situation, and European capabilities should at least be rationalized through pooling arrangements. Nevertheless, the weakness of Europe's air-transport capability is not a critical flaw – unless Europe wished to become a global gendarme.

East Asia, on the face of it, is in the best of situations. Rapid economic growth is generating massive new resources of which only a small proportion goes into defence. 'Modernization' rather than 'arms race' characterizes, at least for the time being, the defence policies of most of the countries in a region which is at peace – after decades of conflict and turmoil. Make profit not war appears to be the region's slogan. But this benign situation is fragile. East Asia, not to mention the Indian subcontinent, has many points in common with pre-1914 Europe: a high degree of economic interdependence, strong economic growth and the ambitions of competing powers. Numerous territorial, demographic or resource-based points of friction exist between China and many of its fifteen neighbours; and the interaction between China, Japan and Korea could prove to be as difficult to handle in the coming decades as it was at the end of the nineteenth century. The difference is that the region has become much more important for the world as a whole than it was a century ago.

The issue in Asia therefore is whether the countries of the region will create institutions and habits of mutual dialogue sufficiently strong to handle peacefully the disparate goals of its increasingly powerful states. The future of the American presence will be a key to answering that question. As long as the US remains militarily and politically engaged in the region, its influence will act as a strategic buffer, cushioning the shock of competing regional ambitions. Conversely, were the US to adopt a hands-off stance, then Asia's internecine antagonisms would be unshackled.

In the coming decades, therefore, war and peace will hinge to a major extent on American intentions and on Asia's ability to resolve its regional differences peacefully. Political decisions and hardware choices may thus combine their effects, although the former will be of more lasting significance than the latter. Warfare will be, as it has always been, the result of humanity's actions, and not a simple function of the evolution of inanimate objects, however 'smart' they may become.

4 The Middle East

BERNARD LEWIS

The End of Modern History

According to a convention commonly agreed among historians, the modern history of the Middle East begins at the turn of the eighteenth and nineteenth centuries, when a French expeditionary force commanded by General Napoleon Bonaparte invaded and conquered Egypt and stayed there until it was forced to leave by a squadron of the Royal Navy commanded by Admiral Horatio Nelson. This was not the first Western advance against the previously dominant power of Islam. But it was the first incursion from the West into the heartlands of the Islamic world.

Bonaparte's arrival and still more his departure demonstrated two important facts: that even a small Western force could conquer, occupy and rule one of these heartlands without serious difficulty, and that only another Western force could get them out.

This began a period during which ultimate power, and with it responsibility, for what happened in this region resided elsewhere; when the basic theme of international relations and of much else in the Middle East was shaped by the rivalries of non-Middle Eastern states. These rivalries went through several successful phases – interference, intervention, penetration, domination and, in the final phase, reluctant departure. From time to time the actors in the drama changed and the script was modified, but the basic pattern remained the same. In the final act of this drama the two external superpowers whose rivalry dominated the Middle East were the Soviet Union and the United States.

Future historians of the region may well agree on a new convention of periodization – that the era in Middle Eastern history that was opened by Napoleon and Nelson was closed by Bush and Gorbachev. In the crisis of 1990–1 precipitated by Saddam Hussein's invasion of Kuwait, neither of the two superpowers played the imperial role which tradition and popular expectation assigned to it; the one because it could not, the other because it would not.

Moscow, once so great a force in Middle Eastern affairs, could neither restrain nor rescue Saddam Hussein. Washington, having freed Kuwait from occupation and Saudi Arabia from the threat of invasion, had accomplished its war aims and unilaterally declared a cease fire, leaving Saddam's regime intact and permitting him, with only minor impediments, to crush his domestic opponents and in due course resume his policies.

As long as the Soviet Union existed, and as long as the Cold War was the main theme of foreign policy, American presence in the Middle East was part of a global strategy designed to cope with a global confrontation. With the ending of that confrontation such a strategy became unnecessary. No discernible strategy has yet emerged to replace it.

The break-up of the Soviet Union brought another important consequence – the emergence of eight new sovereign independent states in Transcaucasia and Central Asia. Two of these, Georgia and Armenia, are Christian; the rest, Azerbaijan, Kazakstan, Kyrgyzstan, Turkmenistan, Uzbekistan and Tajikistan, are predominantly Muslim. All these countries are part of the historic Middle East, linked to it by a thousand ties of culture, language and history. The Tajik language is a form of Persian; the other five Muslim states use languages related to Turkish. The Turks, Persians and Afghans show increasing interest in their newly liberated kinsfolk across the former Soviet frontier. They are also interested in those other Muslim peoples – Tatars, Bashkirs, Chechens, Circassians and others, who remain within the Russian federation. The same interest will in time extend to the Muslims of Chinese Central Asia.

The emergence of a world of Turkic states, like the Arab world that emerged from the break-up of the British and French empires, will be increasingly important in the decades to come, and will have a significant effect on the Middle East to which they are now returning. But there are differences between the two cases. With a few exceptions – Algeria, Aden – British and French rule in the Arab world was indirect and of brief duration. The Transcaucasian and Central Asian territories were annexed by the czars and retained by the Soviets under a thin veneer of federalism. Their experience of imperial rule was in many ways profoundly different from that of the Arabs. Their efforts to disentangle themselves from the embrace of their former masters offer some similarities to the early stages of Arab independence. But they will be dealing with Moscow, not with London or Paris; with a land-based power, not with a maritime and commercial ascendancy. The course and perhaps the outcome of their struggle for true independence will surely reflect these differences.

For the time being, however, Russia is out of the game and likely to remain so for some years to come; America is reluctant to return. This means that in many significant respects the situation reverts to what it was before. Outside powers have interests in the region, both strategic and economic; they may from time to time interfere in Middle Eastern affairs, or even influence their course. But their role will no longer be one of domination or decision.

Many in the Middle East are having difficulty in adjusting themselves to the new situation created by the departure of the imperial powers. For the first time in almost 200 years, the rulers and peoples of the Middle East are having to accept the final responsibility for their own affairs, to make their own mistakes and to accept the consequences. This is difficult to internalize, even to perceive, after so long a period. For the entire lifetimes of those who formulate and conduct policy at the present time and of their predecessors for many generations, vital decisions were made elsewhere, ultimate control lay elsewhere, and the principal task of statesmanship and diplomacy was as far as possible to avoid or reduce the dangers of this situation and to exploit such opportunities as it might from time to time offer. It is very difficult to forsake the habits not just of a lifetime but of a whole era of history. The difficulty is much greater when alien cultural, social and economic pre-eminence continues and even increases, despite the ending of alien political and military domination.

Military and to a growing extent political intervention by the West has indeed ended, but the impact of its science and culture, its technology, amenities and institutions remains and even increases. As in other parts of the non-Western world, this impact has been and will be enormous.

In these circumstances, it is natural that Middle Easterners should continue to assume – and proceed on the assumption – that real responsibility and decision still lie elsewhere. In its crudest form, this belief leads to wild and strange conspiracy theories directed against those whom they regard as their enemies – Israel, and more generally the Jews, the United States, and more generally the West. No theory is too absurd to be asserted or too preposterous to be widely and instantly believed. Even among more responsible statesmen and analysts, a similar belief in alien power, albeit in a less crude form, often seems to guide both analysis and policy. Some even go so far as to invite outside intervention, presumably in the belief that only outside powers have the capacity to make and enforce decisions. A case in point is the constant appeal to the United States to involve itself in the Arab–Israel conflict, oddly coupled with the repeated accusation of 'American imperialism'.

This state of mind is likely to continue for some time, with appeals for support or even intervention to the United States, to Russia and even to the European Union. In time, no doubt, Middle Eastern governments and peoples will learn how to use this window of opportunity to the best advantage – that is, of course, if the window remains open long enough.

Those who accuse the West and more particularly the United States of 'imperialist designs' on the Middle East are tilting against shadows from the past. There is however another charge with more substance – that of cultural penetration.

American culture differs from all its predecessors in two important respects. First, it is independent of political control and extends far beyond the areas of American political dominance or even influence, as for example in Islamic Iran or communist China. Second, it is in a profound sense popular. Previous cultural expansions were limited to political and intellectual elites. American popular culture appeals to every element of the population and especially to the young. It also brings a special message to elements disempowered in the traditional order, notably women. Not surprisingly, therefore, it is seen as a mortal threat by both the defenders of tradition and the exponents of fundamentalist ideologies. How that threat is perceived is clear from Khomeini's repeated characterization of the United States as the 'Great Satan'. No intelligence service is needed to interpret this epithet – just a copy of the Qur'ān. The last verses, the best known along with the first, talk about Satan, describing him as 'the insidious tempter who whispers in the heart of men'. Satan is neither a conqueror nor an exploiter. He is a seducer, most dangerous when he smiles.

The challenge of Western culture has been a major theme in Middle Eastern debate for almost two centuries. American popular culture presents this challenge in its most recent and also its most pervasive form. Middle Eastern rulers, leaders and thinkers have offered and will no doubt continue to offer various responses to this challenge – imitate, adopt, adapt, absorb, or complain, denounce, reject.

Faith and Freedom

When General Bonaparte arrived in 1798 there were only two sovereign states in the Middle East: Turkey and Iran. Today, these are resuming their inescapable roles as the major powers of the region. The regimes in both, in their present form, were founded by revolution – the secular republic of Turkey and the Islamic republic of Iran. Both are inspired by revolutionary ideologies which might be named after their founders as Kemalism and Khomeinism. And both ideologies, albeit in very different ways, are under attack at home.

Today, increasing numbers of Middle Easterners, disillusioned with past ideals and – in many countries – alienated from their present rulers, are turning their thoughts or their loyalties to one or other of these two ideologies – liberal democracy and Islamic fundamentalism. Each offers a reasoned diagnosis of the ills of the region, and a prescription for its cure.

In this struggle, fundamentalism disposes of several advantages. It uses language that is familiar and intelligible, appealing to the vast mass of the population in a Muslim country. At a time of economic deprivation, social dislocation and political oppression, many are ready to believe that these evils are a result of alien and infidel machinations, and that the remedy is a return to the original, authentic way of Islam. The fundamentalists also have an immense advantage over other opposition groups in that the mosques and their personnel provide them with a network for meeting and communication which even the most tyrannical of governments cannot suppress or entirely control. Indeed, tyrannical regimes help their fundamentalist opponents by eliminating competing oppositions.

The exponents of democracy in contrast offer a programme and a language that are unfamiliar and, for many, unintelligible. They have the further disadvantage that the name of democracy and those of the parties and parliaments through which it operates have been tarnished in the eyes of many Muslims by the corrupt and inept regimes that used these names in the recent past. In contrast, appeals in the name of God and the Prophet to cleanse society by restoring his holy law have a force and immediacy unattainable by democrats whose arguments and examples, indeed, whose very vocabulary is recognizably alien. An Arabic loanword like *dimuqratiyya* lacks the resonance of *shari'a*.

But things are changing. In countries where fundamentalists are a powerful force and still more in those where they rule, Muslims are learning to distinguish between Islam as an ethical religion and way of life and fundamentalism as a ruthless political ideology. In countries where they oppose the regime, such as Egypt and Algeria, fundamentalist terrorists have shown a callous brutality that shocks and repels ordinary, decent believers. In countries where they rule, such as Iran and Sudan, they are, perhaps inevitably, disappointing the high hopes that they evoked. The regime of the mullahs in Iran is not noticeably less corrupt than that which it replaced. It is more efficiently and pervasively repressive, and increasing numbers of Iranians, in desperation, are turning against Islamic fundamentalism and sometimes even against Islam itself. Many good Muslims in Iran and elsewhere see in this a mortal danger to their faith and civilization, and there is a growing movement which challenges Islamic fundamentalism, not in the name of secularism, but in the name of Islam. The most serious challenge to the Iranian regime may well come from within its own ranks.

The fundamentalist regimes are also failing by the more palpable test of performance. In Iran, the effects of fundamentalist rule will for a while be palliated by the availability of money from oil and the remarkably skilful use made of this resource in dealing with foreign governments and business corporations. But it is only a palliative, and of limited, duration. In Sudan, where no such palliative exists, the most visible effects of fundamentalist rule are poverty, tyranny and unending internal warfare. The programmes and activities of fundamentalist oppositions in other countries promise nothing better. It is becoming increasingly clear that, whatever political and propaganda successes they may achieve, fundamentalist movements – and governments – have no real understanding of and therefore no solutions for the pressing problems of modern society. Their diagnosis is moral – society has been corrupted and enfeebled by pagan and infidel ways, especially in sexual matters; their remedy is legal – the restoration and strict enforcement of the holy law, that is to say, of those parts and those interpretations that form the basis of fundamentalist ideology. The importance of morality and of law is immense and obvious, but it does not suffice in confronting the pressing economic and social problems of the modern world. The resulting tensions grow daily more serious. They will become critical if these problems persist until the time when oil revenues are no longer available.

A triumph of Islamic fundamentalism would have far-reaching consequences outside as well as inside the region and would evoke sharp responses from other religions – and other fundamentalisms. After the advent of Islam in the seventh century, Muslim jihad wrested vast lands from Christendom and incorporated them in the realm of Islam. Several centuries later, Christianity – a religion with a pacifist core – at last reacted with a jihad of its own, known as the Crusades.

It could happen again. Most Christians – even in the highest ecclesiastical hierarchies – have abandoned the triumphalism and militancy of their forebears. But Muslim triumphalism and militancy could bring a revival, and there are signs that this has already begun. The problem begins with the position of non-Muslims in Muslim states. The very real tolerance once accorded by Muslim states to non-Muslims living under their rule was predicated on their acceptance of the supremacy of Islam and the primacy of the Muslims. When modern ideas disrupt the old consensus, the old tolerance comes under severe strain and is often broken. Attacks on Christians in Iran, in Egypt, in Algeria, in Sudan and elsewhere are reviving old and deep-rooted fears. They have also prompted, in some quarters, a perception of Islam as the new world menace, taking the place vacated by the defunct Soviet Union and its dead communist creed. For the time being at least, this view is an absurd exaggeration of the strength of Muslim militancy and a profound misinterpretation of the nature of Islam.

But the warnings of a new religious response to militant Islam are already there.

In the struggle between democracy and fundamentalism for power in Muslim lands, the democrats suffer from a very serious disadvantage. As democrats, they are obliged to allow the fundamentalists equal opportunity to conduct propaganda and to contend for power. If they fail in this duty, they are violating the very essence of their own democratic creed. Paradoxically it is the Western concern for democratic freedom, even at the cost of Western values and of freedom itself, that sometimes prevents the Muslim secularists from dealing with this problem in the traditional way.

The fundamentalists are under no such disability. For them, winning an election is one of several possible roads to power – and it is a one-way road on which there is no turning back. Fundamentalists, speaking at home, do not even pretend any commitment to democratic choice, and make it clear that, once in power, they would in no circumstances be willing to depart by the road through which they came. On the contrary, it would be their solemn duty to eradicate elements and ideas contrary to the law of God, and to enforce that law against all transgressors. The strength of the democrats, and the corresponding weakness of the fundamentalists, is that the former have a programme of development and betterment, while the latter offer only a return to a mythologized past. The problem is that the weaknesses of the democrats are immediate and obvious; their strengths are long-term and, for many, obscure.

Some speak of a possible compromise between the rival extremes – a type of representative democracy not formally secular, in which a moderate but not fundamentalist Islam might play the role of the established churches in Britain and Scandinavia or of the Christian democratic parties in continental European countries. There is little sign of any such compromise as yet, and at the present time it seems unlikely that any will emerge. But the idea of a combination of freedom and faith in which neither excludes the other has achieved some results among Christians and may yet provide a workable solution for the problems of political Islam.

Until recently, one would have said that the best prospects for the emergence of such a compromise are in Turkey, a country in which most of the population are committed Muslims and in which a parliamentary democracy – albeit with difficulties and reversals – has now functioned for half a century. Turkey was the first Muslim country to establish and maintain such a democracy; it was also the first in which the leader of an avowedly Islamic party became prime minister by electoral and constitutional means. But it is becoming clear that the party which he leads is not just Islamic; it is, for many of its adherents, fundamentalist. The party press reveals attitudes that are anti-Christian, anti-Semitic, anti-Western and, more generally, anti-liberal and anti-modern. Its leaders and spokesmen show affinities – and form alliances – with the most extreme fundamentalist elements in Iran and in some of the Arab countries.

The alarm caused by these developments is increased by reports of the spread of fundamentalist activities in the political, economic and cultural spheres, and, still more dangerous, the acquisition of large quantities of guns and other weapons. As secular elements in the state and more particularly in the armed forces prepare for a showdown, the fear is widely expressed that Turkey might become another Algeria or, more plausibly, another Iran. If that happens, the trouble would certainly spread rapidly, both northwards to the ex-Soviet Turkic states and southwards to the ex-Ottoman Arab states.

But this is unlikely. The Turks, unlike all their Muslim neighbours except Iran, have long experience of sovereign independence. They also have a unique experience of democratic change. One may hope that the Turkish political class will recover the skill and steadiness which it appears to have lost amid the troubles of the 1990s. The Turks have often been leaders in the Middle East – in Islamic empire under the Ottomans, in nationalist self-liberation under Kemal Atatürk, in responsible parliamentary government under his successors. Perhaps they will show the way again.

In either case, what happens in Turkey will have immense and perhaps decisive effects in the region as a whole. A triumph of Islamic fundamentalism would probably spell the end of any hope of Islamic democracy for a long time. A fundamentalist Turkey might, for a while, maintain good relations with Iran, but sooner rather than later the historic pattern of the region would reappear.

An Islamic Turkey and an Islamic Iran would again confront each other as rivals for leadership, the choice this time, as it was centuries ago, being between the Sunni and Shi'a versions of the faith.

In the meantime the fundamentalist movements pursue their distinctive pattern of action – terror at home while in opposition, repression at home and terror abroad when in power. Slitting the throats of harmless villagers in Algeria, bombing parties of uninvolved tourists who are the guests of Egypt – these have become the specific tactics of the movements that we have come to call Islamic fundamentalism.

But what do they have to do with Islam? The Qur'ān states not once but several times that 'No man shall bear another's burden,' that is to say that no one should be punished for the misdeeds of another. Islamic law permits hostages only in a reciprocal voluntary exchange as pledges for the fulfilment of an agreement. The Islamic laws of war prescribe good treatment for women, children and other non-combatants – 'Do not attack them unless they first attack you.' Yet the so-called Islamic fundamentalists seize hostages by force and sometimes torture and kill them, and carry out random massacres of villagers, passengers, tourists and mere passers-by with bombs, guns and kitchen knives.

Some Muslims are already beginning to ask whether the effect of fundamentalist activities is to uphold and defend Islam or discredit and undermine it. The mindless, ruthless, callous violence of so many fundamentalist actions may well strengthen these doubts.

The struggle between democracy and militant fundamentalism is not limited to the Arab and Islamic world. It is becoming increasingly important in Israel. Religion as such has always played an important part in Israeli life. It is, after all, the core of Jewish identity and therefore also of Israeli statehood. What is new in the situation is not the role of religion as such – this goes back for millennia – but the new religio-political ideology, which is gaining increasing support among Israeli Jews and is already a powerful, at times divisive, factor in Israeli domestic politics.

Without the threat of major war from outside, the Israelis will be free to concentrate on their own internal problems and, more specifically, on their own internal differences. In the past, these were on more or less European lines – between a socialist left, a conservative right and a liberal centre. There are signs that this is changing and that the fault line in Israeli politics in the coming years will be less European and more Middle Eastern. This means that the major confrontation will not be between right and left in the conventional Western sense of these terms, but between secular democracy and religious ideology.

The establishment and flourishing of democracy in Israel in the fifty years since the foundation of the state are in themselves astonishing. At first sight, there would seem to be every reason why democracy should fail in this country and in this situation. The vast majority of the inhabitants in Israel originate in countries with little or no democratic experience or tradition. The virtually continuous state of war and the consequent importance of the army and its commanders might easily have led to a military regime – the more so in a region where such regimes are normal. To make matters worse, the Israelis saddled themselves from the start with what must be one of the worst electoral systems in the free world, and then, by the direct election of the prime minister, found a way to make it even worse.

Nevertheless, democracy has survived and even flourished. Because of its enforced isolation from the region in which it is situated, Israel has, for most practical purposes, been part of the Western world, and its democracy functioned naturally in a predominantly Western international environment. For most Israelis, Washington, London, Paris or Rome were nearer than Damascus, Baghdad or Cairo.

But this situation is changing and Israel is becoming, much more than in the past, a part of the Middle East. To some extent, this is due to the increasing proportion of Jews of Middle Eastern origin in the population and therefore the government of Israel; to a much greater extent, to the increasing network of relations with Middle Eastern countries. Middle Eastern influences are already perceptible in many aspects of Israeli life. They are likely to continue and expand. In this respect, the peace process may bring a threat to Western-style democracy in Israel; it may also give much-needed encouragement to the development of democracy in Middle Eastern countries. For example, the Arab League's permanent commission on human rights, founded in 1968, has hitherto concerned itself exclusively with the human rights of Palestinians under Israeli rule. It may now follow the example of the Organization of American States and the Organization of African Unity, with which it shares several members, and look at human rights in member states. There are already active groups in several Arab countries – or in exile – concerned with this issue. They will surely grow in numbers and in influence.

In Israel as in the Muslim lands, the threat to democracy comes not from religion as such, but from a religiously expressed ideology imbuing old terms with new meanings and using – or misusing – the faith and hope of the devout in order to gain and retain power. Faith and piety are perfectly compatible with an open democratic society. State-enforced holy law administered by self-styled holy men is not.

War and Peace

Parliamentary politics, like that other great English invention football, is a method by which rival parties can struggle for victory without violent conflict. Both sides in the struggle observe the same rules and share certain common principles. Both accept either victory or defeat with grace, because both know that victory can never be total nor defeat final. And just as conflicts of interest and policy between rival parties in a democracy can be conducted peacefully, so too can conflicts of interest and purpose between democratic states be pursued without resorting to war.

The position is different when the contending forces are defined, not by politics, not by economics, but by religion. For the old-style religious believer – there is some change among some modern believers – the conflict is not between rival beliefs, rival truths or rival interests; it is between truth and falsehood, and the upholders of falsehood have no rights in the present and no hope for the future. The unequivocal duty of the upholders of truth is to gain power and use it to promote and enforce that truth.

Even the non-religious may admit the value of religion in moral, cultural and above all personal life. But many even of the pious are compelled to recognize the dangers of religion organized as a political force. In the fledgling or embryonic democracies of the Middle East, where co-operation in conflict is still a new and little-known concept, religious parties tend to become fundamentalist, and fundamentalism, by its very nature, is ruthless and uncompromising. Opposing democratic parties may co-operate within the state, rival democratic states may co-operate even in their international disagreements, but for fundamentalists there is no compromise, and dealings between rival contenders fall naturally and inevitably into the familiar forms of jihad and crusade.

How would this affect relations between Israel and its neighbours? Democracies may negotiate and compromise with other democracies. For religions, this is much more difficult and, for fundamentalist religions, impossible. Democratic Turkey is emerging as Israel's closest partner in the region, with a steadily expanding range of commercial, political, cultural and military relations; fundamentalist Iran is the most implacable opponent of the peace process, and will remain so unless and until there is a change of direction in Iran itself.

The peace process began, not because of a change of heart on either side, but because of a change of circumstances – to exhaustion and the realization that the wars in which they were engaged were unwinnable. Israel is no longer the state created by its founders, a pioneer society, rough and tough in its ways, austere and dedicated in its beliefs. It is becoming an affluent and liberal society, still patriotic, but less willing to pay the costs and endure the hardships of maintaining an occupation over unwilling subjects. The Intifada brought this home. After a long struggle, the Israelis succeeded in crushing it, but it became clear that they could only maintain their authority, if at all, at an unacceptable cost, both moral and material, and an unacceptable transformation of the very nature of Israeli society.

On the Palestinian side, too, there is a growing realization that their war aims are unattainable by force of arms and that the continuation of armed struggle against Israel would entail increasing burdens for their own Palestinian people and command decreasing support among their Arab kinsfolk. The decisive change came after two major miscalculations by the Palestinian leadership. They had already made a major mistake by choosing the Axis in the Second World War. They compounded this error by choosing the Soviets in the Cold War and Saddam Hussein in the Gulf War. One may speculate how events would have evolved had the Cold War ended with the collapse of the United States. But it did not, and with the collapse of the Soviet Union, the PLO found itself without a superpower patron. This loss was aggravated by Palestinian support for Saddam Hussein in the Gulf crisis and war in 1990–1. The loss of goodwill in the United States and among the other Western members of the coalition was comparatively unimportant. Much more serious was the loss of the goodwill of the Arab members of the anti-Saddam coalition – the

Saudis, the Kuwaitis and the other Gulf states, who had been their strongest supporters and, more important, their paymasters in the struggle against Israel. They now became increasingly reluctant to pay and were even willing to think the unthinkable – a deal with Israel.

The peace process was thus inaugurated between an isolated and weakened PLO seeking to salvage something from the ruins of their hopes, and an affluent Israel ready to sacrifice some of its gains in order to achieve security for the remainder.

As long as these conditions persist, the peace process between Israel and the Arabs, in one form or another, is likely to continue. It has already survived several severe tests, and will surely face others. A new element of danger arises from the determined efforts being made by Iran and at least two Arab states, Iraq and Syria, to acquire weapons of mass destruction – nuclear, chemical and biological. It may soon be feasible, by the use of such weapons, to destroy Israel. Such an act would inevitably entail the destruction of Palestine and probably also of Jordan. The revolutionary regime in Iran and the governments of the radical Arab states might well regard this as a price worth paying. They are, however, more likely to be deterred by the thought that the same fate might also overtake them at home. Such weapons would, of course, increase the danger of war if their possessors could be sure of an immediate knock-out victory. But, given the sophisticated weaponry of Israel, they cannot be sure, and proliferation may have the opposite effect, of making war less likely through a mutual balance of deterrence. This assumes rationality on both sides, and some have questioned whether such an assumption is valid concerning fanatical religious leaders. Perhaps not, but it seems on the whole probable. After all, even the suicide bombers, before setting out on a mission, make provision for their families. No such provision is possible in a nuclear, chemical or biological war. The fearsome weaponry of the United States and the Soviet Union gave the world the longest period of international peace in the twentieth century. True, there were proxy wars, nasty and vicious, but they had little effect on the outcome of the main struggle. The Palestinians are showing an increasing unwillingness to act as proxies for the schemes of others; the Lebanese Shi'a too may learn wisdom in this respect.

While the peace process will continue because neither side can afford to abandon it, there is unlikely to be any increase in goodwill or friendly relations between Israel and the Arabs. If anything, the movement is in the opposite direction, as greater contact brings greater tension and more opportunity for mutual suspicion and resentment. Attempts to allay these suspicions have often served only to augment them. Deep Arab suspicion is likely to remain whatever government rules in Israel, though Israeli policies may increase or reduce it.

The literature available in Arabic about Israel and, more generally, about Jews, Judaism and Jewish history is overwhelmingly anti-Semitic, based largely on leftovers from the hate literature of the Third Reich. No correctives are available or, in most countries, permitted; even films in which Jews – individually or collectively – are portrayed in a sympathetic or favourable light are usually cut or banned. Arab soldiers and businessmen who have direct personal dealings with Israelis have a realistic appreciation of their human strengths and weaknesses. So too do a small and increasing group of statesmen. The academic establishment, the professions and – most consistently and effectively – the media are and will probably long remain hostile. But there are already some bold spirits – poets and playwrights, philosophers and scientists – who dare seek dialogue and an end to struggle. If the peace process survives, there will surely be more. Among Palestinians there is a growing readiness to meet and even co-operate with Israeli colleagues. Elsewhere, and particularly in countries that have treaty relations with Israel and are therefore, as they see it, exposed to a threat of Israeli economic and cultural penetration, attitudes are if anything hardening. The few who think otherwise are fiercely denounced by their more obdurate compatriots.

This may change with the passage of time and a growth in self-confidence in the Arab world. Until then, the Israelis would be wise to concentrate on economic relations and to content themselves with the cessation of armed conflict and the development of the minimum structure of contact and communication between neighbouring states that are at peace or, to be precise, not at war.

In time, resignation may grow into tolerance, tolerance to acceptance, acceptance to goodwill and even friendship. But this is clearly not imminent, and attempts to hasten the slow process of improvement might halt or even reverse it. The likeliest – and the best – prospect for the coming years is a cold peace in which Israel might expect minimal co-operation from the political and diplomatic establishment to avoid war. Businessmen may co-operate for mutual profit, soldiers out of mutual respect. Intellectuals have neither of these motives, and, with few but increasing exceptions, will trail after the peace process rather than precede and advance it.

In an era when pan-Arab nationalism and the imperialisms against which it was directed have faded into an ever more remote past, the struggle against Israel remains the only common Arab cause, and only Israel's actions can from time to time revive the flagging fortunes of pan-Arabism. Some Israel government policies have already done more for the pan-Arab cause than any Arab leader since Nasser. Similarly Israeli extremism, both nationalist and religious, is nourished and encouraged by the tendency of some Palestinian organizations to resort to bloody terrorism every time there is a hitch in the negotiations.

The peace process still has a long way to go, on a path beset with obstacles and ambushes. It may be halted, deflected or even reversed by acts of folly or fanaticism or by the deadly combination of the two. Even the inexperience of new leaders may cause grave damage. These dangers may come from either side and may provoke a comparable response from the other. But as long as the international and regional circumstances which brought the parties to the negotiating table remain in effect, the peace process will probably continue, surviving both setbacks and crises. If it has not yet achieved peace at the time when these circumstances no longer apply, then the prospects for Arabs and Israelis alike will be very dark.

In the long run the future of Arab–Israel relations will be determined by the outcome of the overarching regional struggle between democratic and fundamentalist ideologies, by the choices made by the peoples and their leaders. The triumph of democracy would eventually lead to a genuine and not merely formal peace. The triumph of militant fundamentalism on either side can only result in continuous and increasingly destructive struggle. The choice between democracy and fundamentalism will, of course, be profoundly influenced by the pace or lack of economic betterment. Democracy and tolerance come easier to the affluent than to the indigent.

The Arab–Israel conflict is not the only factor for war in the region. Other wars, though attracting less attention in the outside world, have lasted longer and caused more devastation. They could easily resume. An obvious starting point for a new war would be an act of aggression by one of the radical and militant regimes. One possibility is Syria, perhaps in the form of a quick, limited move to seize the Golan Heights. But both Hafiz al-Assad and his regime show signs of ageing. One of his major objectives, the subjugation of Lebanon, has already been accomplished – though a serious challenge to Syrian authority could start the fighting again. This will not happen while the present regimes remain in power in Damascus and in office in Beirut. Another objective, the incorporation of Jordan and Greater Palestine into Syria, would involve a full-scale war with Israel; this Hafiz al-Assad would probably prefer to avoid. Similarly the Syrian claim against Turkey for the lost province of Alexandretta would entail unacceptable risks.

Saddam Hussein is another story. Sanctions against him are eroding and trade is increasing between Iraq and both regional and outside powers. Opposition to him is ruthlessly crushed at home and has so far failed to win effective outside support. His international position is improving and sympathy is growing among many in the Middle East and North Africa who admire his successful defiance of the West. For such sympathizers, this more than compensates for his crimes against his own people and against his neighbours. It is therefore not unlikely that, having thoroughly crushed and cowed his own people, he will resume his attacks against his neighbours.

One possible victim is Jordan. He would probably not risk a direct military intervention in this direction, since this would bring him face to face with Israel and into a situation in which action would be militarily dangerous and inaction would be politically demeaning. He might however use his weapons of subversion, sabotage and terror. Feeling safe in his bunker, he might even risk an air attack on Israel with chemical or biological weapons. Israel would of course respond, with unforeseeable consequences.

But most probably this serial aggressor will return to the scene of his previous crimes – Iran, or Kuwait and Saudi Arabia. Of these, the Arab option would be the easier militarily. But an attack on Kuwait or Saudi Arabia might again mobilize regional and then international opposition, and perhaps even drag a reluctant United States back into the fray. His decision will depend on the policy of the American president or, more precisely, on his own perception – after probing and testing – of that policy. If he thinks it safe, this would surely be his preferred target.

An attack on Iran, though militarily more difficult, would be politically easier, since no one – not Europe or Asia, not America or Russia, not even the Muslim powers – would lift a finger to save the mullahs of Iran from defeat. The Iranian regime, by its policies and tactics, has done a very thorough job of antagonizing almost all its neighbours. These would, to say the least, view its downfall with equanimity. By a similar calculation, the rulers of Iran might feel that an attack on Saddam Hussein would be approved, at least tacitly, rather than condemned by the international community.

Inside Iran an almost classic situation for aggression and expansion prevails. An ageing and tiring revolutionary regime enjoys control of a vast network of terror in the region and beyond and a powerful armoury of conventional and, no doubt soon, unconventional weapons. The stress on nuclear development, in a country rich in oil and gas, can mean nothing else. The regime faces mounting discontent among ever larger sections of the population at home. The Iranian revolutionaries are in many ways following the path of their French and Russian predecessors – the struggle of radicals and pragmatists, the terror, the Thermidorian reaction. It is not impossible that the Iranian revolution too may culminate in a Napoleon or a Stalin. They would be wise to remember that Napoleon's career ended at Waterloo and St Helena, and Stalin's legacy to the Soviet Union was disintegration and chaos.

Revolutionary war is not the only threat to the Arab states. There is also the danger of old-fashioned territorial claims by more powerful neighbours – sometimes for part, sometimes for the whole of the national territory. Syria has threatened the independence of both Jordan and Lebanon; in Lebanon the threat has been accomplished. Iraq has several times attempted by various means to make good its claims to Kuwait. It will certainly do so again in the future. Iran lays claim to the whole of Bahrain and has other unresolved territorial disputes in the Gulf area. It may develop claims on Persian-speaking Tajikistan and western Afghanistan. There are other smaller disputes on virtually all inter-Arab frontiers. Though these may for long periods be dormant, they can always be revived for immediate tactical or long-range strategic purposes.

One such is the Egyptian claim to the Sudan. At one time this claim, with the slogan 'Unity of the Nile Valley', was a major theme of Egyptian nationalist ideology and later foreign policy. For some time now the claim has been tacitly abandoned, but it could easily be revived.

Perhaps the most artificial of all the Arab states is Libya, invented by the Italian Ministry of Colonial Affairs in December 1932. Historically, Cyrenaica, the eastern half, was usually associated with Egypt; Tripolitania, the western half, with Tunisia. The frontier between Libya and Egypt was, after some disputes, resolved by negotiation between the masters of these two countries, Italy and Britain. Egyptians might well feel that they are not bound by such imperialist pacts. Some future Egyptian government, tired of the repeated failures of Egyptian policy in South-West Asia, might turn its attention to the more promising opportunities of Africa. Both Libya and the northern Sudan are tied to Egypt by bonds of religion, language, culture and history. The political structures in which they live are alien and artificial in origin and are deteriorating visibly in our time. Some form of union with Egypt might seem an acceptable solution to their as well as to Egypt's problems.

In recent years there have been several attempts, by free choice or by armed conquest, to merge two or more Arab states into some larger union. Almost all have failed. There may well be more attempts of both kinds, but their chances of survival are not great. The one successful example, the establishment of Syrian control over Lebanon, demonstrates that the real threat to existing state structures is not merging but fragmentation.

Centre and Periphery

Perhaps the greatest danger that threatens the Middle East is not wars between states but wars within states. The civil war in Lebanon is the most obvious example. The tragedies of Yugoslavia and Somalia, both on the edges of the Middle East and sharing part of its history, are others. The continuing civil war in Sudan, according to an Egyptian estimate, has already killed five times as many people as all the Arab–Israel wars combined. But the outside world, including most of Africa, seems to view it with indifference. Sudan has little oil, no Jews, no holy places; it has no active well-wishers or even ill-wishers abroad.

For a time, Lebanon functioned smoothly as an open democracy – indeed the only such in the entire Arab world. But that democracy did not survive the importation of other peoples' problems and the intervention, first political then military, of other regional powers. Lebanese democracy foundered in a series of bloody civil wars. As the Lebanese state broke up, loyalty to it became meaningless, and the country disintegrated into a patchwork of tribes, regions, sects and other interest groups, in unending conflict with each other and even within themselves. This anarchic fragmentation was ended only when Syria established effective military control over most of the country and political control over its government. This now embraces the whole of Lebanon, with the exception of the so-called security zone in the south, where a more or less autonomous local Lebanese regime operates under Israeli protection and with an Israeli military garrison. The Israelis, increasingly dubious about the value to them of this security zone, may well withdraw from it when they judge the moment right, possibly – though not probably – as part of a general Israel–Syria settlement.

With or without such a settlement, Syrian domination of Lebanon is likely to continue for at least as long as the present Syrian regime survives.

As in any dictatorship, the death of the dictator will precipitate a crisis especially where, as in this case, there is no generally recognized successor and no established form of succession. Hafiz al-Assad belongs to a minority, the Alawis, that is both sectarian and regional, and the inevitable succession struggle will be complicated and embittered by sectarian and regional as well as dynastic rivalries.

The Syrian state was constructed after the First World War from the ruins of the Ottoman Empire. Its frontiers were defined and its identity determined by agreements between the British and French governments. For Arab nationalists, this state was a construct, a fragment of the greater Arab fatherland. For Syrian nationalists, it was the rump of a greater Syria which included not only Lebanon but also Transjordan and Palestine. But for some of the peoples within its frontiers, even this smaller state with its capital in Damascus was too much. The Alawis of the north-west, the Druze of the south-east, mounted serious rebellions against the central government, and secessionist tendencies also appeared in other regions of the north, the centre and the south. The nationalist aim has always been to merge the state into some larger, vaguer entity. A more likely outcome will be the Lebanese paradigm – to dissolve the state and fragment its territories into rival feuding fiefdoms.

Iraq, another post-First World War construct, faces the same problems and the same dangers. Assembled from three provinces of the Ottoman Empire, the vilayets of Mosul, Baghdad and Basra, it is divided ethnically between Arabs and Kurds, religiously between Sunnis and Shi'a, socially between townspeople, cultivators and nomads. When Saddam's regime faltered briefly in the aftermath of the Gulf War in 1991, all of these centrifugal tendencies came out into the open. While the victorious coalition looked on, he was able to crush these various dissident forces one by one. His successor, whenever and whoever that may be, will certainly face the same challenge. He may not be so fortunate in dealing with it. The Lebanese paradigm is certainly one possibility for the future of both Syria and Iraq.

It is not only imperialist constructs that face the danger of fragmentation. The Kingdom of Saudi Arabia, also a creation of the inter-war period, was not the result of imperial expansion and compromise. It is a creation of dynastic ambition, tribal loyalty and religious zeal. At first sight, the Saudi Kingdom would appear to be relatively homogeneous. There are no ethnic minorities, since all its people – apart from guest workers – are Arab. There are no religious minorities, since Islam is the only permitted religion. Yet there are difficulties. The Arabs are divided by region and more especially by tribe, with an ancient tradition of tribal feuding. The Muslims are divided into Sunni and Shi'a, the latter a minority in the Kingdom as a whole, but massively present in the eastern, oil-bearing provinces. Even the reigning dynasty is riven by factional, sectional and personal rivalries. Economic and social changes are creating new ambitions and new grievances. The vast, ramshackle Kingdom has been held together principally by religion and money. Now, religion is becoming a divisive force, as fundamentalist movements denounce what they see as the impiety of the ruling house and the ruling class; money, once plentiful enough to solve all problems, is now becoming less readily available. The development of both the religious mood and the oil market suggests that these problems will grow worse, not better, in the coming years.

The Kingdom faces no immediate threat of external aggression, at least not in the form of open warfare. But there is a growing danger of subversion at home – some, though by no means all of it, externally inspired.

Against this threat, the magnificent armoury of hi-tech weapons imported from the United States offers no protection. The Israelis learnt during the Intifada that sophisticated weaponry is useless against stone-throwing youths. The other governments in the region are not subject to the same constraints, domestic and international, as are the Israelis, but they too show signs of learning the limits of repression. Even the most advanced of missiles, even the deadliest of unconventional weapons of war, can neither suppress nor deter rioters or terrorists. The latter may even find a use for them.

In one respect Saudi Arabia is better placed than Syria or Iraq – that is, in its enormous size. Most of the country consists of desert, and the centres of population are like islands in an archipelago, separated by vast expanses of emptiness. This makes it easier to contain, isolate and eventually repress any outbreak of active opposition.

What is true of Saudi Arabia applies to a greater or lesser extent to the other oil states of the Persian Gulf. In some respects better situated than the Saudis, in others they are more dangerously exposed, in the immediate neighbourhood of two more powerful states, Iraq and Iran, both using the twin weapons of territorial claims and domestic subversion.

The collapse and disintegration of any one of these states would create a dangerous situation in the region, especially for its neighbours – a threat to the fragile, a temptation to the strong. Here again the civil war in Lebanon and the involvement of its near and even its more distant neighbours could serve as a paradigm for the region.

Not all Arab states face the danger of fragmentation. Some are sustained by long experience of stability and continuity and memories of at least local or regional autonomy. These have combined to produce a common identity, a sense of nationhood that is likely to survive the internal and external problems they may confront in the years to come. An obvious example is Egypt, a nation by any definition. In the future as in the past, it will remain distinctively Egyptian, whatever changes of regime or even of culture it may undergo. Another example is Morocco, like Egypt a creation of geography and history. Other countries whose past gives some hope for continuing nationhood and statehood are Tunisia, Yemen and perhaps – when the Syrians leave – a reconstituted democratic Lebanon.

Though Arab states are the most endangered, they are not the only ones. The trend towards fragmentation will be encouraged by the growth of ethnicity and sectarianism. The seductive idea of self-determination has spread to a number of ethnic minorities no longer satisfied with their previous status.

By far the most important of these are the Kurds, numbering many millions and speaking a language, or rather a group of interrelated dialects, of the same linguistic family as Persian. The Kurds are a very ancient people, but they never achieved separate statehood, and their homeland is divided between the modern states of Turkey, Iraq and Iran, in all of which they have played an important part. Smaller groups are also found in Syria and in the Transcaucasian republics. Of all these countries, Turkey alone has an open society and a democratic constitution. Precisely for this reason, it is the most threatened by the upsurge of Kurdish nationalism. The struggle in Turkey has been very bitter – armed insurrection and terror on the one side, harsh repression on the other. But there are some signs of improvement. There have never been any obstacles to the advancement of Kurds in Turkey even to the highest offices in the land, but always on condition of a total acceptance of Turkish identity and the renunciation of any Kurdish identity. Even the Kurdish language was proscribed.

This is no longer true. Kurdish is freely and widely used and Kurdish books are on sale in the bookshops even of Ankara and Istanbul. There is also a change on the Kurdish side. Hemmed in between Turkey, Iran and Iraq, some Kurds are becoming aware that their access to the outside world can only be through one or other of these countries. Of the three, Turkey – democratic and westward-looking – offers by far the most attractive possibility. One may hope, during the coming years, to see the beginnings of a compromise between Turks and Kurds. This would not involve a Kurdish state, against which all three powers would be adamantly opposed. It could however include a significant measure of cultural and perhaps some regional autonomy, making it possible for Kurds to cherish and develop their Kurdish cultural identity, while being loyal and productive citizens of the Turkish Republic. Some kind of arrangement along the lines of the coexistence of English, Scots and Welshmen in the United Kingdom could provide the answer.

The future of the Kurdish minorities in Iraq and Iran offers much less hope at the present time, and is clearly bound up with the very problematic future course of events in both countries. Both are governed by authoritarian regimes; but both are increasingly threatened by centrifugal sources, both ethnic and religious. In Iran, the Persians properly so called form a bare majority of the total population. The rest belong to other ethnic groups and speak other languages. A potentially dangerous feature is that, on many of the frontiers of Iran, the inhabitants share a language and an identity with the people on the other side. In the north-west, the Iranian province of Azerbaijan adjoins the independent former

Soviet republic of the same name. In the south-west, the province of Khuzistan is inhabited by Arabic speakers very similar to those of Iraq. In the south-east, the people of Iranian Baluchistan share a common identity with the Baluchis of Afghanistan and Pakistan. Along the eastern and north-eastern frontiers, speakers of various Turkic and Iranic languages share a cultural and – perhaps more dangerous – a religious Sunni identity with their neighbours in Afghanistan and in Central Asia. It is easy to imagine a situation in which the central government in Teheran becomes too weak or too oppressive – either could lead to the other – to retain the loyalty of the frontier provinces. And in such a case Iran, too, could follow the Lebanese paradigm.

The danger in Iran, however, is not as great as in Syria, Iraq or Saudi Arabia. Unlike these, Iran is not a new state, nor is it of Western manufacture. It is an old state with centuries, indeed millennia, of sovereign existence and a strong sense of cultural identity which in the past has usually served to counterbalance and in the last analysis to outweigh the centrifugal forces of regionalism and factionalism. This happened in 1926 when a determined and ambitious young officer, seeing his country falling apart under an incompetent shah, saved the unity of the nation by seizing power and establishing a new dynasty. It could happen again.

Oil and Water

Today, with the ending, at least for the time being, of global strategic confrontation, the most important single element in the Middle East, for the outside world, is oil. Middle Eastern countries, now including the former Soviet republics in Transcaucasia and Central Asia, contain the largest proven resources of oil in the whole world, and more are being discovered all the time. But there is growing dissatisfaction with a fuel that pollutes the land, the sea and the air wherever it is used or transported, and that makes the world economy heavily dependent on the whims of such rulers as Colonel Gaddafi of Libya, Saddam Hussein of Iraq and the ayatollahs of Iran. The kings and princes of Arabia are better trading partners than any of these, but continuing uncertainties about their future policies or even in some cases their survival make dependence on them uncomfortable.

For environmental and political as well as economic reasons, a continuous search has been in progress, first for sources of oil other than the Middle East, and second, more important, for sources of energy other than oil. In time, the advance of science and technology, which made oil first useful and then necessary, will make it obsolete, and replace it with cleaner, cheaper and more accessible sources of energy. The exploitation of natural gas may delay but will not prevent this ending. When that happens, those who depend on oil revenues will face a new and bleak reality, and the outside world will no doubt view the struggles and upheavals of the Middle East with the same calm detachment – or, as some might put it, callous indifference – as it now views the civil wars in Somalia and Liberia. Until then, the consumer countries – Europe and the Far East far more than the United States – will be anxiously dependent on whoever rules the oil wells, and will have to devise and apply their policies accordingly. It will be neither a safe nor an easy task.

For the time being, oil remains the major, for some indeed the only, resource. In the oil-producing countries it provides most or all of their foreign-currency earnings. Even in the countries with little or no oil, there is a ripple effect, in the form of subsidies of one sort or another, labour migration and, to a surprisingly limited extent, investment.

This overwhelming dependence on the export of irreplaceable and non-renewable natural resources is obviously dangerous, and when these resources are exhausted or superseded it will become catastrophic. Reserves of non-renewable resources are already falling rapidly, and even renewable resources like water are used at unsustainably high levels. These exceed 100 per cent in Israel, Jordan, the Palestine territories, Libya and virtually the whole of the Arabian peninsula. In addition, the loss from land degradation is currently estimated to cost $11.5 billion a year.

The oil states will face two crises, the first from exhaustion, the second from supersession. A few countries, Iraq, Saudi Arabia and the Transcaucasian and Central Asian republics, still have vast unexploited resources that could last into an indefinite future. The rest, notably Iran, are less well placed. In the early decades of the twenty-first century, they will find themselves bereft of what has become their main resource. In the Gulf states, on a global or even a regional scale, this would be of relatively minor importance. The guest workers will return whence they came or go elsewhere; the states, with their very small populations, will return to the obscurity from which they briefly emerged. But Iran is another matter – a large area with a rapidly growing population, a powerful state supported on the one hand by a militant revolutionary ideology, on the other by an increasingly efficient machine of war. As the revolution approaches its Napoleonic or Stalinist phase, and as the oil resources of Iran approach exhaustion, the rulers of that country, whoever they may be at that time, will inevitably look towards the still vast resources of their neighbours.

The best prospect for the region would of course be of a regional programme of co-operation and development. The past record of the region and the character and habits of most of its present rulers make a bitter struggle much more probable. In such a situation, those countries that have learnt to live and advance without oil revenues, such as Turkey, Jordan, Israel, Tunisia and Morocco, will be at a considerable advantage.

Figures for growth in incomes, exports, job creation and school enrolment vary greatly in the region. Israel, with its relatively well-educated population and its hi-tech industries, leads easily. It is followed by Turkey, with an upsurge of private enterprise in both domestic production and export trade. Some flourishing regional developments have even given rise to the phrase 'the Anatolian Tigers', implying comparison with the soaring economies of East Asia. Of the Arab countries, Morocco, Tunisia and Jordan have the best record and show the greatest promise. Morocco and Tunisia have low military expenditure; that of Jordan is being reduced. All three, lacking exportable natural resources, rely heavily on human resource development. This is reflected in the figures for literacy and school enrolment, infant mortality and life expectancy.

Most of the region lags behind other regions in exports, in private investment, in productivity and in the efficient management of natural resources. Many have failed to improve or even maintain the already low living standards of their populations. Real exports per capita show an overall decline. This will worsen if, as some predict, oil prices remain flat or, at best, uncertain.

An even greater issue than oil – since it directly affects not just some but all the states of the region – will be water. The agriculture of the Middle East is no longer sufficient to feed its people, and the disparity will become worse. The need to feed a rapidly growing population constantly requires more food. The need to house them and the consequent spread of villages and towns reduces the capacity to produce it. Agriculture depends on soil and water. The Middle East lacks the great and fertile plains of other more fortunate regions of the world. Most of its surface consists of mountains and deserts with only limited areas of cultivated land dependent on rivers. Rivers present both technical and political problems.

The technical problems can to a limited extent be overcome by dams and irrigation schemes. The political problems, hitherto quiescent, will be aggravated by this kind of construction. The sources of many of the great rivers on which Middle Eastern countries depend lie in other regions not subject to their control. The headwaters of the River Jordan, vital to Israel and Palestine and Jordan, are in Syria. The headwaters of the Euphrates, life-blood of Syria and still more of Iraq, are in Turkey. The Nile passes several frontiers in its long journey from its sources to Egypt.

In the past, this was not of great importance. It is now, and will be more so as population growth creates an increasing demand for water, and technology an increasing capacity to control it. In the course of time, oil and gas may be exhausted and superseded. Water may be exhausted but it will never be superseded, and, in a not-too-distant future, water will become the outstanding issue between the nations of the region, exacerbating enmities and straining friendships.

Here even more than with oil, there is a choice between conflict and co-operation. Turkey, the only country in the region with an exportable surplus of water, has from time to time offered to export it through pipelines or by sea. Such schemes have come to nothing because of conflict and mistrust between the nations through which such pipelines would pass. In a peaceful Middle East, with a structure of regional co-operation, these schemes could be revived. More important, the countries might co-operate in projects of desalination. For the time being at least, this is the only answer to the water problems of the region. The waters of the sea are inexhaustible and could provide for all needs into an indefinite future. Desalination plants are already functioning in some places, but there are problems, and two in particular. The first is that, with present technology and under present con-ditions, desalination is for most countries economically unworka-ble. The second is that desalination plants are dangerously vulnerable to attack, whether by terrorism or by conventional arms.

In the meantime, some interim measures can and probably will be adopted to secure a more economic use of existing water resources. Growing wheat in Saudi Arabia and vegetables and fruit in the desert emirates may have a certain dramatic value, but is an absurdly wasteful misuse of water and will no doubt be aban-doned when good sense prevails over display. A less obvious but nevertheless significant saving could be achieved by abandoning the growing of such water-intensive and non-essential crops as bananas. Even the great Israeli standby, the orange, will give way to other crops more suited to an arid climate. Significant experiments in desert and semi-desert agriculture are already being pursued at research centres in Israel. These could serve as pilot projects for the whole region.

The growing urgency of the situation is exemplified by some figures released at the annual conference of the Union of Arab Chambers of Commerce, held in Cairo in February 1997. According to these, the Arab population, which reached 252 million in 1996, will reach 290 million by the year 2000, a growth rate of 2.5 per cent. According to figures given by the Egyptian Trade Minister, Arab countries now have to import $40 million worth of food each day to feed their people; 65 per cent of Arab wheat requirements, 74 per cent of sugar requirements and 62 per cent of vegetable-oil requirements are already imported from abroad. A major problem will be to find the exports to pay for these imports.

At the moment the total non-oil exports of the Arab world plus Iran amount to less than those of Finland. As the region becomes ever more dependent on food imports, there will be greater need for manufactured exports. A continuing problem is the lag in investment because of burdensome regulations, low privatization, poor and often deteriorating infrastructure and underdeveloped financial markets. Far from attracting outside investment to the region, wealthy Middle Easterners tend to invest much of their money elsewhere. Conflict and insecurity could only aggravate these trends.

Of all the Arab countries, the ones with the best economic records are Morocco, Tunisia and Jordan. All three function without the oil revenues that have distorted the growth of Saudi Arabia and the Gulf states. All three have avoided the disastrous statist policies that still encumber the economies of Algeria and Egypt. All three devote major resources to education and infrastructure. Tunisia in particular spends more than any other Muslim country on female education. All three have rapidly improving health conditions – including lower infant mortality and greater life expectations. These developments show very clearly the way to greater prosperity through peace and peaceful development. Syria and Iraq show with at least equal clarity the way to disaster through political and economic tyranny and domestic and foreign conflict. There can be little doubt which of these paths the people of Syria and Iraq would choose – if ever they were able to exercise a choice.

The population explosion in the Middle East and North Africa is already producing another important phenomenon – migration of labour. Western Europe has, and in the not too distant future Central and Eastern Europe will have, a relatively high standard of living and a low birth rate. Their southern and south-eastern neighbours in North Africa and the Middle East share a low standard of living and a high birth rate. Modern travel and political relaxation make it easier both to reach and to enter the various countries of Europe. Already the migration of labour, especially from Turkey and North Africa to Western Europe, is seen by many in these countries as a major problem. The peace process between Israel and its Arab neighbours, if it continues, may well produce similar results, as Palestinian and perhaps also other Arab labour is attracted to the expanding Israeli economy.

A significant element in the cash flow of the region is aid and donations of various kinds. By far the most important single source is the government of the United States, which provides a wide range of financial aid for both development and military purposes. The principal recipients are Israel and Egypt, followed by Turkey and Armenia. Barring sudden and violent changes in the region, this aid is unlikely to continue in its present form. Military aid will dwindle as the danger of a military confrontation recedes. Economic aid will be seen as unnecessary where it is effective, and useless where it is not. In Israel, where the military danger shows little sign of receding, military aid will probably continue. Economic aid will be more difficult to justify, as its place in the rapidly developing and increasingly sophisticated Israeli economy becomes less important. Aid to Egypt passes through the U.S. Congress on the coat-tails of aid to Israel, and would probably not make it on its own – the more so at a time when Egyptian policy towards the American-sponsored peace process is seen as equivocal.

Considerable sums also come from abroad in the form of private donations, mainly from Jewish and Muslim communities in the Americas, Western Europe and Australasia. Most of this money is

designated for development, education, welfare and other chari-
table purposes; some of it is diverted to overtly or covertly political
aims. The distinction is not always easy to discern or maintain.
Terrorist and subversive movements of various kinds, some of
them state sponsored, are finding in Europe and North America a
freedom of manoeuvre, both financial and operational, which
they could not hope to find in the Middle East or North Africa.

They are using this freedom to devastating effect. The Iranian
revolution against the Shah took an enormous step forward when
its leader Khomeini moved from Iraq to Paris, where he had
uncensored modern communications at his disposal. Others are
following and will follow this early successful example. Among
the Turkish diaspora in Europe, especially in Germany, both the
fundamentalists and the Kurdish separatists collect funds and
organize subversion. To an alarming extent the war in Algeria is
planned, financed and directed from France. The Iranian government's 'Office of Islamic Revivals', concerned with the promotion
of the Islamic revolution and its ideas in other Muslim countries,
also locates its main financial and operational bases in Europe. At
the same time the Islamic republic is itself threatened by increasingly sophisticated opposition groups using Western democratic
freedom and modern communication to challenge the regime at
home.

There are also transfers of funds within the region, some from
governments, notably Iran and Libya, some from wealthy private
individuals, mostly in Saudi Arabia and the Gulf. In Turkey, the
only Muslim country in the region with free and contested elections, these transfers take the form of suitably disguised campaign
contributions. Even in the older and more experienced democracies of the West, such contributions and their effect are difficult
to follow and document. Their effect will be far greater in the
newer democracies of poorer countries, with less experience in
following the trail of money and measuring its impact. These tasks
will however become easier as the flow of oil money diminishes
and the democracies of the region become more experienced in
detection and counteraction.

Tourism has been described as one of the best prospects for the
region. Certainly there is room for improvement – at the present
time the tourist revenues of the entire region are less than those

of Mexico and about equal to those of Thailand in the 1990s. But the development of tourism, as of so much else, will depend on domestic and regional security. Great numbers of tourists are not likely to brave the dangers of war and terrorism.

With a few exceptions, the economic prognosis for the region remains bad. Productivity is falling dramatically, the creation of new jobs has stagnated, unemployment rates are the highest in the world. The poor are becoming more numerous and, comparatively, poorer. Major economic development will be needed to avoid disaster and this in turn will presuppose the social, cultural and scientific changes needed to bring the Middle East into line with the developed countries of both West and East.

Past and Future

The competition between democracy and fundamentalism will have a direct bearing on another choice – between outward and inward modernization. Outward modernization means accepting the devices, the amenities, the conveniences provided by Western science and industry while rejecting what are seen as pernicious Western values. All too often, this means also rejecting the science that produced these devices and amenities and the way of life that made that science possible. One might put it this way: outward modernization means buying and firing a gun. Inward modernization means learning to manufacture and ultimately design one. This is not likely to happen in countries – like some in the region – where science is taught in schools from fifty year old textbooks.

Catching up with the modern world means more than borrowing or buying modern technology. It means becoming part of the process by which that technology is created – that is, undergoing the intellectual·revolution, the economic, social and eventually political transformation, that precede, accompany and follow technological change.

In this respect, the Middle East still lags far behind other more recent recruits to modernity like Korea, Taiwan and Singapore. It lags much further behind Japan, whose first contact with the West came centuries later than that of the Middle East. The transformation of the 'Asian Tigers' is even more dramatic, and the gap between them and the economies of the Middle East is widening every day. In a region where hundreds of universities turn out tens of thousands of engineers every year, it has become normal for governments and corporations requiring hi-tech construction work to bring in contractors from Korea – a country that only recently emerged from a long period of oppressive colonial rule followed by devastating years of war. Unless the countries of the

Middle East are able to make the transition to the new age, this gap will grow ever wider.

There are three elements which could help transform the Middle East: Turkey, Israel and women – the first previously aloof, the second previously excluded, the third previously suppressed.

Of these, the most important is women. They will, if permitted, play a major role in bringing the Middle East into a new era of material development, scientific advancement and socio-political liberation. Of all the people of the Middle East, women have the strongest vested interest in social and political freedom. They are already among its most valiant and effective defenders; they may yet be its salvation. As in other parts of the world, some women defend and even acclaim the subordination of their sex. Others, never having known anything else, meekly submit to it. But growing numbers, touched by the ideas of freedom and equality and increasingly open to outside influence and example, will rebel against it. Muslim countries cannot hope to catch up, let alone keep pace with the advanced world, as long as they deprive themselves of the talents and energies of half the population and entrust the nurture of most of the other half to uneducated and downtrodden mothers.

The women's movement will still suffer serious reverses in the Middle East. But these, like the excesses of Taliban in Afghanistan and the murderous repression of women in some Arab countries, will not succeed indefinitely. Even in Iran, where anti-feminism was a major theme in Khomeinist ideology, women are already beginning to play an increasing part in some aspects of public life. The influence of women from among the expatriate Muslim communities in Europe and America will also make an important contribution to the emancipation of their sisters who stayed at home.

Turkey today stands before important choices. It may choose, as some of its leaders would clearly prefer, to turn its back on the West and return to the Middle East, this time not leading but following, in a direction determined by others. It may choose, as other Turkish leaders would clearly prefer, to tighten its ties with the West and turn its back on the Middle East, except for those countries that share Turkey's westward orientation and democratic aspirations. In either case, Turkey can and probably will play a growing role in the region. The Turks have greater political experience, a more developed economy, a more balanced society than the Arab states. The Turkish example, perhaps even Turkish leadership, may play a crucial role in influencing Arab choices. The decisions made in Turkey in the near future will determine in which direction Turkish influence will point.

The Arab–Israel conflict too, in one way or another, will profoundly influence the development of the region as a whole. This could be positive or negative. If the struggle becomes more bitter and acquires the enduring quality of some of the other, more ancient quarrels of the region, it will have a corrosive effect on both Israeli and Arab societies, diverting energies and resources from creative to destructive purposes and preventing the progress of the region towards a new age of advanced technology and political freedom.

Peace, in contrast, would help and speed that progress. Even the negative aspects of Israeli rule may unintentionally contribute, in some respect and in some degree, to this process. Almost every day radio and television – including, especially, Israeli radio and television – report on Palestinian protests against Israeli repression, in parliament, in the courts, in the media and in the street, where demonstrators gather to vent their anger. It will not escape notice that all this is an innovation in a region where normally citizens do not sue the government in the courts, and critics do not denounce the policies they dislike in parliament and in the state-run media. Even more important, in most of these countries youths do not throw stones at soldiers, and the latter do not respond to attack with water cannon and rubber bullets. These differences are being seen and understood.

If there is peace, then the peoples of the Middle East, working together, might achieve their own breakthrough as other regions have already done, and resume the creative role which they once played in the history of civilization. One way that this might happen was described in a remarkably prophetic article by T. E. Lawrence – Lawrence of Arabia – published in 1920.

The success of [the Zionists'] scheme will involve inevitably the raising of the present Arab population to their own material level, only a little after themselves in point of time, and the consequences might be at the highest importance for the future of the Arab world. It might well prove a source of technical supply rendering them independent of industrial Europe, and in that case the new confederation might become a formidable element of world power. However, such a contingency will not be for the first or even the second generation . . .

With peace and co-operation between the nations of the region, it might be possible to resolve many problems and inaugurate a great economic expansion. In this, Israel, with its advanced and sophisticated technological and scientific base, would be able to make a substantial contribution. Such co-operation would require the overcoming of many psychological barriers – the allaying of mistrust, the forgetting of grievances, the swallowing of pride. All these are difficult, perhaps impossible, but without them the region has little hope of moral or material advancement.

In the nineteen nineties the combined GNP of Egypt, Jordan, Syria and Lebanon, that is, all Israel's Arab neighbours, was significantly smaller than that of Israel alone. The per capita discrepancy is even greater. According to U.N. figures for the same period, Israel's per capita GNP is seven times that of Lebanon, ten times that of Jordan, twelve times that of Syria, and twenty times that of Egypt. Co-operation could lead to the fulfilment of Lawrence's prophecy and narrow the gap between the two. A continuation of conflicts and boycotts would surely widen the gap.

A Return to Empire?

This window of opportunity will not remain open for ever. Even when its oil and its transit routes, so crucial in the past, are outdated by modern technology and communications, the Middle East will still have some importance – the junction of three continents, the centre of three religions, a strategic asset or danger to be coveted or feared. Sooner or later it will again become an object of interest to outside powers – old powers reviving, new powers emerging. If it continues on its present course, the region, possessing neither the resources of India and China nor the technology and industry of Europe and America, will once again be a stake rather than a player in the great game of international politics.

For the moment, the peoples or governments of the Middle East can to an increasing extent determine their own fate. They may choose the way of Yugoslavia or Lebanon, of fragmentation and endless internecine strife. They may launch – there are some who clearly desire this – a new holy war, a jihad, which would inevitably again provoke, as it did a thousand years ago, the response of an opposing holy war, a crusade. A militant movement or power that defines itself in religious terms will also define its opponents in religious terms and these opponents may sooner or later accept that definition. The so-called Islamic fundamentalists fight for Islam and explicitly reject the notion of patriotic or national loyalties, which they see as pagan, divisive, and – worst of all – the result of Western influence. And since their cause is Islam, their enemies are those whom they see as the enemies of Islam – the followers of other religions or of none. For nationalists and patriots the struggle was waged against Zionism and imperialism. In the language of the fundamentalists these have resumed their earlier names – the Jews and the Christians. No one has a better claim to be called 'Egyptian' than the Copts, the native Christians of Egypt. But attacks on Coptic churches and villages have become a common tactic of the Islamic fundamentalists, acting in the name not of the country but of the faith. Struggles of this kind can only exacerbate relations between the Middle East and the outside world and increase the possibility of a return to empire.

As long as conflict and repression prevail there is little hope of the Middle East achieving a real equality with more advanced countries and therefore of preserving its independence from them. When vibrant and torpid, stronger and weaker societies live side by side, some form of penetration and perhaps even of domination becomes inevitable.

Who would be the players in such a renewed game of great-power politics in the Middle East? In the Gulf War and after, the United States clearly demonstrated its lack of imperial ambition, at least in this region. Important American economic interests remain, and their protection at times requires a military presence, usually at the solicitation of local rulers. But these two interests will dwindle as the oil era draws to its inevitable end. Apart from some promising developments of hi-tech industry – on a small scale and in a few places – there is little else in the Middle East to attract the attention of either investors or predators. The total amount of American private investment in the whole Middle East, according to 1995 figures, was about one-third of the amount invested in Australia, one-fifth of the amount invested in Japan and less than one-tenth of the amount invested in Canada. These disparities have been increasing for a number of years and are likely to become greater in the years to come.

America's major strategic interest ended with the Cold War. Some lesser strategic interests remain, concerned mainly with the threats of terrorism from within the region. Strategic interest will of course revive if and when outside powers become involved.

The European powers, singly or jointly, are unlikely to return to the scenes of their former imperial failures. The crises in Bosnia and Cyprus demonstrated their inability to cope unaided even with problems on their own doorstep. More probably they will content themselves with financial and commercial dealings, with perhaps a little occasional political profit-taking when opportunity offers.

Russia is another matter. For the moment crippled by its internal problems, it is out of the game, and its weakness is painfully revealed in the few unsuccessful attempts by Russian leaders to assert a role in the peacemaking process. But there can be no doubt that at some time in the near or distant future this will change. A country with the resources and numbers, the scientific and technological sophistication of Russia, will not indefinitely remain on the sidelines. Sooner or later Russia will be back, and we do not know what kind of a Russia that will be. It may fall subject to some form of totalitarian tyranny, fascist or communist; it may resume its earlier role as the leader of pan-Slavism or of Orthodox Christianity; it may succeed, after so many failed efforts, in establishing a Russian liberal democracy. It may resume or reject its former imperial ambitions. But this much can be said with certainty: that, whatever kind of regime rules in a resurgent Russia, it will be vitally concerned with the Middle East – a region not far from its southern frontier wherever that may ultimately lie, and linked by ties of history, religion and culture with important elements of the Russian population, including both Jews and Muslims as well as Christians.

The rulers of a new Russia would have several choices of Middle Eastern policies. They might follow the West European example and try to keep on reasonably good terms with as many different groups as possible, while offering effective help to none of them. They might revive the Soviet policy of encouraging and supporting those elements that are opposed to the West and to Israel. Alternatively, they might conclude that militant Islamic fundamentalism is more of a danger to Russia than to the West. Conceivably, they might discover and develop the cultural affinity that exists between Russia and Israel – a society founded by immigrants from the former czarist Russian empire, and recently reinforced by a million immigrants from the former Soviet Union.

The coming century will surely see the emergence of two new superpowers – India and China. Both possess in ample measure the numbers, the resources and the cohesion for such a role. Both – far more successfully than most of the countries in the Middle East – are facing the challenges of modernity and accomplishing the transition to a new age. Both still have major problems to overcome. These may delay but will not prevent the rise of these two new superpowers to a world role.

Both will inevitably become involved in the Middle East in much the same way and for much the same reasons as the European powers in their day. Bordered by Europe in the west, Russia in the north, China and India in the east, the Middle East will be of concern to all of them. Like the great powers of the past, the great powers of the future will meet in the Middle East as allies or rivals, as patrons or masters.

Russia, China and India all have significant Muslim minorities. In the Russian federation, even after the loss of the predominantly Muslim republics, Muslims still amount to some 15 per cent of the total population – a higher percentage than in any part of Western Europe, even after Muslim immigration. A significant proportion of these Muslims, notably the Chechens, the Tatars, the Bashkirs, live in autonomous political entities of their own within the Russian federation.

China, unlike the Soviet Union, has not broken up, and retains imperial control over its Central Asian conquests. These include extensive territories predominantly inhabited by Muslims, most of them speaking Turkic languages. The new-found independence of their kinsfolk formerly under Soviet rule has roused new hopes and expectations among China's Muslim subjects; Beijing's policy of setting great numbers of ethnic Chinese in Muslim territories has aroused new resentments. Increasingly, China will have a Muslim problem, and a growing area of friction with both the Turkish and Iranian worlds. Russia's experience with the Afghans may perhaps give a foretaste of how it will develop.

India has a vast Muslim minority, much greater than those of either Russia or China. Indian relations with Islam have been embittered by a long struggle and, more particularly, by the wars with Pakistan, though here there are signs of improvement. Like Russia and China, but perhaps differently, India will be affected one way or another in its dealings with the Middle East by its own Muslim population.

A Return to Greatness?

In antiquity, the Middle East was the birthplace of human civilization and of monotheistic religion. In the Middle Ages, it was the home of the first truly international and intercultural society, the source of towering innovations and achievements in almost every field of science and technology, of culture and the arts. It was the base of a succession of great and vast empires. The last of them, in many ways the greatest, was the Ottoman Empire. In the sixteenth and seventeenth centuries, it was a mighty world power – its armies twice reached as far as Vienna, its ships sailed as far as Iceland and Sumatra. Since then there has been no Middle Eastern great power nor is there likely to be one until the Middle East has resolved the political, economic, cultural and societal problems that prevent it from accomplishing the next stage in the advance of civilization.

The continuing struggle within the region, with the consequent diversion of energy and resources to the politics and weaponry of war, can only make a resumption of outside interference and domination more likely. If the Middle East falls under the rule of China or of a resurgent Russia, things will be different from the old days. Nationalist delegations will not follow each other to Beijing or Moscow as they used to go to London and Paris, to negotiate with their rulers and put their case before public opinion in the metropolis. Gandhi succeeded against Britain, the Intifada was effective against Israel. They would have had short shrift from such rulers as Hitler, Stalin or Saddam Hussein.

But there is another way – that of peace and progress. The second will depend very largely on the first. This requires from all parties a readiness to compromise on their own claims and a willingness to tolerate the claims of others. Compromise and tolerance have not been much in evidence in the Middle East in the past, but there have been intermittent signs of both among some of the key players. If the different peoples of the region really pool their skills and resources, they may once again make the Middle East, as it was in an increasingly remote past, a major centre of human civilization. If they do not, they and their children face a grim future.

For each and every country and for the region as a whole, there is a range of alternative futures: at one end, co-operation and progress towards peace and freedom, enlightenment and prosperity; at the other, a vicious circle of poverty and ignorance, fear and violence, tyranny and anarchy, hatred and self-pity, leading perhaps in the end to a new alien domination.

5 Terrorism

CONOR GEARTY

Introduction

In the final third of a twentieth century full of moral extremes, a new and virulent evil seems suddenly to be stalking the world, causing terrible violence without a thought and threatening the habit of democratic government wherever it has managed to throw down roots. This supposed enemy of freedom and liberty is not the fascist or communist ideologue of earlier eras against whom wars – both hot and cold – were waged for over seventy years. It is neither as powerful nor so explicit in its ambitions as either of its marauding predecessors, though this obscurity and anonymity are said merely to add to its strength. So powerful has its spell become that its name now describes our times. In the last decades of the twentieth century, it is said that we have been living in the 'age of terrorism'.

Seeming to have sprung suddenly upon us in 1968, the bloody imprints of this violent epoch are said now to be more evident and unmanageable than ever, in the return to violence in Northern Ireland and the Middle East and in the resurgence of such classical acts of terrorism as the 1996 hostage-taking at the Japanese ambassador's Peruvian residence. The violence is also frequently said to have taken on new and even more dangerous forms, such as with the release of poisonous gases in Tokyo's subway in 1995 and the forced ditching of a hijacked Ethiopian airliner in the Indian Ocean in November 1996. Outbreaks of 'terrorism' are regularly presented in quasi-medical terms as symptoms of a contagious as well as an irrational phenomenon, providing no explanation for its actions as it spreads with alarming speed to previously secure locations. It is little wonder that in this supposed 'age of terrorism' anxious questions are increasingly being asked about the nature of Western society, about its apparent vulnerability to attacks of this 'terroristic' nature, and about the degree to which society's exposure to this new enemy now threatens its very survival. Terrorism seems like a modern bubonic plague, carried across borders by human rats and dedicated only to our arbitrary destruction.

It is very easy to get caught up in this transnational panic, particularly when its pessimistic version of reality is endlessly recycled by government ministers, the vast majority of the media and an apparently limitless stream of academic 'experts'. Every bloody incident by every dissident political group anywhere in the world, particularly if it involves Westerners, is instantaneously transformed into further evidence of this new wave of terror, regardless of any local factors or of any historical context that might more particularly explain it. The description of certain violence as 'terrorist' is now something that we take so much for granted that the word has rooted itself in our psyche, bringing with it all those intense anxieties about sudden and arbitrary violence with which as a society we have become preoccupied. So embedded have these assumptions now become that to question them openly, to ask whether there is any such thing as terrorism, or whether we are really in the midst of an 'age of terrorism', no longer provokes the bother of refutation so much as a look of sheer incomprehension. The 'age of terrorism' has become so blindingly obvious to all that the only public debate about the subject that now takes place concerns itself not with whether this worldwide disease actually exists but rather with how repressive and brutal we should be in trying to defeat it.

In light of this pervasive unanimity, the argument that follows might at first sight seem difficult to grasp, even a trifle eccentric. Any thinking which lies outside the mutually reinforcing world of the mainstream inevitably invites such labelling. Let us metaphorically nail four basic propositions to this introductory chapter, the literary equivalent of our front door, so that their oddity may be savoured before our defence of them begins. First, there is no 'age of terrorism'. Secondly, the concept of terrorism has never been a useful or intelligent way of describing political violence and the term is itself now more or less entirely meaningless. Thirdly, and only apparently paradoxically, terrorism as a subject has thrived precisely as a result of this intellectual vacuity, which governments have long recognized and cleverly exploited for their own ends. Fourthly, while democracy may indeed be threatened in this so-called 'age of terrorism', the danger to its integrity comes more from the terrorists' opponents, the states and their armed and police forces, than from the so-called terrorists themselves.

Let us now defend each of these heresies in turn and build our case for the expulsion from public affairs of this fruitless and tendentious preoccupation with a dangerously meaningless label. If we do not act in this way, we face a future in which our political leaders might well succeed in panicking us into regarding our civil liberties as dangerous and therefore dispensable luxuries.

History of a Modern Myth

We begin with this notion of an 'age of terrorism'. It suggests an era exclusively committed to a form of violence hitherto unknown to the world. In fact killing for political gain is as old as civil society itself, and causing terror to make a political point enjoys a similarly ancient if not always respectable pedigree. If this is what an 'age of terrorism' amounts to, then we have never been out of one. In the first century after the birth of Christ, Jewish radicals fought to free Palestine of Roman rule. According to Josephus, the Sicarii were 'brigands who took their name from a dagger carried in their bosom'. Their 'favourite trick' was 'to mingle with festival crowds, concealing under their garments small daggers with which they stabbed their opponents. When their victims fell the assassins melted into the indignant crowd, and through their plausibility entirely defied detection.' The Assassins a millennium later emerged from the same troublesome part of the world and anticipated in the reactions that they stimulated many of the anxieties that dog our 'age of terrorism'. They belonged to the Ismaeli sect of the Shia branch of the Islamic faith and were active in the twelfth and thirteenth centuries. Their contemporary notoriety in the West lay in their preparedness to assassinate the leaders of the Crusades that were then ravaging the Holy Land, with Conrad of Montferrat being their most famous victim, killed in 1192.

The Sicarii and the Assassins would fit easily into most contemporary definitions of terrorism, and they inspired the same degree of fear and loathing among their respective political establishments as our own brand of 'terrorists' do today. The events that actually gave birth to the word in its modern sense, however, involved terror orchestrated not by rebels acting in defiance of governmental authority but by the forces of a state itself. The

Oxford English Dictionary first mentions the word in 1795, after the post-revolutionary Terror in France had accounted for the death of thousands in a short period of deliberate horror between 1792 and 1794. It was precisely because the state was involved that it proved so easy to kill so many. Not for the first time, and certainly not for the last, the power of a government to kill was shown to be far greater than that of any merely rebellious group, harassed as such subversives invariably are by the forces of a hostile state and forced to operate as they must always do without the benefit of a state team of authorized killers, willing to execute their every wish. When the stimulus of the French Revolution had precipitated a largely ineffectual insurgency in Ireland, the revenge killings on which the British government then embarked exceeded in their number the total of casualties for the whole period of the French Terror. Here again was a glimpse into the future, the 'counter-terrorism' of the authorities causing infinitely more 'terror' than the mischief at which it was purportedly aimed.

It has been a grievous mistake to lose sight of this first meaning of terrorism as 'government by intimidation as directed and carried out by the party in power'. In this neglect lies the origin of the current belief that our age is unprecedently swamped with terrorist violence. Somewhere along the line after the French Revolution and before the First World War, 'terrorism' ceased to connote what the word primarily seems to suggest, the bloody but straightforward business of causing terror to achieve political ends, in other words a tactic of violent action available to and capable of being deployed by any actor in a conflict situation, whether it be war, civil war or popular revolution, and whether the actor be a warring state, the government itself or a faction of the governed. In place of this simple approach, emphasizing the 'terror' in terrorism, the meaning of the word gradually changed during the nineteenth century in three vital ways. First, terrorism grew to be identified exclusively with subversive violence. Secondly, it came to be applied to such violence, even in situations in which it did not involve terrorizing the ordinary population. Thirdly, and flowing from both of these, terrorism came to represent a self-standing method of violent subversion which was different in kind from other types of conflict. The result of this linguistic upheaval was that, by the start of the twentieth century, 'terrorism' no longer described the tactic of causing terror, capable of being deployed by anyone in a conflict, but meant something quite technical instead, the use of violence by political subversives who were engaged in such methods in isolation and not as part of a wider conflict. This meant that states and armies engaged in conventional or civil war could not properly be described as 'terrorist' even when they were engaged in terrorizing either their own citizens or the people of an opposing force.

We have been paying a price for these attenuations of meaning ever since they first crept into the language. This is not the fault of the era which produced them. In the relatively tranquil nineteenth century, the fashion for political assassination produced a generation of optimistic tyrannicides, whose enjoyment of the 'terrorist' label helped to shape its meaning, even though the terror they were causing, if they were causing any at all, was to a tiny and extremely well-guarded élite. Terrorism, wrote one whose group had made a series of attempts on the life of Tsar Alexander II, 'directs its blows against the real perpetrators of evil'. Another Russian, writing in 1883, wrote of the terrorist that he was 'noble, terrible, irresistibly fascinating, for he combine[d] in himself the two sublimities of human grandeur: the martyr and the hero'. Of course there was also political violence in Europe which caused terror to innocent civilians as well, such as that in which the Irish Fenians were involved with their dynamite campaigns in Britain in 1883–4 and 1903–5, but the fact that this violence was frequently subversive rather than state-sponsored tended further to confirm the movement of the idea of terrorism away from its late-eighteenth-century French origins.

The concept of terrorism suggested by these nineteenth-century precedents meant that it occurred to no one to describe the horrors of the Western and Russian fronts in the First World War as acts of terrorism. In the 1930s, however, it was as 'terrorism' that the problem of a series of political assassinations was expressed. After the King of Yugoslavia and the Foreign Minister of France were killed by Croatian nationalists in Marseilles in 1934, the League of Nations felt compelled to become involved, setting up a committee of experts to study the problem. In due course two international conventions appeared, on such apparently contemporary concerns as the prevention and punishment of terrorism and the establishment of an international criminal court. Though both conventions were adopted in 1937, neither came into force. It is salutary to consider why this should have been so. By the end of the 1930s, the international community had lost its zeal for feeling anxious about the terrorism which had earlier given rise to such concern. The energy that had generated the intervention by the League of Nations could neither be sustained nor mustered afresh.

Though the problem of terrorism in the sense of political assassinations was no longer a great concern, this did not mean that the issue of violent subversion, or the still larger question of political terror – or terrorism in its original pre-nineteenth-century sense – had also ceased any longer to matter. If anything the reverse had occurred. The use of terror for political ends increased enormously in scale, extending far beyond the focused assassinations of earlier years, at just the moment that 'terrorism' as such was drifting off the international agenda. Indeed, and even more peculiarly, it was precisely because of this huge increase in terror that 'terrorism' as a discrete problem lost its force. What happened was that with the onset of the Second World War and for its duration between 1939 and 1945, political terror became just one means among many through which a great global conflagration was fought. Whereas, in the peaceful inter-war era and before that in the nineteenth century, terrorism had been frequently to the forefront of public concern because it had been one of only a very few forms of political subversion that was then manifesting itself in violence, during the world war that followed its subversive activities were quickly swamped by the depth and range of military operations that surrounded it. The paradoxical consequence of this is that the age of greatest political terror this century is never thought of as an 'age of terrorism', whereas the relatively peaceful times either side of that war have been frequently so described.

We can see this very clearly by considering the effect of an IRA bombing campaign in Britain which began in January 1939 with an ultimatum to the British government to withdraw from Northern Ireland. Here was a terrorist campaign in both the narrow and the broad meaning of the word, in that not only was a violent, subversive group involved but also the methods that were used caused indiscriminate injury to civilians. In the months that followed the IRA's declaration of intent, a series of explosions caused a number of injuries and fatalities, culminating in an horrific bomb which exploded in Coventry's main shopping area on 25 August 1939, killing five people and injuring more than fifty. Perhaps in less peculiar times this campaign would have engendered a climate of fear and anxiety about terrorism similar to that which was to grip Great Britain in 1972–4 and which had briefly threatened to dominate Victorian public life in 1883. Certainly the terrorism seemed more severe than that which had caused such an international rumpus just a few short years before. But, with war with Germany breaking out on 3 September 1939, there was not enough space in the public imagination for the kind of panic that such arbitrary killings would normally have provoked. Nor was a busy government inclined to foster public fear. After one legislative response and some quietly effective police action, the campaign ground unnoticed to a halt in 1940. Its attacks on civilians, though dreadful, were lost in the nightmare of a truly catastrophic war, one which claimed the lives of 30,000 civilians through bombing attacks in Britain alone in its first twenty months. During one night in Coventry in November 1940, German bombers killed more than one hundred times the number of people the IRA had blown up in their attack in the same town the year before.

Our intuitive reluctance to class the many acts of terror associated with the military conduct of the Second World War as 'terrorist' shows how far the word has drifted from its roots. If we take the idea of political terror at face value, as encompassing at its core the arbitrary killing of civilians for political purposes in a way which terrifies the populace, then it is beyond dispute that the war involved both subversive terror and state terror on a truly dramatic scale. We need only think of the French Resistance and Tito's partisans for evidence of the first, and mention the names of Coventry, Dresden and Hiroshima for proof of the second. Some of us might want to argue in the context of the Second World War that attacks on the established pro-Nazi regimes in France or Yugoslavia were justified at the time, just as many of us would remember with admiration the bravery of those German officers who sought at great risk to themselves to assassinate Hitler during the latter part of the war. In the same vein, there is still a lively debate about whether it was right or wrong to use the atomic bomb in Japan in 1945, though nobody (even those who have profoundly disagreed with the decision) has called President Truman a 'state terrorist' for having ordered it.

We are all shy of using the language of terrorism in this way in wartime, despite the fact that such conduct invariably involved the indiscriminate killing of civilians for political ends or to communicate a political message, all supposedly classic ingredients of pure acts of terror. Our reluctance on this score is understandable, and is derived from more than a technical appreciation of the artificial and academic distinction between 'terror' and 'terrorism' that crept into the language in the nineteenth century. It is rooted in a legitimate anxiety about the moral baggage that the word 'terrorism' now carries with it. Intuitively we see the question of the possible morality of many of these wartime acts of terror and violent subversion as not being beyond argument. It might have been right or it might have been wrong to kill this or that Vichy official, to order attacks on German cities to undermine the morale of the ordinary German people, or even to kill millions of Japanese so as to force an end to the war. The point about deployment of the language of terrorism is that the mere use of the word implies that that judgement has already been made. To call an act of violence a terrorist act is not so much to describe it as to condemn it, subjugating all questions of context and circumstance to the reality of its immorality.

These various points can be reinforced by considering the violence that accompanied the campaigns for freedom from colonial rule that were such a marked feature of the post-war world. In the twenty or so years after the defeat of Germany and Japan, an array of peoples across the globe wrenched themselves free from European domination. This series of transitions to independence was frequently accompanied by political violence. In Malaya, Kenya, Cyprus and Aden, British authorities gave in only unwillingly to a pressure for liberation in which calculated, political killing played an important part. The French immersed their nation in even deeper strife, fighting themselves to a standstill in Indochina in the early 1950s and then engaging with Algerian nationalism in a bloody eight-year feud, culminating in the conceding of independence to the country in 1962. These wars of liberation were conducted by subversive forces prepared to fight for their cause in any way that was available to them, whether it be constitutional or illegal. Such tactics frequently included engaging the colonial establishment in the countryside as rural guerrillas and in the cities as covert bombers. They faced states prepared on occasion (as in Algeria) to engage in massive retaliatory terror so as to avert or at least to delay defeat.

Despite the seriousness, depth and bloodiness of these various conflicts, their combined impact was not such as to cause their times to be described as constituting an 'age of terrorism'. This was not because there were no assaults on civilians. The battle for Algiers in 1956–7 involved a campaign of bombing in the city, and many of the other conflicts such as in Aden and Kenya included similarly indiscriminate attacks on civilians. Just as with the Second World War, however, it was the wide-ranging nature of these hostilities that made the terrorist label inappropriate. The situations they encompassed were too serious to be accurately described by such a label. A deeper inhibition on the successful use of the 'terrorist' epithet also existed, rooted in Europe's equivocation about the morality of these wars of independence. Close to the surface in each colonial state lay a body of opinion sympathetic to the aims, if not necessarily the actual violence, of its opponents. Local rebels typically enjoyed wide popular support for both. This popular following underpinned not only rural but also urban military activity of a frequency and force of which contemporary European groups in today's 'age of terrorism' would not be remotely capable. To many among the colonizers as well as the colonized, the struggle for independence was a noble ideal which if it did not justify might at least excuse the means that the fighters deemed essential to its realization. In such a complex environment, the simplistic language of 'terrorism', with its inherent moral condemnation of all subversive violence, was neither appropriate nor frequently successfully deployed. We do not call this colonial phase an 'age of terrorism', because it involved more serious violence than we normally associate with terrorism and also because, just as was the case with the Second World War, we want to reserve our right not to condemn all of the violence that then occurred.

What then are we to make of this 'age of terrorism' in which the experts tell us we have been immersed since 1968? Viewed in historical context, it is clear that the decades since this supposed turning point have for the West at least been a time of unusual peace and stability. There have been a few wars, but these have stayed well clear of the West's public thoroughfares. The colonial insurgencies that had involved the European powers in so much post-war political violence had more or less wound down by 1968, with those that remained (such as in South Africa and Rhodesia) being now mainly squabbles between indigenous peoples and the colonial settlers rather than between the natives and the states who had once sent those settlers there. There had been terrorist campaigns in Europe during the age of decolonization, such as in Northern Ireland between 1956 and 1962 and in South Tyrol during the same period, but, just as was the case with the IRA during the Second World War, these fairly innocuous outbreaks of violence had made little impact. It has been the atmosphere of confident tranquillity that we have enjoyed since 1968 that has allowed the kind of political killing that we have come to describe as terrorism to grab the public imagination in a way that has been out of all proportion to the harm that such acts have achieved. As we have seen, it is of the essence of such violence as it has come to be understood that it takes place in isolation, unconnected to any greater conflict, and that it is subversive in nature. This has been the only sort of political violence on which the West has been at the receiving end for more than three decades. There has therefore been space in the public mind for an emotional reaction, for the sort of neurotic anxiety that would not have been induced had such violence been no more than an unnoticed sideshow in a Western world of greater bloodshed.

Without any great war or massive insurgency to distract us, we have been able to indulge our anxieties about the terrorists' sporadic violence. Concern about 'terrorism' in the West is therefore paradoxically reassuring, since contriving the level of passion that we have voiced about such a minor problem could only be possible in a time of relative peace. The point can be reinforced by considering exactly how much of this political violence there has been during this 'age of terrorism'. The evidence is complicated by difficulties of definition, but whatever yardstick is chosen the numbers of casualties remain historically extremely low. If we restrict ourselves to political violence which crosses borders or is otherwise international in character, the figure for the number of fatalities since the 1960s is on any statistical basis in the low thousands. Certainly there has been no year in which any agency, think-tank or research group, no matter how enthusiastically or expansively it has defined its subject, has ever managed to find more than a thousand fatalities a year from 'international terrorism'. If we add in domestic terrorism, but hold to the notion of such violence being essentially subversive in nature and separate from other types of military conflict, we still arrive at a figure which is in the tens of thousands at the very most.

Dreadful though each of these casualties has been for the victims and families concerned, these figures surely cry out to be seen in proportion. Not only are they historically extremely low, but they also represent only a tiny fraction of the deaths from political violence that have occurred across the world since the supposed outbreak of terrorism in 1968. This is where the self-centredness of the West's habit of treating terrorism as a special isolated type of violence capable of being engaged in only by subversives is at its most exposed. There is an unattractive irony in the fact that during this 'age of terrorism' the number of deaths from what is counted in these statistics as 'terrorism' has been dwarfed by the casualties from the civil wars, communal disorders, genocidal attacks and other forms of political terror that have been gathering pace across the world. The state-orchestrated terrorism of certain homicidal Central American governments in the 1980s alone caused more deaths than the whole catalogue of subversive, terrorist violence since 1968. The victims of political terror in Rwanda, the former Yugoslavia and Somalia in the 1990s have not been included in any statistics on 'terrorism'. The problem of 'terrorism' as it is commonly understood in Europe and North America is very much a Western construct. Its victims may be few but the subject is so defined and its parameters are so arranged that they are almost exclusively Western. In this time of political peace for the West, terrorism represents one of the very few ways in which a European or American can die as a result of political violence. Talk of an 'age of terrorism' shows merely that the West is not content only to control our world, it wants also to define our times.

Seeds of Confusion

The notion of an 'age of terrorism' is so ahistorical and counter-factual that its grip on the public imagination cannot be wholly explained simply by pointing to the lack of other forms of political terror competing for the attention of the Western mind. There are lots of (non-political) ways of dying in the West which are both as terrifying as terrorism and at the same time far more frequent, but which despite their prevalence attract not a fraction of the levels of anxiety which terrorism seems to provoke. This is an obvious point and it might also seem at first glance a mystifying one. The idea of terrorism has not however made it to the top of the international agenda solely through its own efforts. The casualty list has not been the only engine powering its rise to dismal notoriety. The whole concept of a terrorist plague has secured a convenient ally in the form of the many powerful authorities around the world who find themselves immersed in domestic challenges to their own political supremacy. Whereas the concept of terrorism in its modern form may have been Western in origin, this has not stopped states from other parts of the world adopting its language of condemnation. Indeed, for all such governments, whether Western or not, the notion of a wave of terrorism afflicting the entire globe is a tempting and consoling way of characterizing their own problems. It allows them to divert attention away from the local context of such insubordination, which can at times be revealingly embarrassing for the states concerned. In place of this domestic focus, the language of terrorism offers an attractive new emphasis on the international nature of a state's plight, with all nations now seemingly yoked together in courageous adversity like some recently formed brotherhood of victims. It is this neat diversionary trick, not the statistics on subversive violence, which has largely fuelled the terrorist panic that has supposedly gripped the world since 1968.

This can be more clearly seen by considering the uncertainty that continues to surround the meaning of terrorism. Of course the idea of terrorism as inherently subversive in nature, as something that only rebels do, is now deeply embedded in the language, to the advantage of established orders everywhere. Within this restrictive parameter, however, the way governments and national legal systems view the term has drifted apart from the public perception of what constitutes terrorism. That there is any difference between the two may come as something of a surprise. The least you would expect after decades in the international spotlight and endless academic studies would be a fairly clear indication of what terrorism means, making it possible quickly to label this or that act across the world as falling within or without some agreed definition. In fact no such agreement exists. There can be few subjects which are so loud in their claims while being simultaneously so devoid of coherence. One particularly determined scholar once combed through 109 different definitions and produced a set of no fewer than twenty-two components that are to be found in the academic literature from time to time. He did expose a few elements that appeared more frequently than others and which most people would probably intuitively feel to be part and parcel of the quintessential terrorist act. The classic terrorist act in this sense would involve a random attack by subversives on innocent individuals, intended to cause fear, death and injury and thereby to secure political concessions from somebody or some organization other than those who were being directly attacked. This certainly captures the aircraft hijack, the hostage seizure and the arbitrary no-warning bomb, all of which immediately and explicably attract the 'terrorist' label. These were the sorts of incidents that first sparked off speculation about a new 'terrorist age' in the West in the late 1960s.

The subversive violence that became apparent at this time came from three sources in particular. There can be no doubt that the pseudo-colonial violence of groups like ETA and the IRA, the ideological subversion of the likes of the Red Brigades and the RAF and the Palestinian-inspired violence of this period bore many of these hallmarks of classic terrorism. It is this sort of violence that the public generally still has in mind when the image of the terrorist and of the terrorist act is brought to its attention. The idea of terror, of the arbitrary attack on the innocent, remains firmly at the forefront of the word. To governments, however, the word terrorism has come to connote something far broader than this, and broader even than the targeted assassinations of earlier eras. It is now officially construed in terms which are wide enough to encompass within their condemnatory remit all subversive violence of every sort. The popular perception of terrorism as indiscriminate terror has been fanning the judgemental fire inherent in the word, but it has been the official, wider meaning of the word that has driven the counter-terrorist energies of the state, not only in the West where as we have seen concern about terrorism originated, but throughout the rest of the world as well, with many nations wanting for their own opportunistic reasons to climb aboard this anti-terrorist bandwagon. It is this disparity of meaning between the popular and official meanings of terrorism that has made the subject both incomprehensible and at the same time vulnerable to exploitation by governments, both internally and as part of their international diplomacy. This latter manipulation, which we shall consider in our next chapter, has only been possible because of weaknesses that have been present from the start in the whole concept of terrorism. For even when the term was being deployed in its most credible and coherent of manners, as was the case during this brief period at the end of the 1960s and the start of the 1970s, it was nevertheless even then a confusing and distracting label to attach to the conflicts that it sought to describe. It has been the festering of problems ignored or glossed over then that has been instrumental in precipitating the dangerous chaos that has now engulfed the whole subject and which threatens our future freedom.

Let us now develop this point by looking more closely at the problems that gave rise to our so-called 'age of terrorism'. If we turn first to the upsurge of pseudo-colonial subversion, it is clear that the violence that had become a familiar part of the ritual of decolonization in the 1950s and 1960s took an unexpected turn in about 1968. In Spain in that year, the ETA movement which had been established in 1959 claimed the chief of the political police in the Guipúzcoa province as its first victim in its renewed struggle for Basque freedom. A year later, the always potentially unstable political situation in Northern Ireland exploded into the public eye, with the previously moribund IRA gaining a new lease of life from the disorder that suddenly engulfed the Province. In October 1970, members of the FLQ (the Quebec Liberation Front) kidnapped the British trade commissioner James Cross and Pierre Laporte, a minister in the provincial government of Quebec, killing the latter after an attempted escape. All of these movements were quickly deplored by their respective governments as terrorist, and their violence fitted at least one meaning of this term to the extent that it was both subversive and isolated from other forms of insurgency. Unlike the putative assassins of the nineteenth century, however, these groups eschewed entirely the terrorist label and looked instead to the recent tradition of anti-colonial militancy for inspiration and moral legitimacy. This was not as irrational as their opponents might have wanted to believe.

The success of the post-war guerilla campaigns that had produced so many new independent nations had had the effect of making the now expanded international community more inclined than it might previously have been to accept the right of a people to wage a war of liberation against its political masters. This became more apparent than ever just as these violent nationalist campaigns were getting under way. In 1970, the United Nations General Assembly gave its overwhelming support to a Declaration of Principles of International Law Concerning Friendly Relations and Co-operation among States which proclaimed the right of a people to self-determination and to seek outside help for such a struggle. This was followed in 1974 by a further UN initiative which accepted that the concept of international armed conflict should be expanded to include 'armed conflicts in which peoples are fighting against colonial domination and alien occupation and against racist regimes in the exercise of their right of self-determination . . .'. This formulation was added to the Geneva Conventions in 1977, and its effect was inevitably to add further legitimacy to the notion of a liberation struggle by a guerrilla army. All of this international movement was primarily aimed at justifying the battles of the past and at legitimizing the liberation struggles that were still taking place in Africa, against white rule in South Africa and Rhodesia and against the continuing Portuguese presence in other parts of the continent. One of its effects, however, was to appear to underpin other secessionist struggles outside the colonial mainstream, not least within apparently homogeneous national entities in the developed world.

Supporters of the ETA movement in Spain and the IRA in Northern Ireland saw their respective political situations in essentially colonial terms, with both organizations doing no more than exercising their right to struggle on behalf of their respective peoples for their liberation from colonial domination. From the start the analogy was more apparent than real. Spain and the United Kingdom regarded these provinces not as alien colonial outposts but as integral parts of their respective nations, with the secession of either of them being akin more to the amputation of a limb than to the jettisoning of an unwanted appendage. Reflecting this sense of unity, the population in both areas was by no means exclusively drawn from the culture on whose behalf independence was being claimed. In the four Basque provinces in Spain, approximately 65 per cent of the population were native Basques. In Northern Ireland the Irish nationalist community was even lower, amounting to not much more than 40 per cent of the population. Inevitably given these demographic facts, there was no support for the kind of broad fronts that had earlier provided vital support for the push for freedom in genuinely colonial situations. Not even the bulk of the nationalistically inclined communities in either place viewed subversive violence as a regrettable but necessary means to a desired end, as had whole swathes of opinion in such places as Aden and Algeria.

In these circumstances it was inevitable that neither ETA nor the IRA should ever have been strong enough to mount a guerrilla campaign from secured territory or to reach across the whole community so as to make their homelands ungovernable from the notionally hated centre. Isolated subversive violence was all that there was left to do, a consolation for aspiring guerrillas too feeble to mount a proper struggle. It is in this sense that it is correct to describe terrorism as the 'weapon of the weak'. Initially both movements tried to keep the guerrilla model to the forefront of their minds by targeting only specific and (in their view) clearly culpable representatives of the 'oppressive' regime, or by engaging only in actions designed to popularize themselves among their local communities. They tried in other words to keep well outside the popular understanding of the terrorist as the purveyor of indiscriminate terror while recognizing that it was inevitable that they would be so described by their antagonistic governments. We have already seen that ETA's first victim was a local chief of police. In January 1972, the movement kidnapped an industrialist, releasing him only after his company had agreed to rehire 120 dismissed employees, increase the wages of the workforce and grant a measure of worker participation in the management of the company. Another short kidnap a year later produced a similarly attractive package for local workers. In December 1973 ETA managed to assassinate the Prime Minister Admiral Luis Carrero Blanco in a daring attack reminiscent of the tyrannicide preached by nineteenth-century terrorists. For its part, the IRA's violence was initially almost wholly defensive in nature, acting on behalf of its community against both communal and state aggression. When it went on the offensive, its first actions were against police officers and soldiers on duty and other explicit upholders of the allegedly alien British presence.

Existentially pleasing though all this busy and sometimes dramatic violence might have been to both ETA and the IRA, and more militaristic than terrorist though it may have appeared to their respective local communities, it was not obviously leading anywhere. The problem with isolated subversive violence directed at the forces of the state is firstly that it rarely has a sufficient impact to compel any response other than the obvious one of greater repression and secondly that it becomes much harder to pull off after the first few coups, when the forces of the state have inevitably regrouped and improved their defences against sudden urban attack. This had been the clear lesson of the urban guerrilla movements in South America in the 1960s, which had begun full of noble intentions, only to end in a welter of state counter-terror and increasingly indiscriminate subversive violence. This is exactly what happened in both Spain and Ireland during the 1970s and 1980s. As the years proceeded, more and more of the victims of ETA and the IRA came to have less and less connection with the regimes which both movements claimed to be attacking. The notion of the legitimate target was expanded so as to include the vulnerable and exposed as well as the security forces and government ministers, now largely speaking fully insulated from attack. In three years at the end of the 1970s, no fewer than 220 people died in ETA-related violence, many of them unconnected with any supposedly culpable target. As early as 1972 the IRA were blowing up restaurants, hotels and bars and in 1974 a series of attacks in Britain culminated in the blowing up of two public houses in Birmingham, resulting in twenty-one dead and 162 injured, many of the latter horribly maimed. The launching of deliberately or at least recklessly indiscriminate attacks has been a feature of both conflicts in Northern Ireland and Spain ever since.

There can be little doubt therefore that both ETA and the IRA quite quickly reached the point where much of their subversive violence could properly be described as entailing acts of political terror, in the core sense of involving indiscriminate attacks against civilians, designed to inspire fear and thereby to communicate a political message to a wider audience. They had become 'terrorists' in both the popular and the governmental meanings of the word. Despite this, it is by no means clear that affixing this 'terrorist' label to either organization has been at all helpful to understanding or resolving either of the two problems of which they are the most obvious manifestations. The value-laden connotations of the phrase, with its assumption that any activity described as terrorist is necessarily morally wrong, inevitably skews the proper understanding of a difficult and complex situation. Whether it is used loosely to mean all subversive violence or more tightly to describe subversive acts of pure terror, the language of terrorism is the enemy of context, forcing the analysis of any situation down a blind alley of anger at certain violence and blindness towards the rest. It blinkers the discussion of any particular political problem which has manifested itself in violence by compelling a concentration on that violence to the exclusion of the broader picture. From the subversive group's point of view, the definition of terrorism seems contrived so as to produce only one result: moral condemnation of its violence to the exclusion of all larger questions.

The 'terrorist expert' will thus rarely feel obliged to observe that the Spain in which ETA grew to maturity was a fascist state with such habits of repression that the leaders of the relatively quiescent Basque Nationalist Party (PNV) had had to seek the safety of exile in France. The PNV had been in government in the region when Guernica had been destroyed during the Civil War, an act of terror far more barbaric than the worst of ETA excesses, but rarely classed as such in the catalogues of terrorism, on account merely of its having been part of a wider conflict. Admiral Blanco was the last great devotee of fascism and Franco's heir apparent when ETA's brutal removal of him from the political scene made far easier the transition to democracy that subsequently occurred. These are vital facts in any assessment of the legitimacy of ETA's subversive campaign, just as are those that demonstrate how democratic Spain has transformed the basis of the group's claim to freedom. Also important, but obscured by the restriction of the label of terrorism to subversive groups, is the extent to which the tactic of political terror has not been exclusively the preserve of ETA. The hysterically repressive reaction of Franco's Spain to the first ETA killing in 1968 caused more terror to more people than ETA had managed in its first decade of existence. Even democratic Spain has been forced to confront serious allegations of death squads operating against ETA's political associates on behalf of the government. The problem with the 'terrorist' label is not just that we assume all terrorism to be bad; it is also that we naturally consider the reverse also to be true, that everything called 'counter-terrorism' must be good. Such naïvety is a temptation even to democratic governments.

Very similar points can be made in relation to Northern Ireland, about the inequality, discrimination and partisan law enforcement in the Province which had oppressed the nationalist community since the partition of Ireland in 1922, and about the alleged torture, the killings on Bloody Sunday in January 1972 and the other state reactions that followed upon the outbreak of disorder. The point is not at all necessarily to justify any of this subversive violence solely by having regard to its context. It is more modestly to assert that there is such a context, that this violence – some of it certainly horrific, but some of it also undoubtedly highly focused and quasi-military in its execution – comes not from some homeless world plague of terrorism but rather from highly particular parts of the world, with long histories, deep traditions and a series of specific and complicated relations. The simplicity of the terrorist label may be seductive and at times understandable but the effect of the acontextual moralizing inherent in the phrase is to divert public discussion down an intellectual cul-de-sac, thereby invariably prolonging the conflict it is desired to resolve, since it is only by addressing political causes that subversive violence can be properly confronted.

We can also see the same process at work with the second form of subversive violence that burst upon the international scene in the late 1960s as part of this supposed new wave of terrorism. The most prominent of this category of ideological subversives who took their dissent into the realm of the criminal were the Baader–Meinhof group in Germany (afterwards known as the Red Army Faction), the Red Brigades in Italy and the United Red Army in Japan. All three have followed the grim path to ever more arbitrary violence that has invariably characterized the practitioners of isolated political violence of this sort. Without cultural roots as deep as those enjoyed by ETA and the IRA, none of these groups has achieved as much destruction or has endured as effectively as either of these organizations. Nevertheless their driving force has in many ways been an updated version of what had once driven the earlier generation of anti-colonials – a fierce anger against imperialism in general and US imperialism in particular. These groups saw that it was possible to control a country without going to the bother of governing it. This was the excess of which the United States stood accused in the three countries in which these groups operated, West Germany, Italy and Japan. The early impetus for their subversion came from the United States' engagement in Vietnam. Many of their targets were American, and their leaders frequently sought to explain their actions by adverting to what was going on in South-east Asia. There was certainly something odd about the huge concentration on Baader–Meinhof and Red Brigades violence in Europe, of which there was very little, at a time when the US was engaged in a variety of types of horrific political terror as part of its war effort in Vietnam. This violence was however not 'terrorist' because it enjoyed the full force of a state behind it and was not isolated in its execution. So specialized has our definition of terrorism become that, just as was the case during the Second World War, it would seem that the more terrible the act of political terror, and the greater the violence that accompanies it, the less likely it is that it will be classed as terrorism.

All these points come together in the Middle East, which provided the third great platform for the leap into the 'age of terrorism' that supposedly occurred around 1968. It was Palestinian violence above all else that first engendered and then fuelled the panic about terrorism with which we are now so familiar. Viewed in isolation, there is little doubt that there was a sudden upsurge both in 'terrorism' and in 'international terrorism' in the region at this time, however either term is defined. In November 1968 a bomb exploded in a crowded marketplace in Jerusalem, killing twelve people (ten of whom were Jewish) and injuring fifty-five. The explosive was concealed in a parked car. Other bombs followed and in October 1969 five apartment buildings in Haifa were blown up, killing two Israelis and injuring twenty people. The Palestinian quarrel with Israel was also taken on to the world stage at this time, with an El Al jet being hijacked as early as July 1968, but with the pivotal moment of this sort coming in September 1970 when no fewer than 575 hostages were taken in the course of the hijacking of four jet airliners, all of which were dramatically destroyed after the release of the hostages had been successfully negotiated. In the years that followed, Palestinian violence continued to gather pace in the Middle East and at the same time took on a seedier, more desperate and brutal form on its trips abroad. In May 1972, an indiscriminate assault at Lod International Airport near Tel Aviv claimed twenty-eight civilian lives, among whom were sixteen Puerto Rican pilgrims on their way to visit Christian shrines in the Holy Land. In September 1972 came the famous assault on the Israeli quarters at the Munich Olympics, in which a total of seventeen people were killed.

All of this Palestinian violence was of course terrorism in its core sense of involving the terrorizing of innocent civilians in order to communicate a political message. Even when the terror was at its worst, however, the language of terrorism was hiding more than it revealed. The Israeli state whose leaders now reviled these actions as 'international terrorism' had itself been at least partly produced by similar conduct in the past, most notably the bombing of the King David Hotel in Jerusalem in 1946, in which ninety-one people died, fifty-four of them civilians. After the formation of the state, the application of political terror had been one of the prime means by which Israeli territory had been expanded and the control of its armed forces over the region consolidated. In the decades before 1968, the Palestinian deaths at the hands of Israeli forces at such villages as Qibya and Kafr Qasem were etched into the minds of the people in the way that the bombing of Guernica had imprinted itself on the Basques. None of any of this was 'terrorism' because it was all done by the forces of the state. The Arab nations did attempt to wage formal war in 1967 but it was a counter-productive disaster, leading to the loss to Israel of vast tracts of land that had earlier escaped invasion. In the aftermath of the Six Day War, the Palestinian Liberation Organization initially sought in true anti-colonial fashion to mount a proper guerrilla campaign against the Israeli presence in the Occupied Territories, but this floundered on the reality of a far superior military enemy which had not the slightest intention of throwing in the towel. Just as with ETA and the IRA, 'terrorism' seemed the only alternative to passive acquiescence. In their 'will', published in Damascus, the dead Palestinians who had been responsible for the Munich attack wrote of their desire for the world to 'know of the existence of a people whose country has been occupied for twenty-four years, and their honour trampled underfoot. . . . There is no harm if the youth of the world understand their tragedy for a few hours.' In the aerial strikes that Israel launched against Syria and Lebanon in the months after Munich, it was reported that hundreds of civilians were killed. That these were not within the Western definition of terrorism was no consolation to the victims, but it does explain why their deaths, like so many Palestinian losses before and since, went largely unnoticed and unreported.

The Dangerous Utility of an Illusion

We may conclude from this brief survey that even in the darkest age of terrorism, between 1968 and 1974, when arbitrary political violence of a terrifying nature was at its height in the West, the use of the language of terrorism caused more problems than it resolved. The preoccupation with terrorism served only to replace the careful analysis of specific issues with wild, panic searches for general causes, and to divert attention away from real difficulties on to spurious issues, such as the tactics of terrorism or the psychology of the terrorist, as though the rebels under discussion were a type of genetic mutant. In the years that have followed this early phase, governments the world over have exploited the combination of intellectual vacuity and moral judgement inherent in the terrorist label in a way that has hugely facilitated the repressive powers of the states concerned while at the same time greatly confusing the search for solutions to many difficult international problems. The most grievous damage has been done in authoritarian states, already repressive by nature, for whom the Western language of 'terrorism' has been a propaganda godsend, allowing them to present their domestic opponents in a guise that is bound to be anathema to influential world (that is, Western) opinion, and then dealing with them brutally and invisibly, as terrorists rather than as the heroic freedom-fighters that they have all too frequently been.

The most extreme example of such linguistic freeloading occurred in Central and South America during the 1970s and 1980s, where the supposed necessity for strong counter-terrorist action masked state terror of almost unbelievable brutality, by a variety of military regimes whose power was exercised without even a fig-leaf of democratic legitimacy. The 'urban guerrillas' in Brazil and Uruguay were brutally repressed by the mid-1970s, and during the 'dirty war' that followed shortly afterwards in Argentina it has been estimated that over 10,000 people 'disappeared'. In the 1980s, the deaths of civilians caused by Central American military juntas in the name of 'counter-terrorism' reached into the tens of thousands. The levels of terror achieved by these governments and the numbers of killings in which they were involved exceeded, out of all proportion, the subversive violence with which they were purportedly confronted. Throughout even the worst of these excesses the West's preoccupation with the need for strong action against terrorism inoculated its leaders to the political context in which these military rulers were operating.

A similar process occurred in South Africa. As early as 1967, the apartheid government had statutorily defined terrorism as any activity likely to 'endanger the maintenance of law and order'. Not content with such generalities, the legislation went on to specify as terrorist any conduct which promoted 'general dislocation, disturbance or disorder', 'prejudice' to 'any industry or undertaking' or 'embarrassment' to the 'administration of the affairs of the State'. This was not the end of it by any means, with various other forms of direct and indirect dissent or even mild insubordination being also brought into the equation. This name-calling was then deployed in an attempt to equate the African National Congress (ANC) with ETA, the IRA and the other forms of 'terrorism' about which Europe and America were becoming increasingly concerned. Neatly ignored in the analysis, as entirely irrelevant to the assessment of this 'terrorist threat', was the fact that South Africa was ruled by an undemocratic racist regime, which was not only terrorizing its Black majority but was also engaged in aggressive wars against, and the sponsoring of horrifically brutal insurgencies within, the states adjacent to its borders. Bizarrely inappropriate though the language of terrorism undoubtedly was, this ruse enjoyed a great success throughout the 1980s. As late as 1987, the US State Department included the ANC in its publication *Patterns of Global Terrorism*, and in October the same year the British Prime Minister characterized the group as a 'terrorist organization'. It came to an end only when the 'terrorism' finally became unnecessary, with the 'terrorist' movement's leader eventually being fêted by the United States President in

Washington, a city which had itself been named after another violent subversive not dissimilar in stature.

It has been the United States that has been most prolific in its use of the jargon of terrorism in international relations, but it is that country which has also been loosest in its application of any coherent definition to the term. Distinctions between international, state-sponsored, transnational and purely domestic terrorism have come and gone as the US has sometimes condemned subversive violence and sometimes applauded it. At times, such as with the ANC and its neighbouring Namibian liberation movement SWAPO, it has seemed as though the US has been prepared to castigate as terrorist any challenge to any status quo, no matter how mild and popular the subversion or how dreadful or illegal the regime from which power has been sought to be wrested. On other occasions, however, the US has given the impression of being almost enthusiastically anarchic in its support for rebellious factions, most notably with UNITA in Angola, the Contras in Nicaragua and the anti-government forces in Soviet-backed Afghanistan in the 1980s. While occasional efforts have been made to distinguish international from other forms of 'terrorism', it has been neither a desire for linguistic clarity nor squeamishness about violence that has been the driving force behind US policy on terrorism. From the start of the Reagan presidency in 1981, the supposed problem of terrorism has been effectively harnessed as a branch of US foreign policy, with the condemnatory label being deployed to hurt the enemies of US interests while being withheld from US friends and client states, no matter how opprobrious their conduct might otherwise be.

Before the end of the Cold War, the great American enemy was of course the Soviet Union, and in the 1980s a plethora of books appeared dealing with Soviet involvement in terrorism. Replete with evocative titles such as *The Soviet Strategy of Terror*, these volumes sought to link the Soviets with the sort of indiscriminate killing for which the word terrorism stood in the public mind, and for which it was known there was universal disapproval. The then Director of the CIA, William Casey, contributed an essay along these lines called, 'The International Linkages – What Do We Know?' in a volume with the evocative title, *Hydra of Carnage*. At his first press conference as President Reagan's Secretary of

State, Alexander Haig declared in his inimitable style that the Kremlin was today 'involved in conscious policies, in programs, if you will, which foster, support and expand this activity, which is haemorrhaging in many respects throughout the world today'. Connecting the Kremlin with terrorism suited the strategy of the first Reagan administration, since it helped to build up concern about the Soviets, which in turn made the greatly increased defence spending then envisaged by the White House more widely acceptable. The difficulty was that for decades the whole idea of terrorism had been limited to subversive groups acting in isolation. If the subject had up to that point enjoyed even a limited intellectual coherence, it had been rooted in the fact that state authorities were not capable of being terrorists. To solve this problem the US introduced the notion of 'state-sponsored terrorism', whereby it was rebellious groups which were acting in a subversive way in the traditional terrorist fashion, but which were doing so now under the protective aegis of a malevolent state, whose own forces were not however directly involved. Thus Soviet culpability lay not in any actions that its military forces might have been involved in, but rather in its provision of support for such 'terrorist groups' as the PLO and the ANC.

The absurdity of this manipulation of language became most fully apparent in the Middle East. The flimsy nature of the link between the PLO and the Soviets did not seem sufficient to underpin the international terrorist conspiracy for which it was the main evidence. This was particularly true when the connection was being most vividly emphasized, since by the early 1980s the mainstream PLO had long committed itself not to engage in political violence outside Israel and the Occupied Territories. One book, written by a distinguished academic expert and published at the height of the panic in 1982, opened with evidence for his argument that was revealingly comical in its emptiness:

Among the Palestine Liberation Organisation (PLO) and the Popular Front for the Liberation of Palestine (PFLP) rank-and-file in Southern Lebanon these days, the most prestigious badge of distinction that can be worn – weather permitting – is a Soviet-made fur hat. While not of the haute couture variety, Soviet fur hats are the latest thing in revolutionary chic, for possession of one in many parts of the world usually indicates that the owner is a graduate of one of the élite schools and camps operated by the USSR and its allies that train and indoctrinate terrorists and other revolutionaries. With each passing month, more and more fur hats appear in embattled Lebanon and, for that matter, in dozens of other locations around the world. Ironically, they may soon lose some of their prestige value as they become too commonplace.

In 1982, it was not international terrorism, or indeed any sort of terrorism, that had 'embattled Lebanon'. Ever since the 1967 war, Israel and its US ally had used the West's obsession with terrorism as a diplomatic weapon against the PLO, condemning as 'support for terrorism' any recognition that the movement managed to secure on the international front. When the organization secured the rights of a United Nations member nation in 1976, Israel's most senior delegate denounced the organization as a 'loose coalition of feuding terrorist gangs'. And when in 1977 the French authorities expelled from the country, rather than arrested, a senior PLO executive suspected of having been involved in the Munich Olympic killings, the Israeli government recalled its ambassador from Paris, expressing its concern that the incident amounted to 'abject surrender to the . . . threats of terror organizations'. International conferences were held at which the problem of terrorism was earnestly debated by Israeli and other Western 'experts'. One of the most prolific of these specialists was Benjamin Netanyahu, who was subsequently to become Prime Minister of Israel. In one of Netanyahu's edited volumes, *Terrorism: How the West Can Win*, the then Israeli ambassador to the United Nations described the 'war against terror' as 'part of a much larger struggle, one between the forces of civilisation and the forces of barbarism'. It was time, he declared, for the West to 'unite and fight to win the war against terrorism'.

It was this sort of language of counter-terrorism which the Israeli authorities also deployed by way of justification for their use of force both inside the territories they occupied and against neighbouring states. In 1978, a violent attack within Israel by the PLO's military wing, which involved twenty-five civilian casualties, sparked off a full-scale invasion of Lebanon in which some

2,000 people died and an estimated quarter of a million inhabitants were made homeless. Five years later, Lebanon was 'embattled' by a second Israeli invasion, this time far more ambitious in its plans and bloody in its execution. It has been estimated that some 18,000 people died in the course of 'Operation Peace in Galilee' and the siege of Beirut that followed it, the vast majority of them Palestinian and Lebanese civilians. Once again the alibi for this military offensive was a terrorist incident, on this occasion the attempted assassination of the Israeli ambassador to Britain in London, two days before the invasion was launched, an incident for which the PLO was not even responsible. In the distorted language of the times, none of this Israeli conduct was terrorism because it was not done by a subversive group or even by a sponsored subversive group but rather by the full military power of a heavily armed state. Once again, we have the double paradox that the greater the terror, and the more likely it is to have been committed by a Western nation or ally, the less the label of terrorism seems likely to be able to fit.

The military strength of the US and its ally in the Middle East means that neither has had to deploy clandestine, proxy groups to bring about its goals. These can usually be achieved by military operations executed with brutal transparency. For their opponents, however, engaging in such conventional warfare spells certain doom. This was the case in both the 1967 and 1973 wars, just as it was when the PLO tried to take on the full might of the Israeli army in the Occupied Territories for a brief period in 1968. For such groups it has not been obvious why the only method of warfare morally available should be one which necessitates their certain and speedy demise. The penalty for such inconvenient prudence has been to labour under the American-inspired banner of international terrorism. But it is better to have insults shouted at you in the shadows than to be shot dead quietly in the open.

The mobilization of the language of terrorism in aid of America's military efforts in the Middle East has been the final catastrophe for any remaining shred of integrity that the concept of terrorism might have retained after its imposed flirtation with the Soviet empire in the early 1980s and its earlier deployment to mask Israel's territorial ambitions. In the years since the 1982 invasion of the Lebanon, the subject's coherence has completely collapsed. The attacks on the French and US military presence in Beirut in October 1983 which claimed the lives of 300 men were immediately classed as acts of 'international terrorism', even though the carefully chosen targets were military in nature and the objective of the co-ordinated operation was not merely to communicate a message but to achieve through the strength of the force used a clear political end, the evacuation from the area of this multinational force. The 'terrorist' label was not, however, appropriate to describe any of the subsequent aerial attacks on the Sheikh Abdullah barracks launched by the French air force, the revenge car bomb allegedly exploded by the CIA in the vicinity of a Hezbollah leader's office (which killed eighty) or the bombardment of the Lebanese coast by the battleship *New Jersey* which marked the American Marines' withdrawal from the area by raining shells as heavy as cars on to vulnerable villages along the coast. Always discriminating about the kind of death he condemns, the terrorist expert has no interest in any of these violent acts, just as such a person is uninterested in the fundamental question why the US Marines and the rest of the multinational force were in Beirut in the first place. But it is surely not irrelevant to a proper overall assessment of the situation which produced these 'terrorist' attacks on Western forces that the main goal of these armies – the reason they were in the Lebanon – was to return the country to Christian rule under the 1943 constitution, these Christians not only being probably in a minority but also being frequently indistinguishable from the Phalangists who had run riot in Sabra and Chatila in Beirut in 1982, reportedly killing over 2,000 defenceless civilians in just two days.

Nowhere is the subjugation of the terrorist label more obvious than in respect of the notion of the 'terrorist state', to which US policymakers increasingly turned during the 1980s. Having wrenched free of American domination in 1979, Iran was of course immediately placed on the list, not only because of Hezbollah's attacks on the Marines but also because of the hostage-taking to which every Westerner in Beirut had become exposed after the withdrawal of the multinational force. Israel has, however, never qualified for inclusion, not for its overt military terror of course but also not even for its involvement in the notorious

Khiam prison, in which some 300 Lebanese Shias were held without charge or trial in unspeakable conditions of brutality by the Israeli-sponsored South Lebanon Army. Another annual entry in the American list has been Libya, whose various involvements in European subversive violence, though largely unproven, were what provided the justification for the attack on Tripoli and Benghazi by US war-planes ordered by President Reagan in 1986. The number of casualties which resulted from this non-terrorist piece of 'self-defence' – believed to be in the region of thirty-seven dead and ninety injured – marks Mr Reagan out as a more prolific killer of Libyans than General Gadaffi seems ever to have managed to be of Americans. Syria was thought to have been responsible for some of the attacks attributed to Libya, but this nation has drifted in and out of the list of terrorist states according to how well its wily ruler President Assad has been getting on with the Americans at any particular time. In a similar vein, Iraq had long been off the list despite the horrendous nature of the Saddam regime, until its (entirely orthodox and therefore 'non-terrorist') military invasion of Kuwait led to its sudden reinclusion in September 1990. The other regular entrants in this infamous list have all been as prominent for their anti-Americanism as for their 'terrorism' – North Korea, South Yemen and, again inevitably, the ubiquitously evil Cuba.

In view of the manipulation to which the terrorist label has been subject, it is not at all surprising that, by the 1990s, the phrase has lost all traces of what little linguistic discipline it might once have had. It now seems to describe any violence which appears political in nature and which is designed to hurt the West, such as the blowing up of the Pan Am jet over Lockerbie in 1988 and (though the facts are as yet unclear) the downing of a TWA jet off the US coast in 1996. It is now also the word that the media rush to when seeking pithily to explain an act of violence somewhere in the world for which no immediately materialistic (and therefore explicable) rationale presents itself. Thus the gassing of an underground transport system in Japan, the suicidal hijack of an Ethiopian jet off the African coast and the maverick postal violence of the American Unibomber are all classed as terrorist actions, rather than as the erratic, desperate criminality that each might in truth more accurately reflect. As Adrian Guelke has put it in the course of his recent brilliant study, *The Age of Terrorism and the International Political System*, 'Ironically, there would seem good reason to suppose that both the continuity and the coherence imposed on events by the concept of terrorism have been factors in the legitimization of political violence by removing from individuals joining underground organizations or even acting independently of any organization the psychological burden of justifying such violence *ab initio*.' Once the idea of terrorism insinuated itself into common usage in this way, it was only a matter of time before it came to be deployed to describe even non-violent conduct where what was sought to be communicated was a general moral disapproval. Thus in recent years we have had 'eco-terrorism', 'narco-terrorism' and even, after this or that health scare, 'consumer terrorism'. It is as though there is no mischief which does not need to be repackaged as a branch of terrorism for its full horror to be first savoured and then universally condemned.

All of this busy verbal inflation does not come from nowhere. The devastation wreaked on the meaning of terrorism in the 1980s left the word lying open on the ground, its inherent moral judgement exposed to all and available to be occupied by whatever freeloading moralist happened to be passing by. This linguistic anarchy is the price that has been paid for the calculated rape of meaning that had earlier occurred. Despite these consequences, the concept of terrorism remains fully on display in its true home, the Middle East, justifying Israeli assaults on Southern Lebanon in 1995 which involved violent attacks on a United Nations mission there and supposedly legitimizing Israeli demands for a continuing strong security presence in the Occupied Territories, despite commitments made internationally to the opposite effect. The idea of terrorism is not, however, an easily tamed one. That it can take on a destructive life of its own can be seen from the effect that it has had on the implementation of the Oslo Peace Accords, signed by the chairman of the PLO Yasser Arafat and the Prime Minister of Israel Yitzhak Rabin at a ceremony in the White House in 1994. Having secured the 'peace' for which it had long fought so aggressively, neither the US nor the Israeli leadership had any interest any longer in allowing this or that atrocity to destroy the process. The problem, however, was that atrocities were not merely atrocities, they were also 'acts of terrorism' to the 'defeat' of which all other policy objectives had for years been required to be subjugated. Having broken free of the language of terrorism to strike a deal with the arch 'terrorist' Yasser Arafat, both governments now found themselves hostage to the next atrocity, involuntarily beholden to the anxieties that they had earlier so successfully cultivated.

The result of this was that subversive violence which in itself could hardly be said to be capable of challenging the authority of the State of Israel in any meaningful sense was able disproportionately to influence the execution of the Accords. Its inevitable characterization as 'terrorism' fuelled public panic and led the previously terrorist-obsessed Israeli government to seem weak and inadequate. The Israeli right-wing opposition first articulated its opposition to Oslo and then secured political power through the language of terrorism. Arafat may have specifically repudiated the use of terrorist methods as long before Oslo as 1988, but as a result of the Accords the PLO had 'presided over a fantastic explosion of anti-Israeli terrorism', according to Benjamin Netanyahu, writing in 1995. From the hostile Arab perspective, the Accords were equally vulnerable to the sort of emotional havoc that a few well-timed bombs could cause. In late February and early March 1996, four suicide bombings in Israel caused heavy loss of life and helped create the conditions of paranoid insecurity which facilitated Netanyahu's rise to power. The United States President Bill Clinton, acting like an old-style Roman emperor in this new post-Cold War world, immediately summoned a 'Summit of Peacemakers' at Sharm El Sheikh in Egypt. The various world leaders who answered the American call agreed to 'promote co-ordination of efforts to stop acts of terror on bilateral, regional and international levels' and committed themselves to 'ensuring instigators of such acts are brought to justice; supporting efforts by all parties to prevent their territories from being used for terrorist purposes; and preventing terrorist organizations from engaging in recruitment, supplying arms; or fund raising'.

President Clinton knew that this was not just about deploying the language of terrorism to buttress Israeli power in the normal way. The subject has also developed its own US domestic agenda. Every president since Reagan has felt duty-bound to frighten the

American people with wild talk of the terrorist enemy within and without. One week after he had assumed office, Reagan had declared, 'Let terrorists beware that when the rules of international behaviour are violated, our policy will be one of swift and effective retribution.' George Bush had contributed a chapter to one of Netanyahu's alarmist collections in 1981, which was then reprinted in 1989 after Bush had become president. The front cover of another of Netanyahu's works, *Fighting Terrorism*, published in 1995, was emblazoned with the commendation 'excellent', offered by a still optimistic Robert Dole. Now Clinton stepped neatly into this new presidential tradition. As his close adviser Dick Morris later revealed, he had during 1996 advised the President of the three 'big things' that it would take for him to drag himself out of the third into the second tier of American leadership. The third of these was 'to break the international back of terrorism by economic and military action'. 'That's a good list,' Clinton had allegedly replied to the adviser. 'It puts things into perspective.'

The True Threat from Terrorism

The concept of terrorism is more than merely the meaningless plaything of international diplomacy. In recent years it has also been deployed within democratic states so as drastically to restructure the relationship between the individual and the state, to the former's profound disadvantage. This is the meaning of the fourth of the heretical propositions set out at the start of this essay, that while democracy may indeed be threatened in our artificial 'age of terrorism', the danger to its integrity comes more from the terrorists' opponents, the states and their armed and police forces, than from the so-called terrorists themselves. Viewed in historical perspective, it is remarkable how fear of terrorism has justified legal changes that would otherwise surely have been unthinkable.

Take as our first instance the United States of America. It will come as no surprise that there are at least four definitions of terrorism lurking within the law, with each being sprung into action by the authorities as and when it is required. In the absence of much serious subversive violence within its borders, the US has dealt over many years with its indigenous 'terrorism' not as a universal threat requiring special measures but as a series of particular forms of criminality, which is all generally that these groups have ever amounted to. After the Oklahoma bombing in April 1995, however, the atmosphere quickly changed, with the Clinton administration proposing that the FBI be given access to personal financial records, including bank accounts and credit card and telephone bills, to assist their investigations, and also that the Bureau be given new wiretapping powers. Inevitably there has also been a foreign dimension. Speedy procedures to deport aliens who are 'suspected terrorists' have also been sought. In the mammoth Terrorism Prevention Act 1996 that followed Clinton's politically contrived concentration on the 'terrorist threat', not even the constitutionally protected right to free speech escaped attention. Congress has gone out of its way, under the guise of counter-terrorism, to starve foreign groups inimical to government interests of the capacity to communicate directly to the American people. The Act allows the Secretary of State to designate a group a foreign terrorist organization, after which it becomes a criminal offence to provide material for it. Following on such a designation, the authorities may order the freezing of the group's financial assets. Free speech remains, but no one will be listening. In a separate and particularly draconian section, the Act makes it an offence for a US citizen to engage in various financial transactions with countries deemed by the administration to be 'terrorist states'. We saw earlier how this label has degenerated into little more than a contrivance of US foreign policy. Now we see it being deployed to consolidate US power over the whole world, since in the post-Cold War era any state refusing to acquiesce to US interests risks a designation that will deprive it not only of American business, but of all business everywhere in which Americans are involved, which in practical terms means most of the business in the developed world.

This latter section has provoked an angry response from the European Union, but here too there has been a transformation in the nature of policing, almost all of it covertly effected and much of it driven by a perception that the 'war against terrorism' requires a common police front-line. In 1976, an informal liaison group to deal with terrorism, policing and customs issues of common interest was set up on a purely informal basis within the European Community. Named TREVI, this body provided an intergovernmental forum with meetings every six months at ministerial and official level. TREVI was joined in 1979 by the EU-wide Police Working Group on Terrorism (PWGOT), made up of representatives of all the then EC countries plus Finland, Norway and Sweden. In 1990, TREVI secured a permanent secretariat and in the years that followed this initiative the practice grew of exchanging 'counter-terrorism liaison officers' between states in the Union, whose role it was (and remains) to provide the host police forces with information and advice on terrorism. None of these developments has been subject to any statutory or political control, a state of affairs that is likely to persist even after the EU

Council of Justice and Home Affairs, set up under the Maastricht Treaty in 1992, has been fully implemented. The complaint is of course not about the principle of co-operation in the proper discharge of police duties in respect of law enforcement; it is about the way in which such an informal network has been allowed to develop on the margins of legality and without adequately transparent political accountability. Terrorism may not have been the sole driving force behind these developments, but the secrecy and autonomy in which these police operations are perpetually shrouded owes much to the intimidatory power of the label.

It is to the United Kingdom that pessimists about our freedom should look for a depressing glimpse of the future. Britain has been exposed more than most nations to the 'counter-terrorism' ethos on account of a combination of three factors: a genuine problem of violent subversion in Northern Ireland; a government unsympathetic to civil liberties which enjoyed a continuous hold on power for eighteen years; and the absence of many of the checks and balances on executive power that are to be found in most Western democratic nations. The effect of the supposed necessities of terrorism on the civil liberties of the citizen has been quite extraordinary. In Northern Ireland, the authorities first reacted to subversive violence with conduct that was at and beyond the margins of illegality. The internment of suspected members of the IRA was introduced in 1971 and held sway as a principal policy for some four years, during which allegations of torture and ill-treatment were frequently made in respect of the treatment of many of those who were then in police custody. This phase of the conflict was also marked by the highest levels of deaths that have been endured in the Province since the disorder began, a worrying proportion of which at this time were at the hands of the security forces. The most controversial of such incidents was the shooting dead of fourteen unarmed protesters in Derry on 30 January 1972, in an incident which was subsequently to enter Irish nationalist folklore as 'Bloody Sunday'.

From about the mid-1970s, the state embarked on a new tactic of criminalization, whereby subversive violence was no longer to be dealt with by military-style means but was rather to be processed through the courts as a brand of terrorist criminality. The propaganda advantages to the authorities from this change of tack were obvious, but the unattractive reality continued to be that the subversives enjoyed a large measure of active and passive support within their own communities and this was not likely to be easily changed by a state-sponsored labelling exercise. The policy of criminalization and of 'police primacy' therefore inevitably required the wholesale truncation of the rule of law if it was to be effective. This is exactly what has happened in Northern Ireland when the new approach began to take effect in the mid-1970s. The breadth of the criminal law was immeasurably widened so as to facilitate the bringing of charges against suspected 'terrorists'. Those who are arrested may be denied access to a lawyer for up to forty-eight hours and may be held in custody without charge for as long as seven days. The right to silence, both for a suspect in a police cell and an accused before a court, has been emasculated and may now only very rarely be effectively invoked. Trial by jury has become a thing of the past for 'terrorist' crimes, with all such cases now being heard by a judge sitting alone. Despite the absence of political violence in Northern Ireland, the government has not rushed to the resuscitate the rule of law.

These modifications to the rule of law have been particular to Northern Ireland, but the changes that have occurred in the rest of the United Kingdom on the basis of the supposed threat of terrorism have in many ways been far more sinister and have also survived the outbreak of peace. To start with, the driving force behind the restriction of civil liberties was the violence in Northern Ireland. Thus, in legislation passed in 1974, Parliament empowered the authorities to proscribe 'terrorist' organizations and to arrest without warrant persons suspected of being involved in 'terrorism', if needs be restricting their movement within the UK through the use of a form of internal banishment called 'exclusion orders'. These powers were initially deployed only against persons suspected of involvement in Northern Ireland-related violence, which was an important qualification given that the Act defined terrorism in the broadest possible terms as 'the use of violence for political ends', including 'any use of violence for the purpose of putting the public or any section of the public in fear'. It was therefore an important but barely noticed moment when in 1984, in the midst of the scare about international terrorism that marked the first Reagan presidency, Parliament agreed to extend the arrest and detention powers in the terrorism legislation to suspected 'international terrorists'. It has been on the basis of the need to deal with 'international' as well as Northern Ireland-related 'terrorism' that the police have subsequently secured for themselves unprecedently wide powers to stop and search vehicles and pedestrians and to throw up cordons around whole areas as part of this or that counter-terrorism operation.

The way in which these latter powers were secured is characteristic of how the fear of terrorism is deployed by the authorities to coerce the democratic process into compliance with its will. On Friday, 29 March 1996, it emerged that in the government's view there was an urgent need for fresh counter-terrorism law, so as to prevent an imminent IRA campaign which it was said was set to commence in Britain in the course of the next few days, to commemorate the eightieth anniversary of the Easter Rising. The official opposition was quickly tamed by a couple of confidential briefings and the Bill was printed, and rushed through both the House of Commons and the House of Lords in the course of no more than a couple of days in the following week, which was Easter week. A measure that had never been publicly heard of on a Friday was law by the following Wednesday. Those few MPs who expressed concern about this process in the Commons found that the government and opposition were not only prepared to agree the Bill but were also agreed about pushing it through with no more than a few hours of debate permitted to discuss its merits. No IRA campaign subsequently occurred, despite the fact that the new powers did not appear to have been deployed immediately or extensively by the police. Critics of the measure pointed out that it could hardly have come as such a sudden surprise to the police and Security Service that the eightieth anniversary of Easter Week was due in 1996. It also did not seem to have occurred to the planners of the Bill that the commemoration of Easter 1916 was in any event not due in the week that the legislation was enacted, since Easter is a movable feast and Easter in 1916 had occurred in late rather than early April.

None of this mattered to Parliament, which allowed the spell waved by the repressive wand of 'counter-terrorism' to magic away freedoms which had been hard won over generations of civil libertarian struggle. The same rhetorical power may well shortly ensure the application of the 'terrorism' laws to domestic subversives, such as the environmental and animal rights groups, that have engaged so actively and successfully in direct action in recent years. In late 1996, it almost secured a place on the statute books for a Private Member's Bill which would have criminalized in Britain the planning of 'terrorist' crimes abroad. Given the broad way in which terrorism is defined in British law, condemning all violence for political ends, this was a truly outrageous proposal, which risked turning the British authorities into the law-enforcement agencies of various police states. The authoritarian leaders of China, Burma and Indonesia, for example, would no doubt have welcomed the opportunity to have had those of their courageous opponents who have escaped to Britain transformed into convicted terrorists for the crime of continuing to try to stand up to them. The proposal has never fully disappeared from the political agenda. The ultimate degradation of language will have been reached when it will have become possible to brand the Dalai Lama as an international terrorist for his defiance of China's will in Tibet.

Looking Ahead

The central argument in this essay has a simplicity that is almost naive. There is a depressingly large amount of political violence in the world and many ways in which it manifests itself. These include war, civil war, covert war conducted by proxies, guerrilla warfare, large-scale communal fighting and the sort of isolated subversive violence that has come to be known as terrorism. Each of these ways of engaging in conflict may involve but does not necessitate the use of terror as a political weapon. By terror, we mean the launching of a reckless or consciously indiscriminate attack on civilians in order to communicate a political message to a third party, who will invariably be the real enemy. Viewed in this way, terror can be seen for what it is, a tactic available to any combatant or covert combatant in any hostile situation. We have recounted examples of terror being used in the Second World War, by both Churchill and Truman as well as by Hitler. We have also seen how the tactic was deployed in the course of various colonial conflicts in Africa in the 1950s and 1960s. It is a sadly familiar feature of the part-communal, part-separatist violence that has engulfed Sri Lanka and the Punjabi region of India from the early 1980s. Terror is of course also one of the tactics to which many subversive groups – 'terrorists' in the sense just described – have turned when they have been engaged in a covert campaign of sporadic violence against their own national authorities. Indeed because of the relative ineffectiveness of this kind of violence when targeted solely on well-defended official and military targets, we have seen how engagement in it, however focused initially, seems to lead almost inevitably to more and more killing of civilians.

Three points emerge from viewing 'terror' and 'terrorism' separately in the way described above. First, terror is not all that those we describe as terrorists do. Indeed it is something which they might never do or might strive always to avoid. Second, 'terrorists' have no monopoly on terror. It is a tactic available to all, and has frequently been employed with deadly abandon in non-terrorist conflict situations. Third, the immorality of engaging in violent conflict for political ends can never be simply assumed, and this is as true of terrorist campaigns as it is of any other form of political warfare. Our society has been built on bloodshed and has defended itself violently when the need has arisen. Political violence has made us what we are. It is not even clear that the tactic of political terror is always necessarily wrong in every conflict situation. Terrible examples of just this form of warfare during the Second World War are still felt by many to have been a horrible necessity. What we can be slightly more sure about is that the use of the tactic of terror by a terrorist group will invariably be ill advised, at least for reasons of inefficacy if not also for reasons of immorality. But it is quite impossible to say *a priori* that the use of violence short of terror by any subversive group is necessarily wrong. Everything depends on context. What is heroic under an authoritarian regime will be less so in a properly functioning democracy. The violent defenders of a community oppressed by the brutality of a police-state are in a different category from young men and women whose violence is proactive and unprovoked by earlier, direct aggression. The choices forced on a contemporary Nelson Mandela cannot be equated with those of a latter-day Andreas Baader.

The language of terrorism in its modern usage cuts across all these distinctions. It rushes to condemn wherever it finds political violence of which it disapproves. By eliding terror and terrorism, it wrongly suggests that only the terrorist engages in terror. It ignores not only political context but also our history, and that commitment to justice and fairness which has made us less uncivilized than we might otherwise have been. It is a verbal Trojan horse through which much of the liberty and freedom that make us what we are risks being set aside by the repressive reflexes of the 'counter-terrorist' state. The stakes here are higher than are usually supposed. It has only been in the twentieth century that the moral force of democracy has finally triumphed against the rival opposition of fascism and of communism. The form of this victory is still up for grabs. The optimist will say that Western society is bound to continue to develop along truly democratic lines, slowly but inexorably growing into a culture in which civil liberties and human dignity are universally respected and in which our political leaders are routinely not only elected but also held genuinely accountable for the power that they exercise. This benign scenario is however by no means inevitable. The victory that the democratic West has won over its fascist and communist opponents was only possible after the people of the West had won democracy for themselves, against ruling élites that were on the whole markedly disinclined to surrender their privilege. It is this internal battle that has been only half-won.

The West remains a place of great inequality and injustice, despite its apparent commitment to popular rule. The winning of the franchise has not yet produced the equality of opportunity and the universal respect for human dignity which many of its supporters assumed would be its inevitable consequence. Democracy in the West needs to be revived and reinvigorated so that its early promise can finally be realised. Those who have most to lose from a change of this sort have never truly conceded victory to the democratic revolutionaries. They are always vigilant for the chance to turn back the egalitarian tide. If they are successful, we will have a different more malign form of democracy in the future, one in which the form of self-government may remain ostentatiously in place but in which real power will be exercised elsewhere, without publicity, accountability or vulnerability to popular pressure. In such a society, it will be vital to extinguish all manifestations of public discontent. The self-justifying authoritarianism of the exigencies of 'counter-terrorism' will then achieve its full flowering, as the chief means of quietly, apparently morally, destroying all unacceptable dissent. It is for the reader to evaluate which scenario is the more likely to result. We can only be sure of one thing, at the end of this inquiry. The loose language of terrorism has become too dangerous to be acceptable in any healthy democracy.

6 Europe

HUGH THOMAS

Introduction

The present essay is the third which I have published on the subject of Europe. The first, *Europe: The Radical Challenge*, was written in 1973 in an attempt to persuade the then Labour Party that Europe was an opportunity, not a threat. Indeed, the title of that book was originally *Europe: The Radical Opportunity*, but the publisher thought that 'challenge' sounded more dynamic. The second essay, *Ever Closer Union*, was published at the beginning of 1991, in an attempt to make the same point to the Conservative Party. In some ways, that book was an open letter to Mrs Thatcher, who was still Prime Minister in the summer of 1990 when I finished the book. But events swept her away between that moment and the time of publication, which occurred in January 1991 on the unpromising day of the outbreak of war in the Gulf.

The present work, written in response to an invitation by George Weidenfeld, who also published *Europe: The Radical Challenge*, tries to deal with some of the problems facing Europe in the future. Historians are not well equipped to prophesy. But they can at least hope.

*

This question of Europe's future seemed at one time likely to become a matter for debate in the general election in Britain of 1997. Kenneth Clarke has said that he thought that that election should have concentrated on the successful way in which he had managed the economy. But in the event that triumph, for such it seemed, played less of a part, and the Conservative campaign was allowed to revolve around Europe: essentially whether the Labour Party was going to be too 'weak' on the matter. Hence the old-fashioned cartoon of Tony Blair on Chancellor Kohl's knee, which might have appeared in *Punch* in the 1890s. But in the end the word 'debate' was too sharp a word for the exchanges in April 1997. For there was nothing in the way of what used to be known as argument. The 'Schengen *acquis*' did not figure in any party political broadcast, nor the three rather elegant pillars of the untidy edifice known as the Treaty of Maastricht. John Major, it is true, in a dramatic appearance on television, did demand a free hand from the nation in respect of negotiating the European currency.* Yet he seemed to be addressing his own party more than the electorate. The late Sir James Goldsmith made some rousing speeches, in improbable places. But if Blair made a powerful speech about Europe's future, I missed it. A serious discussion not only about what Britain's place in the European Union is or should be, but what that Union should become, did not occur.

Nor did the election manifestos suggest that much thinking had gone on. Many, perhaps most, Conservatives declared, to nobody's surprise, that they were against what Alan Clark, in his electoral address to the voters of Kensington and Chelsea, spoke of as a 'centralized federal European superstate'. That phrase cropped up in many other addresses. The phraseology was either cynical or stupid: for if the individual, or perhaps it was a committee, who (or which) wrote the sentence, was saying, 'Well, of course, we are against a federal Europe which is centralized because everyone knows that the idea is a contradiction in terms. We can thereby keep our hands free to plan any Europe we like', then the phrase was cynical; but if the drafter did not know that the word 'federal' means 'decentralized', then he was an ignorant dolt.

Most Conservative candidates also showed that they disliked the idea of British entry into a European currency. Furthermore, they also opposed any increase of the powers of the European Parliament, even though the Deputy Prime Minister, Michael Heseltine, in 1990 devoted an entire lecture, published rather improbably, as it now seems, by the Centre for Policy Studies, to the theme of the 'Democratic Deficit' in Europe.

But it would be unfair to suggest that the Europsceptics had no

---

* This was the speech in which John Major spoke of the phrase 'ever closer union' as 'Eurobabble'; which sounded strange on the lips of a man who once was proud of his achievement in inserting those very words into the preamble of the Treaty of Maastricht in place of mention of the 'federal purpose'.

view of what Europe should be in the future. For they presented themselves as Gaullists. They would have agreed with the sense of the rhetorical questions put by General de Gaulle in September 1960 when he asked: 'What are the realities of Europe? What are the pillars on which one can build it? In truth, they are the states . . . which have the sole right to order and the authority to act. To imagine that one can build something which is both effective and at the same time beyond or above the states, is a chimera.' The Europe which the Eurosceptics said that they wanted to see, and they repeated the statement *ad nauseam*, was 'a Europe of nation-states'.

Before we consider what that phrase may mean nowadays, it is desirable to recall what New Labour seemed, before they reached power, to want of Europe. They were determined to win the election and seemed perturbed lest any positive statement of theirs on the matter might lose them one or two votes. Blair, on his first outing to the continent, later told his fellow heads of government that the British voters were 'viscerally' critical of the European Union. All the same, the Labour Party manifesto, late on, in its pleasantly glossy pages, made the rather weary promise, 'We will give Britain leadership in Europe.' That was what the Conservatives had promised at numerous elections in the past, which they had won. That should not be left unremarked, for it was a real change from the Labour manifestos of the old days of Michael Foot and the unEuropeanized Neil Kinnock, whose sights had seemed so rigidly limited to the white cliffs of Dover.

The Labour manifesto of 1997 also stated, more modestly, that Britain 'will be *a* leader in Europe'. The text insisted that the Labour Party when in government would make 'a fresh start in Europe'. That, it was made known, would be done by various tactical compromises, of which the only specific ones to appear before 1 May 1997 were to consider introducing the idea of proportional representation as the voting system for the European parliament, and a willingness to sign the Social Chapter of the Treaty of Maastricht, on which matter Major had secured one of his famous 'opt-outs' (the ugliest of political expressions in an era obsessed by verbal shorthand). The Labour Party also pronounced itself willing to consider an extension of qualified majority voting in future decisions of the European Council.

These declarations were accompanied in the manifesto by two pictures, both encouraging to the Europhile: first, a blurred photograph of a first-class coach of the Eurostar, suggesting that the party was about to set off, in style, for a destination of importance; and, second, one showing Blair accompanying a thoughtful President Chirac. The manifesto certainly read as a document of a party which was more enthusiastic about Europe than the Conservatives, and some candidates sounded most amicable towards the whole adventure. The would-be Labour member for Kensington and Chelsea, for example, was quite lyrical. 'Britain's future', announced Robert Atkinson, 'lies in its enthusiastic participation in the European Community and its further development.' So far so good, though, of course 'the European Community' has already been 'further developed' to become the 'European Union'. 'Robert', the voters of Kensington were told (a harbinger of the age of Christian names, which looks set to engulf political life, with its anxious emphasis on informality), 'Robert' thought that Britain should be 'actively involved' in the creation of a common currency and, once 'the conditions are right and, after a positive referendum vote, we will join'. For Atkinson believed rather generally in 'a unified European voice'.

But, when it came to saying what New Labour's long-term expectation was, the Party seemed remarkably close to old Conservativism: 'our vision [it was, of course, a 'vision', not a mere opinion] of Europe is of an alliance of independent nations choosing to co-operate to achieve the goals [which] they cannot achieve alone'. Nations, admittedly, not 'nation-states'. The words were evidently carefully chosen. How, we wonder, could that word 'alliance' have emerged? After all we had been endlessly assured that nothing in the Labour campaign was left to chance.

The manifesto of the Liberal Democrats, like that of the Labour Party, also had 'a vision' for the future. This phantom seemed more robust than anything which had figured in the manifestos of the two larger parties. In a paragraph entitled 'Positive leadership in Europe', the Liberal Democrats said that they hoped for a 'European Union that is decentralised, democratic and diverse': three good Ds, which could turn into a good slogan for what is desirable in Europe in the future, including for people who are not Liberal Democrats. The manifesto did mention too the 'European Union', an expression which the other two parties eschewed, and announced that the third party aspired to create 'a strong and united Europe', which 'respects cultural traditions and national and regional identities'. On other matters, the text of the Liberal Democrat manifesto was unfortunately as vague as that of its rivals. There was a requirement that Britain should 'play a leading role in shaping Europe', though it was still unclear in what key that part as a prima donna would be sung. The party also said that it wished to democratize the institutions of the European Union. But there was no explanation of how that miracle would be performed. The Liberal Democrats wished to allow the entry into the Union of the 'new democracies of Central and Eastern Europe'. But then so does everyone else.

Apart from the manifestos, something like a debate on the future of Europe was carried on by a few literate voters in the columns of *The Times* and the *Daily Telegraph*. Most of the letters published in these papers seemed to be hostile to the European Union, above all to participation in a common currency, but they were balanced by occasional interventions by realists, such as the Air Commodore (retired) who wondered whether it was worth trying to preserve British sovereignty when the armed forces had been shrunk to such a low level. Sir Edward Heath, stung by the Referendum Party's misuse of a statement which he had made in 1971, wrote a powerful article in the *Daily Telegraph* explaining that he had, through a vote in the then House of Commons, gained approval for the sharing, not the abandonment, of sovereignty. On the other hand, there was no sign that the correspondents wanted to talk in detail about the Treaty of Maastricht or its planned revision. Competition policy? Transparency? Subsidiarity? Those were not even 'visions' to the canvassers as they walked purposefully along the quiet back-streets with the almond blossom dripping in the late-April rain.

Perhaps, it may be said that the explanation for the lack of explicit discussion about Europe's future is that, now as in the nineteenth century, foreign policy is still not made by reference to the voter. Ministers may 'entreat' the electorate's [the average elector] opinion about the schooling of children or the limiting of drink, as the great historians of Victorian Africa, Robinson and Gallagher, remarked, 'but the higher statecraft of empire and world security they usually managed to seal off from his ignorant enthusiasms . . . foreign policy . . . was still made at house parties, not by the man in the street or the man in the stock exchange'. If the phrase 'house party' sounds inappropriate, the correct expression could be the weekend conference at Ditchley Park. But more likely the real reason is that Europe, a concept which lives on a mezzanine floor between foreign and domestic policy, raises momentous questions which are just too complex to be dealt with in the way that elections are nowadays carried on, with very few set speeches and no heckling.

*

A few weeks after the Labour victory in May came the French election. Now it might have been supposed that there, in the country of Montesquieu, inspirer of constitutions and inventor of schools of political thought, the future of the European Union would have become entirely clear. Yet Europe played even less of a role: that of an elderly uncle in a play by Giraudoux, it might be said, if I am allowed to prolong the dramatic metaphor. The Socialists and Communists made evident, in a joint statement of 29 May, that they thought that a strong Europe was desirable in order to face in common the perils of 'globalisation'. But they were against 'the Europe of King Money', and 'ultra-liberal Europe', two bogeys which appear in Paris as bloodthirsty to the left-wing mind as that of 'Socialist Europe' seems in the *salons privés* of the Eurosceptics of London. Lionel Jospin said during the campaign that he was not against the common currency, but he wanted to impose conditions on the Euro, which would otherwise be unacceptable. That tough talk seemed to imply that French Socialists would like a 'soft' Euro, not a hard one. But surely that meant that there might then be no Euro at all?

Of course, the French Socialists were in a difficult position. They were travelling in a rather old-fashioned carriage with the Communists, who were against Europe, bag and baggage. Yet the modern European agenda had been largely written by the two most distinguished French Socialists of recent years, Jacques Delors and François Mitterrand.

Philippe Séguin, who had led the campaign against the French signature of the Treaty of Maastricht, on the same parochial nationalist grounds as the British Eurosceptics, repeated that he thought that that document had been responsible for most recent evils. But, all the same, what was done was done, and one could not go back on the issue settled so long ago. Very statesmanlike! Yet Europe for Séguin had also too often been at the mercy of 'the pupils of ultra-liberalism': a view which those in England who sometimes agree with him politically, such as the Baroness Thatcher, might have been astounded to hear. All the same, he has since become established as the accepted leader of the French right, and his views – sorry, his 'vision' – will no doubt be heard more of.

*

The reason why there was no debate about the future of Europe during the British election of 1997 was because the two large parties were in agreement. They neither of them wanted the country to withdraw from the European Union. But at the same time, on what has seemed the central issue of the continuing role of the nation-state, they were as one. Neither would have been happy to talk as the Commission did, in their subsequent document *Agenda 2000*, of some new idea being a 'step on the way to the unification of Europe'. True, after the election, the new Labour government did show itself on the surface as more friendly, or appreciative, than its predecessor had been, at least in the latter's last stages, towards the country's European partners. The *Financial Times*, than whom there is no greater friend of the European Union, felt able to entitle one of its early editorials after 1 May, 'Eurodawn'. A new Minister of State for Europe, Douglas Henderson, a Scot, like most of those who manage Blair's administration, went to Brussels to say that he and his colleagues looked on Europe as an 'opportunity', not a threat; while the new Foreign Secretary, Robin Cook, repeated the burden of a statement of his in February that, if the European currency were to go ahead, and turn out a success, Britain would have to join it: not perhaps exactly a suggestion of leading Europe, but, all the same, politically realistic;* and fully in keeping with a comment made years

---

* The earlier statement was that, if the currency functioned well, 'it would take a very sober and serious calculation to stay out beyond 2002'.

ago by Jean Monnet, the Inspirer, as De Gaulle mockingly called him, to Lord Plowden: 'You English, you will never join an organization with an abstract goal. You will only join an institution which is working.'

The Labour government also immediately announced its intention to subscribe to the Social Chapter – an obligation which, in practice, was the reverse of sensational, for all that had been done up till then under what Conservatives liked to speak of as its baneful aegis had been to oblige large multinational companies to establish 'works councils' for consultation, on the German model; and there was also an obligation to provide three months of unpaid leave for parents of new children, a directive which needs to be fulfilled by June 1998. These were very modest innovations, but the British self-exclusion from the Chapter had been unpopular among the other European governments, which thought that it derived from Perfide Albion's calculated determination to refuse to adopt minimum standards of living for workers, and so gain a competitive economic advantage. The Conservatives, of course, fear (and that included some of the Europhile wing of the party) that, one day, under the Social Chapter, all kinds of old-fashioned impediments to money-making may be introduced and Peter Lilley, by then Shadow Chancellor of the Exchequer, drew attention to the fact that the government took this step without making a statement in Parliament, but he uttered no further complaint. After all, the Labour Party had 'a mandate' for this policy.

New Labour also made one or two other positive moves just after 1 May. Thus Blair at Noordwijk, near Leyden, in the Netherlands, seemed to have sought a compromise over the question of Spanish fishermen seeking cod in British waters. The Bacalao problem seemed to have been resolved at last – but what had really been done seemed a little obscure later on. He also said that Britain wished to be 'a major player' in Europe, by becoming a third party to the friendship – or is it an alliance? – between France and Germany, a desire scarcely calculated to please the only other socialist Prime Minister in a large country in Europe, Sig. Prodi in Italy. The effect of the declaration of that ambition so bravely stated was anyway diluted somewhat by the new Secretary for Defence, George Robertson, who, though in the past usually seen as a 'European', was quick – too quick, surely – to say that Britain would not collaborate with any of the ideas for a European 'pillar' of defence within NATO which Alain Juppé's government in France had been toying with. ('Pillars' are the essential nouns for the politics of the late 1990s).

Blair at Noordwijk in the Netherlands also seemed to suggest a new approach, his own contribution to his party's 'new start', no doubt, when he reflected that the European idea had to be made more attractive to its citizens – and, of course, since Maastricht we have all become 'citizens of Europe' – by ensuring the discussion of things which interested them, such as the questions of employment, health, fraud and the environment. Europe should be less concerned in the development of its institutions, he added. Blair was heard with respect. His political skill is admired. But what was he really saying? Did he mean that the Union should take over responsibility for health?

In fact, the Labour government was also showing that, in respect of some matters, it was inclined to see eye to eye with the Eurosceptic wing of the party which it had displaced. Blair, for example, was at pains to say, early on, that Britain would not be joining in the arrangements for the end of frontier controls, as conceived in 1985 on that mysterious island on the Rhine, Schengen – is there an atlas which mentions it? Or is it too a vision? – and later, at the meeting of European heads of government at Amsterdam, successfully argued that that exclusion should be legally protected: an action which indubitably distanced Britain from one of the main themes of the European system. Both the Foreign Secretary in the House of Commons and the Lord Privy Seal, in their speeches on the first day of the debate on the Queen's Speech, announced that they, like the Conservatives, believed in nothing less than or, rather, nothing more than, 'a Europe of nation-states'. The relaxed, world-weary style in which the latter made his announcement – I heard it – sounded as if he were saying we are perfectly ordinary carnivorous men and women. Cook repeated that he wanted to make Britain 'a leading player in a Europe of independent nation-states', a way of putting the matter which actually sounded more old-fashioned than the words of his predecessor Malcolm Rifkind, who, in a lecture before the election, explained that he hoped Britain would 'work for a

European Union which draws on the strengths of the individual nation-states'.

Thus both the leaders of both of the larger parties in Britain are still talking about the 'nation-state' with an affection suggestive of an undergraduate on a course of political theory glad to have absorbed at least one comprehensible idea from his crowded syllabus.

*

The expression 'nation-state' is a relatively new one. For it did not have a history before 1914 and, indeed, the earliest example of it cited in the Oxford Dictionary dates from 1918. At that time, the now forgotten Oxford historian J. A. R. Marriott, wrote, in one of his many books, *The European Commonwealth* – a concept not recently put to use, incidentally – that the 'ultimate genesis' of the First World War was '[to be] sought . . . in the existing European polity . . . based upon the recognition of a large number of nation-states, entirely independent and co-equal'.

Whatever its origin, the expression has a precise meaning. A 'Europe of nation-states' was what, in the sixteenth century, replaced the universal empire of the middle ages, supported by an equally universal Church. Europeans in several countries began thereafter to give to the head of the 'nation-state' much of the loyalty which had previously been offered to the still undivided Church. The idea of the nation-state grew up in Tudor England, Valois France and Spain of the Catholic kings, and in Portugal of the Aviz dynasty, and was slowly copied in Medicean Tuscany, Holland and Sweden, and then in Prussia, but it was not till 1870 that Germany and Italy achieved the consummation.

These developments took place before the era of mass communications. It was, all the same, the work of print. Everyone recalls how Victor Hugo, in his *Hunchback of Notre Dame*, imagines a scene in a cell in a monastery in front of the great cathedral in the early days of printing. An archdeacon, Dom Claude, gazes at the colossal building and then at a printed book, an obscure volume printed in Nuremberg. Alas, he says, 'this' – the book – 'will kill that' – Notre Dame. The Archdeacon meant that the Church would be destroyed. He was half right. The Reformation would not have been carried through had not Luther's works been available in print and nor, in the end, would the nation-state have been born had it not been for newspapers and pamphlets. It was those, after all, which ultimately made possible 'the imagined community', in Benedict Anderson's clever expression: the assumption by millions that they have something in common with other millions whom they would never meet, but who share their culture and their language. Print enabled poets, publicists, novelists and historians of the nineteenth century to assemble ballads, standardize languages and create histories out of myths.

It is true that the historian of the Italian Renaissance, Burck-hardt, when talking of the state as a work of art, 'the outcome of calculation and reflection', dated the birth of the enterprise earlier than the invention of printing: to, indeed, the ruthless govern-ment of Frederick II in Sicily, in the thirteenth century. All the same, the philosopher who first wrote coherently of the merits of this new system was Macchiavelli, who, in the early sixteenth century, made evident, in *The Prince*, that he thought that the best ruler was one who had no sense of international obligations, and who pursued his own success regardless.

France, and I daresay that there is significance in the difference, talks not of 'la nation-état' but of the 'état-nation' (Spaniards, like the French, also put the state first: 'estado-nación'). Whatever the significance, a recent article by the ex-editor of *Le Monde*, André Fontaine, described the slow process whereby the idea of France came to triumph, though that country was dominated by petty particularisms till the early nineteenth century. That national victory of the centre over its component parts, he asserted, was achieved by 'the growing use of the classical French language, the common faith in liberty, the abundance of cultural treasures, and the beauty of the landscapes'.

So the ideas of our modern politicians, Eurosceptics or New Labour as they may be, seem to have a respectable intellectual provenance. Macchiavelli may have been in the end looked on as a criminal by the Florentines but his standing as a philosopher remains.

There are several things to be said about the notion implicit in the expression. First, during the last few centuries, most of the large European nation-states became international empires. So those in Britain who declare themselves as proponents of 'a

Europe of nation-states' are asking us to turn back the clock several hundred years and imagine ourselves as we were in the sixteenth century, before, say, Sir Humphrey Gilbert took possession of Newfoundland in the name of Queen Elizabeth I; and before France established herself even earlier in her engagingly named first colony, France Antarctique, of Rio de Janeiro, in Brazil, in the mid-sixteenth century.

Second, many in Britain may think of themselves as living in a nation-state, but that gives a false impression, since she has, as Conrad Russell has often pointed out, for a long time constituted a multinational undertaking, given the continuing presence of the Welsh, the Scots and the Northern Irish in the kingdom. The same is true of some other European 'nation-states'. In Spain, for example, no one would doubt that Catalonia and the Basque country are nations. Brittany, Lombardy and Bavaria are in much the same relation to France, Italy and Germany.

A third point: the Europe in which we live is no longer a congeries of independent and sovereign nation-states, at least not in the old sense. For example, European law, though modest in its zone of operation, takes precedence over national law, and that has been the case since 1958 in the case of the Europe of the Six, and since 1973 in the case of Britain. Lord Denning used to complain that 'the Treaty is like an incoming tide [of laws]. It flows into the estuaries and cannot be held back.'

We have, too, something which, there is no escaping admitting it, is close to a federal system of politics in respect not only of policy towards state aids and competition, but also agriculture, fisheries, trade and the environment. There was certainly nothing like it in the days of Sir Humphrey Gilbert, and even the Catholic Church was a persecuted sect in the country in those days.

Fourth, and perhaps most important, the idea of the nation-state since 1918 on the continent of Europe has been discredited, even if it has not been so in Britain, for the reason that is implicit in the quotation cited from Marriott's book. This discrediting on the continent derives from the fact that the wars of 1870, 1914 and 1939, not to speak of the many wars earlier on, seem to most people of a liberal temperament to have been mainly caused by that very system of nation-states which Eurosceptics seem to love. The German Foreign Minister Klaus Kinkel in an article written on the occasion of the fortieth anniversary of the Treaty of Rome, said: 'For centuries, foreign policy in Europe was characterized by coalitions and counter-coalitions of great powers, by violence and war. The idea of European integration has enabled us for the first time to break effectively and permanently with that infernal spiral.' Jacques Delors said, at the same time: 'Yesterday Europe spelled fear, hatred for one another, and a succession of fratricidal wars. Today it spells unity.'

Thus for Kinkel and Delors, as for other continental Europeans, the nation-state appears too small, and too destructive, a political entity for our time. An invention of the Renaissance, the thing had its positive side in the sixteenth and seventeenth centuries, it could be allowed, for it had broken the irresponsible independence of feudal noblemen, and imposed a national order. But the way that the nation-states had grown in Europe in the nineteenth century, each with strong nationalist ideologies, their national versions of history and their national armies, led directly to August 1914 and September 1939. It is true that many capitalists, like artists, had by then already left the nation-state, or had never joined it. Politicians would follow, after 1945.

These views can of course be challenged. Some historians would say that, in those disgraceful days which Kinkel was denouncing, war broke out because so many European countries were absolute monarchies or, at least, autocrats, guided by aristocracies. Now that we are all democrats, the danger of war, so this argument goes, has vanished. Did not Aristotle say that the reluctance, even the incapacity, of democracies to mount wars of aggression was one of their virtues? Did not even Margaret Thatcher say the same in one of her most successful speeches, in Brussels appropriately, in 1978?

All the same, wars have often occurred because the honour of one country has been offended, and then attacked, by another. Middle-class men and women can be offended at least as easily as aristocrats. Democracies are not insulated from chivalrous sentiments.

Anyway, whatever the truth of the matter (about which it is improbable that any panel of historians from the fifteen members of the European Union would be able to agree), the common perception on the Continent is that the nation-state has been the guilty party in modern European history. That judgement was the first motor behind the idea of the European Common Market, then the Community and, finally, the Union. The requirement after 1945 was therefore to establish something more than a simple loyalty to the state – inspiring some international obligation, say, in order to maintain peace in a continent which had experienced more destructive wars than anywhere else. In comparison with it, Latin America, say, always considered by the ill-informed as a 'violent' place, has been an oasis of peace.

So our British view of a Europe of nation-states without qualifications has little echo beyond Calais. To quote again from Klaus Kinkel: 'today no one can seriously defend the idea that it is possible to pursue with success national interests, whether they are alone or in changing alliances. That would only be to revive the nineteenth-century *politique* which has inflicted so much suffering during our century.' Sir Michael Butler, an experienced British ambassador in Brussels, after describing how Europe had learned to collaborate with each other, through the *engrenage* – that excellent word meaning the meshing together of practices and institutions – so subtly devised by Jean Monnet, made the same continental point in a book written in the 1980s, when he explained that we are all leaving behind 'forever [the old] insistence on the unfettered sovereignty of the nation state'.

Even Spain and Portugal, so different and so long isolated, suffered governments which for a time at least acknowledged their intellectual debt to Nazis or Fascists.

Britain, however, has had no recent experience of invasion, much less of occupation. British Fascism seemed to be a private club of eccentrics. When Jean Monnet went to London in 1950 in order to try and persuade Britain to support the Schuman plan, the editor of the *Economist*, Geoffrey Crowther, told him that there would be 'a battle' precisely because Britain 'felt no need to exorcise her history'. Though the country had lost much, she preserved the trappings of her 'nation-state' not just unaltered during the Second World War but, in some ways, enhanced. Indeed, our nation-state functioned as never before in war in the 1940s, and perhaps as no other liberal society has ever done. The dedication as well as the feat of organization of resources and manpower still amazes. In his wartime orations, Churchill celebrated Britain as a tight little island, threatened by a great continental enemy as she had been at the time of the Armada in 1588, but at the same time the head of 'a mighty empire': a good reminder of our country's engaging capacity to have two distinct versions of her destiny at one and the same time.

Further, after the war, when the Empire began to unravel, and when our economic superiority in Europe, which we had for so long taken for granted, faltered, and when even the 'Special Relationship' with the United States began to seem unreal, the nation-state appeared one thing, perhaps the only thing, of which we could be sure. We might not be able to build aircraft, our car industry seemed increasingly peripheral, but we had the English state. The triumph of the nation-state in 1945 was followed by the achievement of the welfare state. Hence the beginning of Britain's distancing of herself from the European integration which began in 1951, and hence, too, the reliance which British politicians, left and right alike, place even now on the idea of the nation-state.

Professor Anthony King summed up the current national attitude to these things rather well when he reflected in early 1997 that the British wonder, in respect of the European Union, 'What is all the fuss about? Why the rush?'; and add, 'We are not going to war. The case for further integration is at best a case at the margins . . .'

The British old-fashioned view of a Europe of states is shared by some Continental politicians. In his book, *La Segunda Transición*, the future Spanish Prime Minister, José María Aznar, for example, wrote of desiring a Europe of 'national states [*estados nacionales*, actually, not *estados naciones*]'. There is also the clever Professor Pedro Schwartz, who has spent so long in England, working on Jeremy Bentham, whom he understands so well, that he became a natural Eurosceptic, even if he writes in Spanish. There are Schwartzites in Austria and in Sweden. For Jean-Marie Le Pen's Front Nationale, President Chirac is 'the little *télégraphiste* of Maastricht'. The Front Communists agree with the Front Nationale, at least on that issue.

Who is right, then, the Eurosceptics who consider the state a work of art in Burckhardt's sense, which should not be altered? Or the Monnetians, who have created a more subtle and more modern masterpiece? Well, war in the early twenty-first century within Europe looks unlikely. All the same, it would be unrealistic to suppose that Europe has changed 'irreversibly' for the good. The Yugoslav experience may seem extreme to cite but the wars there provide a good example of what can happen if a political superstructure is removed. Would not a large-scale, haphazard revival of the system of the old nation-states risk renewal of old rivalries? Why should those not turn into wars? Nations like individuals are as good as the rules allow them. High levels of intelligence and culture are not a recipe for peace. The best educated of European nations, Germany, was the most aggressive one in the early part of the century. It is no use saying that we are all now so civilized that there is no chance of a war between, say, France and Germany. In most respects, politicians are less well educated than they were a hundred years ago (who in England at the front rank of active politicians is there to compare with Salisbury, Balfour, Morley and Rosebery, all of them admirable writers, to consider English statesmen only of 1897?). There are British politicians who give the impression of fearing the Germans, despising the Italians and hating the French.

The nation-state is threatened not only from above, from the international or supranational angle, but from below. Three major countries in the European Union, Germany, Italy and Spain, have ample powers devolved to autonomous governments. Britain is set to embark on a major constitutional experiment in Scotland and Wales. Brittany and Corsica continue to be concerns, at the least, in France. The European Union's committee on regions is at the moment a minor influence but it could be important in the future. Indeed, the European Union, through the way that its subsidies are allocated, and through the way that its members of parliament are elected, is already giving energy to such regional or national movements as have not received a fair standing in the old structure of nation-states. This will probably continue. A second chamber of the European parliament might even one day be considered to reflect this.

Yet there is a major qualification to this obituary of the nation-state. The unexpected Professor Alan Milward, the best historian to write of the making of modern Europe, has, in his *The European Rescue of the Nation State*, argued not only that there is no antithesis between the nation-state and the European Community, but that the latter saved the former. Without the process of integration, declared Milward, the West European nation-state might not have retained the allegiance of its citizens in the way that it has. He developed this interesting argument with skill. He might have recalled that, actually, the European Union has never proposed the abolition of the nation-state. What it has ensured has been for the nation-state to be obliged to carry into effect the ideas which, through the *engrenage* of Commission and Council of Ministers, it has proposed. Here is a continuing role for the state in Europe – a 'leading role', indeed! – which neither Monnet nor Delors questioned. For the essential point about the Union, as it has developed and as it expected to develop, is that it is the civil servants of the nation-state which carry into effect the ideas of that super think-tank, the Commission, once they have been approved by the Council of Ministers. There is no group of itinerant Eurocrats, dressed in discreet loden overcoats, patiently travelling from Euro-airport to Euro-airport, seeking to act as an international civil service. Whatever is done (or not done) to achieve a European Defence Community, it will surely be national armies, linked in ways with which NATO has familiarized us, which will carry out the decisions of national officers.

*

If, therefore, it is inadequate, and even naive, for politicians, or commentators, to suggest that the future of Europe can still be exclusively or primarily one of nation-states, what really are the possibilities? And what should be aimed at?

A serious picture of what is to come might be expected to be available from the European Commission, which to quote Hervé de Charette, the French Foreign Minister until the 1997 election, is the 'mécanisme d'incitation, vecteur d'imagination' in Europe. Yet the idea of planning for the long term has usually been eschewed by the Commission. That institution's purpose has been to suggest ways in which some practice, product or new step forward might be harmonized. Sir Michael Butler thought that 'most ministers and officials have long since tacitly agreed that it would be useless and divisive to spell out a constitutional aim. A federation? ... A Confederation? ... It is best to leave such questions aside.' He added, 'most old Community hands would agree that we should leave the [question of the] destination of the journey [which] we are making together unanswered'. He ended his discussion of that subject with the rather bland reflection, 'the Community is setting a good example. To go on doing so one does not need to be able to say where it will be in 2000 [he was writing in the 1980s] . . . It is enough for it to keep going.' Even *Agenda 2000* does not speak of Europe's future in a way which would satisfy a professor of political theory at even the most humdrum of universities.

To ask for a long-term plan from a member of the Commission is thus to seem naive and old-fashioned and to miss the point that the Commission is primarily concerned with the *engrenage*, on the assumption that, as a Conservative Party manifesto in the European elections of 1983 remarkably put it, to think of the longer term of Europe is dangerous. Europe is like a bicycle: if one keeps pedalling, one will remain standing up. Or, to use that once favoured travelling metaphor, Europe is a train about which it is childish to ask the name of its final stop.

'It is enough for it to keep going'! When, a few years after Sir Michael Butler wrote those words, people began to think that the Union had become too intrusive, the Commission cleverly dusted down a word which they had in the attic, and wheeled into play 'subsidiarity'. Well-worn by years of useful service to the Papacy, the word seemed to express the right idea: nothing should be done at the Community level 'if it could be better or even as well done at the level of the state'. How often was that sentence trotted out in the early 1990s! But useful though the word 'subsidiarity' was, it was as Nurse Cavell said of patriotism in Brussels (think of it) in 1915, 'not enough'. The idea of power being divested from the top downwards was confusing and difficult to imagine; and who is to decide what is better? Better for whom? The European Court of Justice? The judges have been unenthusiastic. Surely a dangerous precedent would be set.

If the Commission is deliberately unclear about what it wants to see eventually achieved, what about other European leaders? Chirac, Kohl, Aznar, Prodi, how would they like to see the future, and how will it work? Do they not have in mind a future harbour, still beyond the next cape, to which the pacquet-boat (yes, I am daring a new transport metaphor!) of European integration will one day finally draw in, where the engine of directives and regulations will cease, and where the grateful burghers of the new Europe, in their gold chains of office, will stage a banquet of thanks in honour of the Commission? But on the whole those continental statesmen who express themselves on the matter echo the Commission's attitude. Thus, to quote again the German Foreign Minister Klaus Kinkel: 'the question is often put, what will be the final form of the European Union? United States of Europe? Europe of nations? Partnership of nations? It's a theoretical debate, a vain debate. For it is useless to make abstract speculations on this subject because the European Union is in a permanent state of construction.' Certainly, that is current German policy. An unnamed German diplomat commented on one of Malcolm Rifkind's lectures last April: 'Mr Rifkind wants to know what the final goal of European integration will be. But we Germans see this as an historical process where no one knows the conclusion.' Sir Michael Butler has, too, explained

> There may be no agreement among those around the European Council table about exactly where the Community [that is Union] is journeying to and at what speed. I suspect that many of them do not give this question serious thought, even once a year. But they know in their bones that we are all journeying together towards real European unity.

All the same, that 'theoretical debate' on which Dr Kinkel elegantly pours scorn must be desirable. Are not institutions plants which live on, and need, theories? Or, to adjust the metaphor, if you are planting an oak tree, it is desirable to know where the walls of the garden are. 'Europe' is now not much appreciated by its 'citizens' in any country. *Agenda 2000* admitted that at the time of Maastricht 'the general public had not kept up with the accelerating pace of institutional change in which they did not feel properly involved'. The mood is sour. Beethoven's Fifth Symphony plays to an empty hall. The flag of twelve golden stars hangs limply on its blue background. The main explanation is that people do not have an idea of the extent, and the limitations, of the European competence. A clear picture would surely make it easier for the idea of Europe to be understood, and so accepted.

*

In order to see what that clear picture might look like, it is desirable to recall the original purposes of the new collaboration between the European states after the war.

The first impulse was to prevent war by increasing the connections between peoples and economies, between business and unions, so that the idea of conflict would become unthinkable. Everything would be intermeshed. Dr Adenauer summed up that stage, in his down-to-earth way, when he said, at the moment of the birth of the Coal and Steel Community, 'since the production of the Saar will be pooled, one cause of tension will be removed'. He had himself been interested in such ideas in the 1920s.

Second, the aim was to enable the Europeans to become richer. That laudable goal clearly had a political purpose too. If Europe could abolish poverty, then one of the most important grounds for rivalry and strife would be removed. Everyone knows Keynes's remark about how harmless men are when they are given over to the pursuit of wealth. In addition, a prosperous Europe, it was argued in the 1950s, would be one which the Soviet Union would find it difficult to subvert. The consequence was the establishment, first, of the Common Market, then of the single market and, finally, of the plan for the single currency.

The third purpose of the post-war initiatives was to enable the European nations to play a part in world politics in a way that they think that they can no longer do as independent states. President Chirac, when in Prague in the spring of 1997, talked of European power as deriving from a more integrated Europe, which, he added, was in the Czech, as well as the French, interest: 'c'est votre interêt, comme c'est le nôtre'. Jacques Delors has explained, in his own way, that one purpose of European union was to bring an end to the 'geopolitical and economic decline of a continent which had invented the ideas of the universal, of democracy and of human rights'.

The idea of Europe as a third force between the United States and the Soviet Union always underlay continental European thinking, even though it did not play much of a part in Britain, whose mainstream politicians, on the left as on the right (though not always their artists nor their intellectuals) have had a tolerant, appreciative and sometimes even subservient attitude to the United States. But, again for both sides of the political spectrum, the notion that world power is to be forever in the hands of the president of the United States has often seemed at least an irritant, if not an insult and a reproach. The rejection of the idea of the '*imperium* américain' has been the one idea which has united right-wing and left-wing European intellectuals, from General de Gaulle to André Fontaine. Before the fall of the Soviet Union in 1989 and since, editorial writers on *Le Monde* have indeed written regularly of the need to escape from 'la tutelle des Etats-Unis'. The only difference is that Europe is now to be the second force, not the third one.

The former French Foreign minister, Hervé de Charette (and he was surely expressing an institutional view from the Quai d'Orsay), said:

'Europe' [is] a formidable amplifier of power [*un formidable amplificateur de puissance*] for each of the countries who are members of it, as much in respect of economics as in respect of international activity [*rayonnement*] . . . [for] we do not want a world dominated by a single great power, but one organized on the principle of multipolarity. France has reason to wish to be present everywhere [a remarkable statement!], to be involved in all the great debates of the world, and to be a major player in international affairs.

On another occasion, he explained that 'the "Euro" will become one of the two great currencies in the world', and he added, in the same interview, that he hoped that Europe would be able to act as a single negotiator in the next great battle about free commerce expected to begin in the year 2000: 'L'Europe doit combattre sans complexe.' That is not just a French *folie de petit grandeur*: Germans have similar ideas. In the words of Kinkel about monetary union, 'the Euro is not an end in itself. It is indispensable to enable Europe to continue to play a part in the first division of the world economy.' The view was reflected in *Agenda 2000*, which stated that 'the strength of the internal market should be used to promote the Union's interests *and presence* internationally' (emphasis added).

Whether the world would, in fact, be better off with two or three great powers rather than one is a question which few seem anxious to ask. The United States is often incompetent or even embarrassing in its international policies – think of President Bush's pathetic justification for his intervention in Panama – but one benefit in having the United States as the single global power is that it is, *à la longue*, a country which would prefer not to exert authority at all outside the United States. The Soviet Union devoted much effort over many years in depicting the United States as an aggressive imperial state, but that was really a self-portrait. When thinking of the United States, it is better to remember the benign picture of a globe with only one great power sketched in the suggestive last pages of *The Pursuit of Power* by W. H. McNeil.

In all these matters, the Inspirer would have been a good witness. For Monnet knew the United States well. He had met David Lilienthal when still in French rather than European politics, and tried to copy the Tennessee Valley authority in the region of the Rhône.

Another dream in Europe has always been one for the recovery of a unity lost long ago. Abel Matutes, the Foreign Minister of Spain, in early 1997 said,

Four hundred years ago, tradesmen plied their craft across the continent, scholars moved between its great universities, its different coins were universally acceptable, thanks to their gold or silver content. But the dimension of 'Europe' became obscured with the formation of the so-called modern state in the sixteenth century. This process continued until it reached its apogee with the emergence of the nation-state after the French revolution.

Though Matutes was speaking as a minister in a government of the right, there is no traditional nostalgia there for the Spain of the Catholic kings. Equally, Hervé de Charette has recalled that 'Charlemagne, Charles V, Napoleon and others tried to reunite Europe by fire and war. This time the unification is being done peaceably.' De Charette forgot to mention the idea of recovery of the Roman unity, but who can doubt that it was in his mind, as it was in 1988 when, at Bath, in the Pump Room, a great Roman building, the then Deputy Prime Minister, now Lord Howe of Aberavon, spoke so passionately in favour of British entry into the European monetary system?

*

To think about the long-term future of Europe is rendered both more complicated and more interesting by several unrelated matters: first, there is the likelihood, or must we now say the probability, that the plan for creating a European monetary union with a single currency will go ahead in the near future; and, second, there is the possibility that the European Union will in the next ten years see many new members, perhaps ten, perhaps as many as fifteen. Third, there is a chance that, when those two enterprises, monetary union and enlargement, have been carried through, we shall see as a new task an effort to re-create a European Defence Community. There will be other challenges. A harmonized tax policy? A return to consideration of the democratic basis for the Union?

No one, first of all, can be expected to predict the consequences, economic, political or psychological, of the monetary union. They will be immense. The Italian Foreign Minister and ex-Prime Minister Lamberto Dini was right to comment that it would be 'the largest and most decisive transfer of sovereignty of the last forty years'.

And what of the consequences? In the long run political union has been seen by some as a possible, even a logical, outcome of monetary union. Financial policy, with the management of the public debt and fiscal planning, has, in the twentieth century, become the core of the sophisticated nation's activity. So Chancellor Kohl has described monetary union as being the prelude to political union. But what kind of political union he did not make at all clear. Kenneth Clarke, who managed a most successful economy in Britain, has said that monetary union need not necessarily lead to political union. That is entirely true. Some argue, in reply, that the German customs and monetary unions of 1834, the Zollverein, made possible the eventual political union of Germany. Correct. But there was no causal connection. The unification of Germany was achieved not by the slow evolution of a confederation with a monetary union into a federation, but by three wars, which enabled Prussia to emerge as the dominant country in the multi-state Germany of 1815, wars themselves inspired in a calculated way by Bismarck. (Bertrand Russell, in *Freedom and Organization*, argued that the unification of Germany was the best example in history of 'a great man successfully pursuing a single aim'.)

The economic consequences are also unpredictable. The Belgian ex-Commissioner Etienne Davignon declared that the 'single currency is the only thing that can unleash the full potential of the single market'. At the very least the single currency, it would seem, would prevent those 'competitive devaluations', as the French put the matter, which 'enable countries to gamble selfishly against their neighbours'. A writer in the *Financial Times* at the end of May 1997, Wolfgang Munchau, pointed out sensibly that there would be winners and losers in consequence of such a change. The Euro would certainly become a new reserve currency, he thought, a good development all round, since the world's monetary system would thereby become less ill-balanced. There would probably be a redistribution of wealth within the European Union, in unexpected ways; many sectors of the economy would be affected unevenly, some small banks would close, and big companies would prosper. Munchau also thought, though, that the effect of monetary union would be bound to be deflationary to begin with, because the new European Central Bank would err on the side of caution, but in the end the Euro would inspire growth, if in quite unpredictable places.

As for the enlargement of the European club, the consequences are even more difficult to predict. The Treaty of Amsterdam in June 1997 stated specifically that any European state which respects the various principles of liberty and the rule of law which the Treaty named could apply to join. In 2020 AD, with perhaps as many as thirty members, the population of the Union may be approaching 400 million. The number of these members is less important than the fact that the whole of Central or Eastern Europe, including probably the Baltic states and Balkans, and including the countries of ex-Yugoslavia, must be expected to have joined the Union by that year. 'Prague and Cracow are as

European as Paris and Cambridge,' the *Economist* has reminded its readers. These states are all poorer than those in Western Europe, and though the admission of the obvious candidates would increase the population by 100 million, the wealth of Europe would probably only be augmented by 5 per cent. Most of the states concerned have been outside the domain of Western European assumptions not simply during the era of Communism, 1945–89, but in some cases always. For example, much of Poland had been governed from Moscow since the 1790s, and some of the Baltic states since even earlier. Rumania may have been the Dacia of the Romans but it was also the Wallachia of the Turks.

The assimilation of these countries will, therefore, be difficult, but the prospect should all the same be an inspiring one. At any time before 1989, the idea that all the lost provinces of the East (or are they of the Centre?) Europe to the Carpathians – fortunately not to the Urals – would be able to participate in the European banquet would have seemed a wreck of a 'dissolving dream'.

First, consider the effect on the existing structure. At the moment every large state has two commissioners, every smaller state one. Every state has a judge on the European court. How can that membership possibly be sustained? Then there will be the impact on the European Parliament. At the moment, that institution has a life which is increasingly recognizable as that of a legislative body, and some of its debates are already important, if usually badly reported in the press. But how would thirty states be satisfactorily represented? Would there have to be a chamber of a thousand? Or would there perhaps have to be two chambers, constructed along the basis of the United States Congress, with an upper house representing nations along the lines of the Senate, and a lower one representing the peoples in direct proportion to their numbers?

However that matter is resolved, it is obvious that a few countries might seek to press ahead, as suggested by the German Christian Democrats a few years ago, to form a core, even a directorate, in such an enlarged Europe. Jacques Delors, pointing out that expansion would demand greater control at the centre, seems to agree:

in order to prevent the union of thirty states from being reduced to a mere economic area, it is necessary to accept that, at the same time, some of the thirty countries must go further than others and constitute a federation of nation-states. So these countries will be the vanguard of a European power, autonomous in both defence and foreign policy. If expansion is increased without this, we can say goodbye to the idea of a great Europe. We would go directly to a 'Europe-space' and, since spaces have no souls, when difficulties arise, the countries concerned would simply return to re-establish tariffs, frontiers and protection.

Hervé de Charette, though from a different political party to Delors, said the same more clearly:

Those who have always pursued the project of a federal Europe will not abandon it. In this greater Europe which we are now building, a small number of states will be the pathfinders [*éclaireurs*]. In this perspective, France, with the collaboration of Germany, will set about organizing a newly reinforced co-operation ... During recent years, we have thought that we could do two things at the same time: to pursue the federal project and also expansion. Now to speak of a federal Europe suggests that we are talking in terms of being inspired by the American experience, where power came down from the top.* But in Europe power is coming up from below. As for enlargement, it has been damaged all along by fundamental contradictions [*contradictions existentielles*]. Then Britain and the Scandinavian countries have always shown themselves doubtful about the federal idea. The only way ahead is to pursue the two projects in different ways.

De Charette was then asked by his interviewers if he, like Delors, supported 'a federalizing core inside a confederal project'. 'That is a good formula,' replied de Charette, who in so speaking was perhaps unconsciously echoing a phrase in Balzac's *Les Chouans*, where a revolutionary soldier speaks of France as 'a traveller with a mission to carry a light'.

---

* This reflection shows the Foreign Minister's ignorance of De Tocqueville's work *Démocratie en Amérique*, where he argues that it was the contrary.

So it must be expected that, with expansion, France as well as Germany will be among the 'federalizers', and among those who envisage a Europe of two tiers: the *éclaireurs* and the rest.

These ideas are an expression of the idea of 'Flexibility', the current word for allowing different members of the Union to progress (but where to?) at different speeds. This concept has had several earlier names: 'variable geometry', for instance, had its day, as did 'Europe *à la carte*', or was it the other way round? Am I wrong or has not the humble 'closer co-operation' already taken the place of 'flexibility'? The concept has had as many changes of name as English Whig peers had in the early eighteenth century at the time of the Glorious Revolution. Anyway, whatever word is used the concept is a dangerous one. Delors must know that the suggestion would not have been considered *communautaire* by any of his predecessors as President of the Commission. Picking and choosing could ruin the whole picture. The *Economist* quotes Pascal Lamy, who was once *chef de cabinet* to Delors, as austerely saying: '"flexibility" is the easy answer, but it is not necessarily the best one'. The approval of the idea at Amsterdam seemed to suggest a danger that numerous associations would threaten the whole consitutional order set up under the Union.

If, however, there is to be any inner directorate, it would be better to permit it to develop informally, rather than provide for it expressly in a treaty, as, say, the Cabinet grew in England. That would enable the identity of the *éclaireurs* to change. Who knows, one day Britain could aspire to be one of those?

If there were no such core, simple arithmetic points to some delicate problems: with thirty members of the Union, a majority of the states voting in the Council of Ministers could achieve a simple majority while representing only 15 per cent of the Union. If voting is to be weighted according to population, there could be other anomalies: for the four largest countries (Germany, France, Britain, Italy) could achieve a simple majority, even if all other twenty-six member states opposed; and the two most populous members (Germany and Britain, say) would have as many people as the combined population of over twenty of the smallest states. Of course, simple majority votes or votes achieved by unanimity would be preferable, but it is hard to see that those arrangements would work, since they would give power in Europe to small countries. Perhaps, in the light of how badly small European states have been treated in history by large ones, that would be fair, but politics cannot be a matter of retribution for past wrongs. The arrangements for dealing with this matter agreed at Amsterdam in June 1997 were notoriously unsatisfactory.

The economic consequences of enlargement on the scale envisaged would also be considerable. Agriculture, for example, plays a large part in the lives of the candidate countries, and their products are able to be traded quite well on the world market as it is. The *Economist* thinks that if these countries are admitted in the late 1990s the cost of the Union's agricultural budget would increase by half as much again. Enlargement would no doubt be spread out over many years but, even so, countries such as Spain and Portugal which at present receive substantial subsidies (through the so-called cohesion funds and the structural funds for regional and social policy) would be certain to find these diminished.

*

In the last few years, discussion has begun again for the reconsideration of the European Defence Community, and by the year 2010 the matter could easily seem as important an item on the European agenda as the monetary union is today and as expansion will be for the next ten years.

The subject has had a curious history. The first attempt at a Western alliance was the so-called WEU, Western European Union, established in 1947 by the Treaty of Brussels between Britain, France and the three Benelux countries. This was the core of what became NATO in 1949, with other European nations being added (Italy, Denmark and Norway) and two North American ones (the United States and Canada). But an idea for another more integrated scheme for European defence was one of the first aims of Jean Monnet in the 1950s. The French Minister for Defence in 1950, René Pleven, devised a scheme for a European army which would make possible the collaboration of West Germany in the defence of Western Europe. Italy, the Benelux countries and France would have collaborated. The United States supported the plan, but the British position was characterized by its usual hesitations, Churchill articulating the national mood when he at one moment called for regular meetings of European defence ministers and the next speaking of the very idea of a European defence force as being 'a smudgy amalgam'. That European defence force would have been fitted in as the European pillar of the already constituted NATO.

The idea was generally accepted in the parliaments of all the countries concerned except for France, though the nature of British commitment was obscure. In the end, after many debates, the plan was defeated in the French National Assembly during the prime ministership of Pierre Mendès France by a combination of Gaullists and Communists. Germany was soon allowed into NATO as a member in her own right, though not without further upheavals on the matter.

The concept was then left on one side for about forty years. From time to time, the matter would be raised indirectly. For example, President Kennedy's administration, under the influence of the Under-Secretary of State, George Ball, talked about the desirability of establishing a European pillar in NATO. There were numerous ideas for trying to ensure a European common market in armaments, if not in defence, through such bodies as the European Programme Group. But nothing much transpired, until the original aim of NATO, the collapse of Soviet imperialism, was obtained. Then in 1990, six months or so after the fall of the Berlin Wall, mention of a European dimension to NATO for the first time appeared in the communiqué at the NATO meeting in Paris that year. Then people began to wonder whether that old alliance WEU might not be revived as a way of ensuring a revived European defence collaboration and, within a short time, France came to be interested. Perhaps that was a way whereby that essential country could be persuaded to return to the new NATO. Meanwhile the French and Germans began largely token defence collaboration and Spain, still anxious to show her international respectability, was willing to participate. Defence was discussed at Maastricht but the subject was firmly placed in that zone of collaborative efforts which were to be intergovernmental. In early 1997 the French government was shifting from this position and was talking of the desirability of ensuring that WEU might be adapted to come under the control of the European Union by the year 2010. Already, as the Treaty of Amsterdam reminded us, the WEU as a body has 'access to operational capability'.

This idea upsets Britain, the strongest supporter of NATO. Her spokesmen, whether Conservative or Labour, have thrown up their hands in horror at any idea of a genuine common defence effort, on the ground that it is desirable for Britain to maintain her close association with the United States in matters of intelligence. Still, those doubts did not prevent the Amsterdam Treaty including a statement that the Union should 'foster closer institutional relations with the WEU with a view to the possibility of the integration of the WEU into the Union, should the European Union decide'.

In the long run, the intellectual basis for British 'Atlanticism' will have to be reconsidered. Of course it would be desirable, for the foreseeable future, for the main European nations, whether singly or through WEU or through some other organization, to remain a part of NATO. But in the twenty-first century there will be numerous security requirements for Europe in which the United States will not be primarily interested; and the United States will have her own considerations in Latin America, the Pacific or the Caribbean.

*

There would seem at first sight to be three immediate institutional choices for the future of the European Union: first, a continuing, calculated and of course sophisticated refusal to deal with such matters as the frame within which we operate, in the interests of maintaining the present *engrenage*; second, an acceptance of Europe as a confederation, that is a permanent and close-knit association of otherwise independent nations (*not* an alliance, since alliances can be reversed); and, third, a federation, and the fact that the 'F' word is unpopular in Britain cannot effect its exclusion from the possibilities – for it is not everywhere unwelcome, and there is a simple logic to it.

There is also the chance that one state, such as Britain, could either withdraw from what is happening in Europe ('secede') or negotiate for herself a special position, off-shore of these alternatives. The withdrawal of Britain, though it would be disturbing to those who believe in the European adventure, would not destroy the enterprise, though the withdrawal of either France (essential in the first thirty years of the new Europe) or Germany (even more essential now, with the prospect of enlargement eastwards) would do so. Ferdinand Mount in his *The British Constitution Now* thought that no state could be said to have lost her sovereignty if she had the right to withdraw from a federal system and '[in] 2002 . . . it is surely a reasonable bet that any discontented member would still retain the right to leave [the Union]'. So Britain's stance as a possible solitary, but presumably benign onlooker, a distant figure with binoculars on the south coast of England, should be briefly considered, at the end of the discussion of the other possibilities.

*

Though Sir Michael Butler and his friends in Brussels may mock the word, Europe is already a 'confederation', as that word has been traditionally understood. The German constitutional tribunal a few years ago said as much. It is surprising that we do not speak more in these terms. 'Confederation' is an old-fashioned concept but none the worse for that. Indeed, that old-fashionedness could help understanding.

There have, actually, been rather few confederations of states. The best modern example may seem to be Switzerland, but the country long ago developed what most people think of as a 'federal' identity. Indeed, for all its title, the 'Swiss Confederation' was considered in the eleventh, and most intellectually respectable, edition of the *Encyclopaedia Britannica* to be a 'federation'. If Gibbon had only written his history of the rise of the Swiss Republic, instead of that of the decline of the Roman Empire, we might know better the reason for that.

The weaknesses of a classical confederation in Greece, the Amphyctionic League, were often discussed by the authors of the United States' federal constitution. James Madison, in the Federalist papers, number 18, was at that time seeking to boost the argument for federalism. For the newly independent states of what had been till recently British North America constituted a confederation. As a result of Madison's and Alexander Hamilton's reminder of the dangers of a weak confederation in the Greek style, the independent states then associated in the federation which became the United States. Hamilton had been speaking of the need for that ever since 1780, when he had told James Duane that 'the leagues among the old Grecian republics . . . were continually at war with each other and, for want of union, fell a prey to their neighbours'. As everyone knows, in 1861 the southern states in North America broke away from this federation to form the 'confederacy', a term usually used thenceforth to indicate an association which would turn out to be less than permanent.

If Europe is at the moment a confederation, it is neither a tidy nor a classically shaped one. It is a rambling Gothic edifice, more like, oddly enough, the old British Palace of Westminster than a continental chamber of deputies, with classic pediments. It is also a more complex enterprise than what existed in the United States before 1789, or indeed in any confederation of which history bears record.

The complexity is suggested by the fact that the Treaty of Maastricht provided that the two so-called pillars of common endeavours covering foreign and defence policy, on the one hand, and justice and home affairs, on the other, should be intergovernmental, not intragovernmental, even though there would be a European dimension to both, and even though the Treaty of Amsterdam of June 1997 seems to have already changed matters somewhat.

The present system in Europe has by and large done well. People would not be so afraid of it had that not been so. A reminder of some of the achievements is at this point desirable. The common agricultural policy, for example, has seemed unfair in Britain but, on the continent, it has had the positive effect of allowing farmers to be competitive while avoiding the eclipse of the working population of the countryside, as seems to be happening in Britain. British agriculture is so efficient that it hasn't benefited from the Common Agricultural Policy but that 'efficiency', with its extensive use of chemical fertilisers, has destroyed wildlife on a colossal scale. The Union's regional funds have assisted the economic development of Ireland, Spain, Portugal, Greece, the south of Italy and even parts of France. The Single European Act of 1987 inspired about thirty directives designed to improve health, safety and security in factories and other places of work. European trade policies would not have had the success which they have enjoyed had each country had to negotiate separately with, say, Japan, much less the United States. The idea of social Europe seems in England to be clumsy, and interfering but, with its insistence of collaboration as well as competition, it has helped to save the cities of the continent from turning into the social desert which, with some exceptions, those of the United States have become. Relations between France and Germany are better than they have been since the death of Charlemagne. As a new institution starting from scratch, the enterprise inspired by Monnet in 1950 has transformed the political and economic face of Western Europe. It is the great international political success of the second half of the century.

The political innovations have also been astonishing. No previous confederation before has asserted so subtly that it is an agency making possible the complicated idea of 'shared sovereignty', whereby otherwise independent states pool certain powers in order to use them in common.

This last idea, as we all know, is rejected by some English politicians, who insist, in the uneasy calm of their constituency consulting rooms, that sovereignty is something so pure that it can be neither divided nor shared. One slice of it taken away and the whole is ruined. But perhaps the matter should be more carefully considered. Suppose the slice is only a small one, and affects only the cream-making industry, for example? Perhaps sovereignty is only lost when over half of what is important is subtracted and given to another authority? Did membership of NATO not affect sovereignty at all? After all, by committing ourselves to that Treaty, we prepared to let the most powerful, and symbol-dominated, part of our national endeavour operate permanently under the command of a North American general. Sovereignty, it should not be forgotten, was a concept devised by the French philosopher Jean Bodin at the end of the sixteenth century. It was not known before.

*

The idea of seeing the future of Europe indefinitely in confederal terms has some weaknesses: first, as noted earlier, the Union already has federal elements. The institutions and the ideologies of the Union and its predecessors have always had at their core a federal purpose. Monnet may not have had a long-term plan: his motto was probably that of Danton: 'On s'engage et puis on voit.' But all the same the statement, which he drafted and which set the Iron and Steel Community on its way, in 1950, was explained at the time as 'laying the first concrete foundations of the European federation'. In a letter to the French Prime Minister Georges Bidault, sketching out his ideas in April 1950, Monnet wrote, 'The contribution [which] an organized and living Europe can make to civilization is indispensable to the maintenance of peace. To achieve that Europe must be organized on a federal basis.' De Gasperi, the Italian founding father, was fond of saying: 'European patriotism can develop only in a federal Europe.' Luigi Einaudi, President of Italy from 1948 to 1955, saw national sovereignty as 'the enemy number one' of human culture. Robert Schuman, who moved fast from being a typical French foreign minister to one who thought the division of Europe into small states 'an anachronism, a nonsense, a heresy' (the last being his strongest term of abuse), did not mention the word 'federation' (nor 'federal') on 9 May 1950 when he launched in Paris the Coal and Steel Community, but he did speak of 'European construction' and 'a Europe solidly united and strongly built'. Given the attitudes of these 'saints' of the early days of European integration, as Alan Milward calls them, it is not surprising that the Treaty of Rome of 1957 too seemed to have been dictated in order to create the embryo of just such a Europe.

It may now appear, especially to the dwindling band of optimists who recall those far-off days, that, since the Luxembourg compromise of 1966, those federal ideas, conceived in such different circumstances, no longer mean anything. Yet the mention of a federal purpose was something which those who wrote the first text of the Treaty of Maastricht wanted to place in that document's preamble. Those who work in the Berlaymont building think of themselves as Monnet's heirs. Though the Union may be at the moment a Gothic edifice, most of its architects always aspired, and aspire, to turn it into a more classical one. It was because the founders of the Coal and Steel Community hoped that it would in the end mature into a federation that Britain refused to join it in 1951, thereby preparing the way for an unprecedented half-century of political failure as far as Europe is concerned.

Federalists survive too, and not only in politics. For example, Helmut Werner, until recently president of Mercedez Benz, whose products have for long bound together by autoroute the aristo-crats of the new Europe, told *Le Monde* in March 1997, 'we must end up with a federal Europe which will, to begin with, [only] include France, Germany and six or seven other countries'. The late French Foreign Minister de Charette's remarks about seeking a federal core at the heart of a confederated continent should be recalled.

The notion of federalism has also existed in Britain, and in unexpected corners, not only as an enemy to be baited, but sometimes as a solution to be embraced. Were not Lord Robbins and Professor Hayek, patrons of the new right, once federalists in the 1930s? Then, some fifteen years ago, I found myself chairman of a Conservative Party study group about Europe before the election of 1983. My friends and I visited the late Nicholas Ridley, at that time Financial Secretary to the Treasury. He assured us that he thought federation was the only serious possibility for Europe in the long run. Otherwise, he thought, 'the thing will sooner or later fall apart. That's an unpopular view, I know,' he went on, 'but I see no alternative.'

Ridley's statement was made when the Europe family consisted only of nine members. With fifteen, he would presumably have been even more certain. With thirty, it might seem inevitable.

It is curiously necessary to repeat that the word 'federal' spells the reverse of the idea of centralization. If one wants to avoid excessive intervention from Brussels, federalism is a word with a less intrusive meaning than the expression 'ever closer union'. That last expression suggests that there is no end to the process of unification. Federalism has a quite different connotation.

Like the word confederation, federalism has a good classical ancestry. The Thessalian, the Boeotian and even the Arcadian federations all have a place in the pantheon of ancient polities. There are as many doubts as certainties. Was the league of the cities of Latium a real federation? Historians dispute the matter. In all these entities, at all events, the states delegated a part of their functions, or powers, to a central authority in their common interest. At present, as we all know, Germany, the United States, Canada and Australia are federal states, with the *Länder* or the states in possession of lavish, and not easily changeable, powers. These federal entities have been among the most successful of the polities of the late twentieth century, and partly because of the nature of the devolved powers.

In the United States, the federal authority has become stronger, over the generations, and the federal government in Washington is much the strongest institution in the world. That was not inevitable. The powers of the *Länder* in Germany have not diminished after fifty years, and the increase of the power of the federal government in the United States can be directly explained by the climb of that country to world power. Some nominally federal states, such as Mexico, have been so only in name, and troops known as *los federales* were made fun of in hundreds of popular ballads. By the same token, some federal states have had such a weak central authority that they have fallen apart. One example was the First Spanish Federal Republic, where the centrifugal motion of the peripheral cities and provinces was too strong for the centre to survive. The consequence was to make the word 'federal' a dread one in modern Spain, and for reasons very different to what has inspired the common British dislike of the same word.

It is curious that the idea of a federal Europe has been rejected by market-concerned conservatives in most countries. Their opposition to socialism or statism, as the late Keith Joseph used to put it, is comprehensible and logical. But it is hard to see why they do not accept that, for private enterprise to work effectively in Europe, a federal order would be desirable.

*

Yet the full federal consummation is improbable. For none of the major Western European states covets it, with the possible exception of Germany, if by that is understood a replacement of the existing heads of state by, say, a European president, and some parts of the upper civil services of the states by a federal European bureaucracy, with loyalty only to the Council of Ministers in Brussels. However different defence and security requirements will be in the twenty-first century, most Europeans for the foreseeable future will prefer to retain control over their armed forces. Finally, the European Parliament would not seem ever likely to be able to compete in vitality with existing legislatures. It is true that the British Parliament, with its long uninterrupted history, is in a different category to its sisters in other countries, many of which have thoroughly revised their institutions on new principles in the last generation or so. All the same, a European parliament, with members from everywhere from Riga to the Canary Islands or Skye to Athens, speaking in twenty-five or so languages, through interpreters, would not begin to be able to provide the intimate security made possible through national parliaments.

Thus it would probably be best to assume that the European Union in the future will remain a confederation with federal elements or, just possibly, a federation with confederal ones.

No doubt all these uncertainties should be cleared up. The obscurities of what the European Union aspires to are disconcerting and lead to fears that the aim is to harmonize everything, making impossible the diversity which the Liberal Democrat manifesto in the British general election of 1997 very properly spoke of as being a necessity. Professor Anthony King has said that the European Union needs 'some kind of clear operational doctrine, like those spelt out in the American, Australian and Canadian constitutions [or the German, it might be said] about what properly belongs to the component nations of the Union and what properly belongs to the Union itself'. He added: 'of course, one can have long disputes about what ought to be done at what level, but it seems to me that, as long as the muddle remains as great as it appears right now, and as long as the European Union seems to be imposing solutions on Britain, there is going to be unhappiness'. Frank Vibert, in a book published in 1997, argues much the same. His most important point is that 'the assumption that political integration in Europe can continue to be pursued by indirect means [that is, economic means] is a false one. It insults the instincts and the intelligence of the peoples of Europe.'

Vibert made this suggestion, of course, for the whole of the European Union, not just the British, but it seems likely to be disliked more by the British than by any other nation, because of our own lack of a constitution. I remember hearing Enoch Powell, at a conference held in the UNESCO building in Paris on the impact of the French Revolution, in 1989, say firmly that the reason why the British would in the end reject the European Community, as it then was, was that they could not be expected to approve of a written constitution, such as was offered by the Treaty of Rome.

The distinguished minds who operate the European Commission may insist that such a document as Vibert suggests is not necessary since, after all, a constitution can be extracted from the existing treaties. But those treaties were written by experts, perhaps for experts. There must be something wrong with a treaty such as that of Maastricht which even Europhiles cheerfully admit that they cannot read. It was a document drawn up by a committee.

In 1839, faced by a rebellion in Canada which clearly could be justified in democratic terms, the then Prime Minister, Lord Melbourne, requested Lord Durham, his High Commissioner in the country, to write a report with a view to finding a new deal in the territory, which would avoid the risk of rebellion such as that which had led to the independence of the thirteen colonies seventy years before. The consequence was the Durham report, which found a way, through 'dominion status', of maintaining the loyalties of the Canadian territories by allowing them to manage their own affairs. We need just such a document now in relation to the European Union, to determine the status of member states in relation to the Union. The report should, like the Durham report, be written by a single good writer, who knows the ropes in Brussels as well as those in his own polity.

Our new Lord Durham should, of course, go further than merely summarize what exists. He would have to deal with matters which the Commission does not regard as part of its business, and should anticipate problems which have not yet arisen.

The all-important preamble to our new Durham report would embody general truths and purposes, such as are suggested quite well for once in Chapter I, Fundamental Rights, of the Treaty of Amsterdam. The explicit requirement that the Union should respect the national identities of its member states might be expanded to cover regions. The British notion of direct political responsibility for ministers should also be in some way implicated. This section would be hard to write if it is not to be a string of platitudes adapted for modern European political purposes. 'Ever closer union', which has had a good run for its money, should be avoided and allowed to wither away. Even if the phrase is qualified to indicate a union of peoples, not of states, it is desirable now to make evident that there is no intention to harmonize everything, from the size of brandy glasses to the way we deal with child criminals. The comparative word 'closer' has a vague sense, after all, that we can never get as close as Monnet would have liked to that forbidding matron of Calais who is standing wishing to press us to her ample bosom as we emerge from the Eurotunnel.

From the rest, there should also be a clear explanation of the idea expressed in the much maligned White Paper of 1971 for 'the sharing and enlargement of individual national sovereignties in the general interest'. It is an unusual idea which is at the heart of the whole process of the European Union. Economic and monetary union would also have to figure, as would the need to accommodate future applicant members, perhaps, as suggested by the French, with their fertile imaginations, by setting up a 'permanent conference' of all such nations. The new Lord Durham could then do worse than spell out more carefully than has been done hitherto what 'subsidiarity' means in practice.

The complex but subtle voting system in the European Council will probably have to be simplified.* Then the issue of diversity could be more seriously and institutionally addressed. 'Gardons notre diversité!' demands Jacques Santer. How? It is scarcely enough simply to say, 'Europe must return to respect the principle of nationalities.' There should be an institutional backing for this. The French sometimes speak of in-laws as the *famille adverse*. What about a commissioner *adverse*, specially charged to question each act of harmonization?

*

As for the idea of a British withdrawal into the borders of Europe, Britain on the elbow of Europe, say, rather than at its heart, an attempt has recently been made by the former Home Secretary

---

* Today it is possible to obtain a majority vote in the Council of Ministers if it is sustained by 58 per cent of the population of the Union. In the Europe of twelve the percentage was 63, in that of the Six it was 70. France has suggested that it might be less than 50 per cent in an expanded Europe.

Michael Howard to describe what this would mean in practice, in a pamphlet of 1997, *The Future of Europe*. Howard asked for the 'repatriation' of several undertakings which his government and its predecessors, mostly Conservative, had conceded to 'Brussels' – agriculture and fisheries, naturally, but also drinking water (because, Howard implied, namby-pamby men in Brussels are asking us to waste money treating our water to an unnecessary degree), safety and health. In the *Sunday Times* Ferdie Mount described the resulting arrangement as 'a free trade area with knobs on', but, if that is so, the knobs were very badly polished, for it is hard to see them. The fact is that nothing like this will be accepted by Britain's continental neighbours, nor by Ireland. General de Gaulle tried in the 1960s, less than ten years after the signature of the Treaty of Rome, to abstract from the then new Common Market its supranational content. He failed and, even if Britain were twice as powerful economically than she now is, it is improbable that she would have any greater success.

There is some historical ground for the Howard plan. Britain has spent most of the last four centuries trying to prevent the unification (or reunification) of Europe. As late as 1951, Anthony Eden warned Winston Churchill against the Pleven plan for a European army on the ground that it was federalist. To join Europe wholeheartedly, even Professor Sir Michael Howard (a Europhile and no relation to the ex-Minister) has admitted it, would be to turn her back on five centuries of history. He stresses the Protestant side to the English tradition, in the broadest sense of that word, and thinks that 'even for Europhiles [such as himself], it is annoying that the European Community should have been founded on a treaty signed in Rome'. Britain has fought, often, against all the four major countries of the European Union, Germany ('Jerry'), France (the 'Frogs'), Spain (the 'Dagoes') and even Italy (the 'Wops'), so that the minds of even badly educated people are full of vague memories of far-off battles against them, especially at sea. 'Sink me the ship, master gunner,' ordered Sir Richard Grenville in Tennyson's poem about a naval fight with Spain in the sixteenth century, 'sink her, split her in twain!/better Fall into the hands of God, not into the hands of Spain!'. For English nationalists, that huge Spanish vessel, the *Santa Maria*, bearing down on the little *Revenge*, stands for continental power, whether of Philip II, Louis XIV, Napoleon, the Kaiser or Hitler.

Britain, it is true, embarked on her membership of the Union on a slightly false basis. For Harold Macmillan applied in 1961 to join what was then the Community on the assumption that General de Gaulle's 'Europe of Nations' had won the day. Having been rebuffed in 1963, both Harold Wilson and then Edward Heath returned to the policy as if it had been a national challenge, without perhaps taking into account that De Gaulle's idea of a 'Europe des patries' had been outmanoeuvred and that, by the 1970s, the General had, in the words of Sir Michael Butler, 'failed to break the Community mechanism, and the process of integration was picking up speed again'.

The difficulty facing a Britain outside the mainstream of European powers is that she would still be affected by European politics and economic decisions, but would be unable to affect them. The 60 per cent of Britain's trade which is now with the countries of the European Union might drop a few points, but there would still be a sizeable amount of it. Many British citizens would presumably hold bank accounts in Euros. Britain would wish to be involved in at least the decisions of NATO but, if she 'repatriated' so much of her European activities, she would not be in a position to influence, nor hold back, the development of Western European defence, even as a European pillar of NATO.

On the whole, it might be better for Michael Howard (the ex-Minister) and those who think like him to go the whole hog and advocate withdrawal absolutely from the European Union, and then hope to negotiate some position similar to that of Norway or Switzerland. It would probably come to that in the end anyway. Of course, that did not seem desirable in 1983, in the high days of Thatcherism, when the Conservative manifesto stated that 'withdrawal would be a catastrophe . . . as many as two million jobs would be at risk. We would lose the great export advantages and the attraction to overseas investors which European membership now gives us.' But the world has changed since then, and some Eurosceptic Conservatives, who think of themselves as Thatcherites, talk of or hint at the charms of a tight little island outside all regional groupings except perhaps for a close friendship with the United States. But most countries in the twenty-first century are likely to participate in some kind of regional organization, the United States included, and we have known since Anthony Sampson's life of Harold Macmillan appeared in 1964 that the United States is likely to take more seriously a Britain within the European Union than one without.

The Howard plan for Europe would give Britain a place similar to that which we had in the sixteenth century: an offshore island, to recall Paul Johnson's book of that title, which in a reprint turned into 'a History of England'. That sixteenth-century island differed from our present one not only in the size of its population but in the fact that the union of the English and Scottish Crowns had not occurred; and, though predictions are not easy, there must be at least a chance that the union with Scotland would not survive a Howard repatriation.

*

Predictions and hopes

1. The European Union of the future will be a grouping of twenty-five to thirty states, with over 400 million people. It should be recognized that the task of ensuring that these new members fit in successfully will be as difficult a task as founding the original Coal and Steel Community of the six nations.

2. It is assumed that a European monetary union will have been established, with a common currency generally in use by about 2005 AD. This will have psychological as well as economic consequences which cannot be foreseen, but they will be vast.

3. With the number of member states envisaged, a federal state might seem logical. But it would probably be impossible to ensure liberty with a society of that size, there is no thought of building a federal civil service, and there remains doubt whether an effective European Defence Community can be ensured.

4. An effective, subtle and well-written scheme for a confederal union with some federal elements should be worked out. The scheme would be largely based on the present treaties.

5. Since committees cannot write, a single man or woman should be asked to write this, rather as Lord Melbourne asked Lord Durham to write his report which led to the development of the idea of 'dominion status'.

6. This author will plan for the maintenance of democratic activity at the national level, and European parliamentarians might be associated in one way or another with their national parliaments.

7. The *engrenage* of institutions (Commission, Council of Ministers, Council [i.e. heads of government], Court, committee of permanent representatives, Court of Auditors) which has been such a mark of the first forty years of modern European innovation will continue.

8. New institutions or offices will be devised to prevent excessive or unnecessary harmonization. A 'commissioner *adverse*' might be named to ensure this.

9. A Europe of the regions will be promoted, perhaps by a separate chamber in the European Parliament.

10. Within the confederal union, a group of states will see themselves as pathfinders. These *éclaireurs*, headed by France and Germany, will associate informally.

In the long term, by, say, the year 2050 AD, the success of the European Union will probably have inspired other groupings of nations each of which will have surrendered an element of their sovereignty in order to influence those parts of their neighbours' policies which affect them. The North American free trade area, the Central American common market, the Russian Commonwealth of States are indications of what is likely to occur. By the year 2050, surely, the nation state, *pur et dur* of the French revolutionary era, will everywhere have vanished.

7 Moral Values

A. C. GRAYLING

Preface: Predicting the Moral Future

Prediction is a mug's game. Consider horse-racing: you can be an experienced punter who exactly knows the form and going, but your horse might lose nevertheless. Yet this is a simple species of prediction where chances are calculable. It is infinitely otherwise with social attitudes and practices, where 'chaotic' effects – in the mathematical sense of small initial factors ramifying into large differences later – apply to already complex questions. The difficulty increases when one adds the fact that, in thinking about moral values, there is a close relationship between saying how things might be and how things should be – at very least because when one says 'matters will probably be thus' one is immediately tempted to add either 'and so they should' or 'they should be otherwise'; for moral debate is not a neutral matter, but concerns the realm of action, choice, and the character of life, where bare description never seems enough.

Given the difficulties, how can one venture to make predictions about morality? One might suppose that as history is, at least to some extent, the mirror of the future, one might seek there for instruction. There is some truth in this; but, on such large questions as the moral evolution of societies, the derivable lessons tend to be general, often ambiguous, and sometimes contradictory. Moral history can seem endlessly cyclical, with periods of austerity succeeding relative liberalism, which in turn liberalize after a time, only to retrench again. Sometimes there seems to be an inertia in human affairs, reversing progress at every opportunity of war or disaster. But such remarks are tendentious; history, including moral history, never exactly repeats itself; and nothing is ever quite lost from the argument of time. Moreover there is always a danger of our reading present value-judgements back into the record; for example, commentators used to say that, in its successful republican youth, Rome was austere and chaste, and that the voluptuousness of its later imperial stages was a symptom of decline. When we do this, history cannot teach us about our future, for it is (absurdly) being made to take lessons from our present.

But there is indeed something to be learned from the history of morality. It is that it consists in a struggle – a Heraclitean one, as the flux back and forth shows, and a Herculean one, given how much of the happiness of mankind is at stake – between what, for brevity, one might call 'liberal' and 'conservative' values. I speak of the history of the Western world – the world of essentially European and Judaeo-Christian origin. The only safe prediction about the future of morality in this world is that it will continue the self-same struggle, with no real ascendancy between either party, but with each thinking that the other is ascendant – and occasionally, to the real distress of the other, with one of them temporarily being so. Most people, as individuals, never belong fully to either party, but hover between, tending to err on the liberal side in respect of their own conduct and on the conservative side in respect of others' conduct. One large difference between the parties is that when the conservatives have the upper hand they actively persecute the liberals (in the past going so far as to burn them at the stake), whereas the liberals, when ascendant, cause conservatives no greater agonies than those of disapproval and chagrin.

But there is something else to be said about the future, the most important thing of all. This is that it does not exist: it waits to be made. Therefore the future of morality depends upon what we choose it to be. It is not there, laid like railway tracks running forward into time, for us helplessly to trundle along them, surprised or dismayed by what comes into view. As masters of the future, our duty is to think as clearly as we can about what kind of people we wish to be and what kind of life we wish to lead; and then to choose, and to act, as wisely as we may.

As a contribution to choosing the future, the rest of this essay sets out the conservative and liberal views – firmly on the side of the latter, for to repeat: morality is not a neutral matter – not in predictive, but in polemic mode. I return to the question of prediction at the very end.

Introduction

This is an essay in moralizing, not in moral philosophy. It is a brief essay, and therefore summary. The questions it addresses are complicated and delicate, and have been, and continue to be, discussed in the wider debate that society has with itself in many different forums, from academic seminars to newspaper columns and beyond. This is a contribution to that debate, and presupposes it; but it is also an argument for a change of perspective, which if accepted would help to change the debate's terms.

The difference between moral philosophy and moralizing merits comment. Some moral philosophers deny that it is their job to moralize – that is, to offer guidance, and to say how one should choose and act – on the ground that they are no better fitted to do so than anyone else. Instead they see their task as clarification of the concepts used in moral debate (for chief examples: 'goodness', 'right', 'duty' and 'obligation'), together with investigation of the reasoning employed about them. Moral philosophy thus conceived is a neutral, purely descriptive task, which studiously avoids offering views about how to live.

This is a recent development. Past moral philosophers were concerned to identify and enjoin the good life, and to recommend ways of resolving the problems whose occurrence is guaranteed by the complexity of human existence. Given the three facts that life is a demanding business, that many search for guidance in how to live it, and that most who offer to guide them do so from tendentious religious or political standpoints, it seems not just a pity, but a dereliction, that moral philosophy has turned its back; for philosophy is the enterprise of reason, which tries to take the large, clear view, guided by logic and the facts – from which, therefore, one might reasonably hope for more judicious results than partisan faiths or factions can offer.

In any case, moralizing needs moral philosophy. In moralizing one has to reason from principles, which in turn require grounds. Although what follows is an act of moralizing, it therefore also includes at least something of its justification.

Most of what I say will be regarded as mere common sense by some, and as highly controversial by others. Past example shows that it is hard to persuade the latter to think and behave differently; but the argument with them must be continued nevertheless, for their views remain influential – and, arguably, harmful.

To most, discussion of morality suggests discussion of a familiar range of topics: the family, sex, drugs, crime; the implications of medical advances; standards in public life. But this perception of what matters most is not universal. It is chiefly believed in the Anglo-Saxon West, in Muslim countries and in China. This geo-social remark is intended to give pause, as reminding us that in (for example) non-Anglo-Saxon Europe, especially northern Europe, not all of the problems listed, least of all sex and drugs, seem quite so acute; not because people there indulge less in either, but because they are more tolerant of both. A comparative study of moral attitudes across the world's societies would indeed be instructive, among other things showing that one reason why North America and Britain differ from continental Europe in the noted respect is that more austere, less tolerant varieties of Protestant Christianity have been influential there. It might also show that where Christian or Muslim missionaries have not penetrated, the peoples of Africa, South America and the Pacific islands perceive the moral realm differently – as they still do in India, and once did in pre-Communist China.

These generalizations are intended to keep before us the thought that moralities are socially constructed and historically shaped. It is healthy to remember that what is taboo or acceptable in one culture might be the reverse in another. At very least, that fact should make one keenly re-examine one's own values.

The Great Moral Questions

But the great moral questions – the most important and urgent ones – are not about sex, drugs and unmarried mothers. They are, instead, about human rights, war, the arms trade, poverty in the

Third World, and inequality and injustice everywhere. These areas of concern involve truly staggering horrors and human sufferings. In comparison to them, the parochial and largely misguided anxieties over sex, drugs and the other matters that fill newspapers and agitate the 'Moral Majority' in America and Britain, pale into triviality. It is itself a moral scandal that these questions preoccupy debate in comfortable corners of the world, while real atrocity and oppression exist elsewhere. This is not to deny that the parochial concerns are important, for they are: but, as I shall argue below, their importance lies in what is almost invariably the opposite of what moral conservatives think.

The claim that human rights violations, war and Third World poverty are the greatest of moral problems hardly needs explanation or justification. The piteous agonies of refugees, the starving, the massacred, the tortured, the imprisoned, are eloquent in their own case. It is astonishing how many in the world's comfortable regions are nightly able to witness the plight of their fellow humans, only to turn off their television sets and forget what they saw. Perhaps the reason is that individuals feel helpless in the face of so much and such profound suffering. Beyond making a donation to a suitable charity – and there is a reasonable limit to what one can give – the next step in active concern threatens to consume too much of one's time and resources, thereby disrupting one's own projects in life.

This suggests that it is better for governments to take action, as the collective agency of the people they serve. Impelled by their electorates, they could, and on this view should, act in concert to halt those among their number who violate their citizens' rights, or make war. The United Nations organization embodies a noble aspiration to this end; but in practice it is enfeebled by its members' divisions and its lack of funds, so that the good it does is limited. But it still does good at times, not least in representing ideals – among which its Universal Declaration of Human Rights is central.

Human Rights

When the UN came into existence at the end of the Second World War one of its earliest acts was to respond to the appalling atrocities of the preceding years by boldly committing itself to the ideal of treating every human individual in the world as possessed of basic entitlements, and of trying to protect them. The Charter of the UN, adopted in 1945, affirmed 'faith in fundamental human rights, in the dignity and worth of the person, and in the equal rights of men and women and of nations large and small'. Accordingly the UN established a committee to draft a Universal Declaration. The committee worked swiftly, and the Declaration was adopted in 1948 without a dissenting vote. At the time it was particularly welcomed by Third World countries and subjects of colonial rule. Since then the Universal Declaration has been supplemented by two Covenants, respectively on political and civil rights and on social and economic rights, and dozens of further international instruments, jointly constituting an International Bill of Human Rights.

It might seem that these resolutions have little practical worth, because human rights violations continue everywhere in the world, often in the grossest forms. Yet their mere existence has unquestionably reduced the number and severity of violations, and gives powerful aid to individuals and groups opposing them, as witness the patient endeavours of non-governmental organizations at the annual sessions in Geneva of the United Nations' Commission on Human Rights. Progress is slow – painfully so, usually – but it represents a striking historical departure. One of its chief effects is that the International Bill of Human Rights now weighs significantly in international legal proceedings. This is one of the most optimistic signs for the world's future.

The Universal Declaration is a bold document. It starts from the claim that 'all members of the human family' enjoy 'inherent dignity and equal and inalienable rights' and that upon the recognition of this rests our best hopes of achieving the great universal desiderata of freedom, justice and peace. Disregard for these rights led to the barbarities of the Second World War, vivid in the memory of the international community, which, as it emerged from their shadow, sought to renew its hopes for 'a world in which human beings shall enjoy freedom of speech and belief and freedom from fear and want'. Recognizing that such aspirations merit the protection of law, the UN's Declaration sets out to describe what that law should encompass. The chief provisions are that all human beings are born free and equal in rights; that these latter include life, liberty, and security, freedom from slavery and cruel punishment, recognition before and protection by law, freedom of movement, freedom to express views, to participate in the government of the state, to have an education, to own property, to practise a religion, to have time for leisure, to make choices in personal life, and to enjoy peace. Correlatively, the Declaration recognizes that everyone has duties to others and to the community, which in sum make it possible for others to enjoy the same rights also.

These principles by now seem commonplace to people in the West, for whom they state a mere minimum of expectation. But to the majority of the world's population they are still ideals rather than realities, and for anyone languishing in political detention, or in the shadow of a harsh regime, they represent precious aspirations. Philosophical discussion of the basis and justification of rights continues; but one could abbreviate it by *laying claim* to those rights, defending one's arrogation of them on the ground that history has taught us what best promotes human flourishing, and that enjoyment of these rights is essential to it.

One main purpose of ethics might be to help people see that human rights are chief among the moral issues facing the world, and to urge them to act accordingly. People need only decide to do something about the problems thus identified; at the very least to write, and to keep on writing, to their political representatives, demanding collective action; and voting accordingly – and never forgetting that the truly important moral questions lie here. If there is an arena where the greatest challenges for the future lie, and with them therefore the greatest need for moral heroism and endeavour, it is in the sphere of human rights. The development of science and technology shows us that, as a species, we have grown clever; their misuse for war and oppression shows us that we have not yet grown wise. Moral heroism is required for us to teach ourselves wisdom.

I shall say no more about the great question of human rights here, because it speaks for itself. There are other social and political questions of relevance to ethics that do not always speak for themselves; in particular, those about poverty and inequality cannot be left aside, because in all their forms they touch the nerve of debates about the good life in the good society. Accordingly I mention them again below.

'Morality' and 'Ethics'

The remainder of what follows treats of some of the standard and familiar problems in moral debate, involving what are seen as threats to 'family values' and allied concerns, which for most people, as noted, turn on questions about marriage and divorce, sexual practices and behaviour, drug abuse, and such dilemmas as abortion and euthanasia. This list is not exhaustive, but it covers central ground.

It helps to recognize a distinction between narrow definitions of 'morality' as conceived in modern times (chiefly since the eighteenth century) and a more inclusive, classical conception of 'ethics'. As the notion now operates, morality applies just to parts of life, chiefly to interpersonal relationships; and it invariably concerns such matters as marital infidelity and malicious gossip. No one thinks that eating bananas is a moral matter, nor how a person works, or what colour he paints his house. The philosophers of classical antiquity thought differently. For them all of life is an ethical matter: one lives and does well as a whole person, and both one's flourishing and effect on others flow from one's total character. For this reason life has to be considered – 'the unconsidered life', said Socrates, 'is not worth living' – and it can only be considered if it is informed.

Questions about ethics, therefore, as against those having to do with more narrowly conceived morality, are questions about intelligent human flourishing – which is to say: human well-being and well-doing. They therefore seek answers not only to questions about what sort of people we should be, but about what sort of society we should have – so that the best we can aspire to be can have the best environment to thrive in. Thus ethics and politics, as Aristotle saw, are continuous.

Grasping the distinction between morality and ethics is important because it helps us to promote the latter. Morality is about what is allowed and forbidden in particular realms of behaviour; ethics is about the character of one's personality and life. Therefore the groundwork of ethics is not rules and codes, admonitions and sanctions, as in morality, but an education of character whose primary target is the inculcation of thoughtfulness, insight, taste and tolerance. The admittedly utopian conviction thus embodied is that from success in such an enterprise ethical society will grow; and in such a society the permissions and prohibitions with which morality concerns itself will be unnecessary because already comprised in the mutual respect and tolerance constituting the relationships among its members.

I turn to these larger considerations later. The best way of showing why they are worth promoting is to work through the main moral (in the narrow sense) debates that bedevil Western societies. Discussing them shows that the moral problems we think we face change character when viewed from what in the end is seen as an ethical perspective.

Two Facts and Two Demands

Most people are capable at times of being well judging and careful, and able to think things through in a generous frame of mind. In such moods one can recognize two facts, and two demands entailed by them, which are profoundly important to ethical considerations – and yet which are, as is often the case with profundities, simple.

The first fact is that we (for *any* 'we') have a good idea of what, in a general way, conduces to human flourishing. One can interpret the Universal Declaration of Human Rights as stating that understanding in full, but it can be put more summarily. Shelter, warmth, food, companionship, health, freedom, security: this is easily the list of desiderata which – irrespective of their historical or cultural setting – most people would acknowledge as among the necessities of a good life. Of course there is much more, of more complex and diverse kinds, that make for full human flourishing, for humans are intelligent and creative animals: all the arts and sciences, and the various amenities of civilization, show what we have found attractive besides.

The second fact might at first seem to conflict with the first. It is that there is a great variety of human interests, not all of which one can be confident of understanding. No one can see things from everyone else's point of view; few can expect to achieve real insight into the needs and desires of others merely on the basis of knowing their own.

The conflict between the two facts is merely apparent. A relativist might dispute the first by saying that, if we think we know what people elsewhere or at other times regard as desirable, we risk misinterpreting them according to our own parochial views. But this argument is at best only half right, for the first fact is that we have a perfectly good general understanding of what makes for human flourishing, even if – as the second fact then adds – we have to learn more to discover what is sufficient for such flourishing on an individual basis, taking background considerations into account.

Two demands follow immediately from these two facts. The first is that if we know the least of what makes for the flourishing of others, then, if those others lack it – or are offered the opposite of it by, say, oppressors or natural disaster – this makes a call on us. To know that another is without the minimum that makes for human flourishing, and to ignore the fact, is wrong – or at very least, deeply imprudent; for, in a world in which people recognize others' needs but ignore them, one will oneself be sure to suffer as a result. Therefore, even on minimal prudential grounds, people do well to act in such a way that this is not a world in which we perceive but ignore each other's needs. (Below I give grounds for saying that it is not merely imprudent but unethical, in the inclusive classical sense, to act this way.)

The second demand is that, when we recognize the variety of human needs and desires, our first step must be to tolerate that variety, because it is so great that, as noted, we cannot always expect to have a ready insight into it; so the only way to avoid being mistaken, or prejudiced, or motivated by ignorance, is to be open-minded. Again the point can be substantiated by appeal even to the lowest motivation. We each wish to live our own lives and make our own choices, and in doing so to be respected or at least tolerated by others. We wish for sufficient latitude from others to carry out our own projects, even when they do not understand what our projects mean to us. Because we wish this to be a world where this happens, we have to extend the same consideration to others.

The Limits of Tolerance

This generosity is premised, as noted, on the insight that we cannot expect to understand, without sympathy and the right kind of effort at least, people whose concerns are different from our own, especially if they inhabit other conditions or cultures. But this is not mere mindless tolerance; it is neither unqualified nor irrevocable. For there are intolerable acts – murder, rape, torture, oppression, warmongering and injustice – whose perpetrators, whoever they are, step absolutely beyond the pale. This suggests a familiar principle: that whatever anyone does, he should be free to do it provided it does not harm others, and allows them to pursue their own goals under the same condition. This principle only says what one must not do – namely, that one must not interfere with or harm others. The first demand is stronger, having the form of a positive injunction: it says that we should help others when we recognize their need.

All this implies that the great sin is harm to people (which includes failing to help when one sees the need). One should say: the great sin is harm to other sentient creatures; but, although this is correct, I shall restrict discussion to humans here, for it is at least clear that they have a special place among sentient creatures, as having closer interests to our own, and as being capable of more various kinds of suffering.

I characterized the two demands at their lowest denominators, to show that even if we are merely self-regarding it is prudential to obey those demands. But of course I believe that we do far better with an ethics which adds other-regardingness to self-regardingness. This is done by recognizing and respecting others' interests, so that by a thoughtful mutual navigation of concerns we always seek the best, and at times accept the least bad, for ourselves and each other, taken together. The justification is that living thus is more satisfying and fruitful for everyone concerned than if one met these demands merely out of self-interest; and the kind of world in which most people felt this way would be a better-quality world than one in which mere self-interest prompts us to tolerate, and occasionally to help, others when it is useful to ourselves to do so. For one would not always find it useful to help others; indeed, the imperatives of competition and advantage-seeking would often make it harmful to oneself to tolerate or help others; so such a world would only be patchily mutual at best – and, even then, for not very edifying reasons. It has to be admitted, alas, that this describes our world as it is.

These remarks touch on matters of importance in several further ways. They bear on a truth that gives much of the point to ethical and political debate, recognized as seamlessly connected. This is that in human communities both resources and sympathies are limited; that competition between individuals and groups is therefore inevitable, and can, and often does, lead to conflict; and that therefore we need laws, rules and traditions to ameliorate our relationships, and to resolve conflicts. On the front line of these are ethical considerations, which enjoin a certain mutual attitude between people – of respect, consideration and trust-keeping; of kindness where appropriate and fellowship where possible – and which constitute the reasons for a person's acting in one way rather than another when his actions affect others.

With these thoughts to hand, we can now turn to the standard questions of moral debate.

'Family Values' and Values

Most debate about morality clusters around a set of problems, or perceived problems, which are most easily identified by the proposed ideal with respect to which they are thought to fall short, namely, the morality of 'family values'. The concept of a model family and its behaviour is central to this view. That model is of a happy nuclear family of two parents, one of either sex, with obedient, well-socialized offspring, living together in the same household into which others come only by arrangement and temporarily. None of the family use illegal drugs, and if they use legal ones (alcohol, nicotine) they do so moderately and sensibly. The parents limit their sexual interest to one another, and the offspring engage in sexual activity only when, as adults in their turn, they have committed themselves to a responsible relationship – standardly, a permanent monogamous marriage – with a member of the opposite sex. This family is economically independent, socially responsible, law-abiding and observant of contemporary norms.

That is the minimum that a model 'family values' family should be. More evangelical supporters of this ethos urge us, in addition, to be against abortion, homosexuality, divorce, pornography, and too much welfarism (on the grounds that people should take responsibility for themselves), and in favour of hanging and other very severe punishments for crime. They also strongly oppose the use of drugs – some of them include the legal drugs too, as temperance and prohibition movements show. Many supporters of 'family values' justify all these views on religious grounds.

This ethos is complex and interesting. Arguably, it is a mixture of something right and much wrong, the latter stemming from traditions of thought – principally religious – which are themselves complex.

What is right about this conservative ethos is that it recognizes, and makes central, the value of settled domestic affections, by which I mean those that sustain long-term, committed, co-operative relationships based on affection and shared interests at the core of private life. Without doubt such affections, as found in the happiest marriages and most flourishing families, are a great good. It is scarcely needful to list their benefits. But such affections can be, and are, enjoyed in a large variety of ways, of which the 'family values' model family is only one, and – as its short history shows – a rather unsuccessful one. Moreover, the 'family values' school takes its attitudes to sex and sexuality, marriage and fertility, drugs, crime and the nature of society, to be the corollary of their belief in the nuclear-family version of what promotes domestic affections. This, arguably, is a mistake – and sometimes a tragic one, as we can see from the number of social problems it causes. Conservative morality, in other words, is the problem, not the solution, in much that causes difficulty in society. This is because it is repressive and prohibitive in ways that cut across the grain of human nature. As a first step to seeing why, consider the family in 'family values'.

The Nuclear Family

The nuclear family is the 'family values' preferred model. Of relatively recent origin – it is a Western urban industrial phenomenon – it is proving notoriously unsuccessful, because it suffers both structural and ethical flaws. The structural flaw is best described by contrast with what it replaces. For much of history the typical family was (and elsewhere in the world still is) a small community, often consisting of more than two generations of people not always related to each other genetically or by marriage, in which the caretaking of children was effected chiefly by other children, grandparents, servants or economically unproductive (because, say, disabled) members of the household. In such families incest was by no means uncommon (if a man's wife were pregnant or menstruating he might turn to his eldest daughter), and the associated facts of life – disease, mortality, poverty – were familiars. Death gave family life a character quite different from how it now is in the West; it made most childhoods and marriages short.

In the 'family values' nuclear family, psychological and physical burdens are borne by a small inwardly focused group. Traditional extended families were diffuse in structure, offering varieties of channels for managing emotions and resolving conflicts; but the nuclear family intensifies both by diverting them all inwards. To this structural flaw is added an ethical flaw relating to the principles that govern the relationships in this enclosed small group. This is that these relationships are intended to be both permanent and exclusive. Divorce and adultery (not to say the even more problematic ways of relieving the claustrophobia – and hence tensions – of nuclear family life, such as drunkenness, violence and incest) are strongly disapproved of, so not only is the group cooped up together in a small emotional space, but the exits and safety-valves for the resulting pressures are blocked. The results are familiar enough: 'family breakdown' is a lamented commonplace, on which many social ills are blamed. It is a tribute to the human capacity for deceit and self-denial that complete breakdown occurs in 'only' one out of two or three nuclear families, although one does not know what greater costs are sometimes paid in keeping nuclear families together.

In an effort to shore up this inherently unstable family model, the conservative ethic has to stigmatize much that is neutral or even good across the whole range of interpersonal relations and private recreations, not least among them sexuality. The chief aim is to contain the pressures that threaten to explode the nuclear family, if possible by persuading people not to feel them in the first place, but anyway forbidding their expression. A nuclear family works where one of the marital partners is submissive or compromising, and the children are dutiful – and, say, a religious commitment has imposed strong internal controls on temptations that might disrupt these attitudes and the bonds they sustain. A family nourished on religious doctrines which encourage such an outlook is exactly the 'family values' ideal. But it is immediately obvious that it is premised on self-denials and beliefs for which there are no independently good reasons; the only reason for their acceptance is to protect the 'family values' family from breaking down. Urging them, therefore, is rather like urging someone to give up breathing on the grounds that he will never thereafter catch 'flu.

Divorce and Marriage

Because the modern nuclear family figures so importantly in their outlook, moral conservatives are hostile to divorce, which represents the termination – in their view the failure – of a nuclear-family project. Yet divorce is often a good thing; it gives people a chance to start again, or – which is as great a good, if people could only recognize it as such – to live alone: solitary life is not necessarily lonely life, but can be a strong and productive mode of existence, and very peaceful.

Divorce allows freedom and flexibility for everyone, but especially for women, to make changes when change is needed in their domestic arrangements. Marriage without the possibility of divorce is a life-sentence based on decisions made (usually) at a time when the participants' judgement was immature, and anyway influenced by pheromones or fashions. Without divorce, the result is unchangeable, no matter what new circumstances arise. Divorce is often a miserable experience because it signals the loss of affections important to one or both parties; but it is even more wretched when society makes divorce difficult, so adding to the problems of those experiencing it.

Like abortion, divorce is a question of personal freedom. It is about people starting afresh, remedying mistakes, getting back on course with other decisions and choices, to construct lives worth living.

There would be no divorce if there were no marriage. Marriage is a central pillar of the 'family values' view, not merely in the desirable sense of a long-term committed relationship, but as a legally constituted one which controls the age and sex of the parties to it (it says who can enter it, and when), and dictates what they can and must do in it, and on what terms, if any, they can leave it. So viewed, legal marriage looks like a monstrous public interference in personal relations, and it is surprising how many people still go in for it. Aside from their religious interests (and – more trivially – the fun of dressing up for the ceremony, the usefulness of getting presents, or the unmeaning claim that 'getting married shows commitment'), couples asked why, instead of just living together, they choose legal marriage, tend to cite the interests of children they might have. Bastardy considerations might once have made sense of this point, but are an irrelevance now.

The truth, no doubt, is that people continue to marry merely because it is traditional and in so doing they perpetuate an institution which originated for inequitable social and economic reasons, chief among them to control the sexual activity and fertility of women, and thus to ensure that the property men bequeath has a better chance of going to children who are truly theirs.

One-Parent Families

But questions about children's interests always touch a chord, and are therefore important to 'family values' supporters, not only in their defence of nuclear-family marriage but in their correlative attack on one-parent families. Children's interests, they claim, are served best by the former and are at risk in the latter.

Is this true? What matters to children is love, stability, a good diet and opportunities to play and learn. It does not matter how many parents they have or even whether the person or people who look after them are their biological parents, so long as the relationship is a secure and permanent one. Biological parturition is no guarantee of the social skills required for parenting.

The problem with one-parent families is the absence not of one parent, but of resources – in short, poverty. Social hostility – with its roots in religious condemnation – to sex and childbirth outside marriage leaves a stigma, and the result is economic punishment: moral conservatives are reluctant to 'subsidize the irresponsibility' of unmarried women and teenage girls who get pregnant, even more so when they do it more than once. This reluctance amounts, one is obliged to say, to a Canute-like opposition to biological forces. It is in animal nature to mate, and hence sometimes to reproduce; only human animals try to control sexual activity and reproduction for social, religious or moral reasons; and only humans punish deviation from what they have decided, in some place at some point in history, to regard as a norm.

As this point iterates, conservatives use their ideal of the family to promote and justify their views about sex, drugs, abortion and society at large. On each of these questions the 'family values' view is as disputable as its view of the family itself. I consider them in turn.

Sex and Morals

If sexual activity were allowed its natural place in human life it would consume less time and energy than it now does. Sex occupies an absurdly inflated part of the moral horizon, and in many respects is surrounded by muddle and even misery, because prohibitions, anxieties and what amounts to social rationing exaggerate its importance ('the hungry individual thinks only of food'), and in some cases distort it – for frustrated instincts are more prone to seek unusual, sometimes harmful, outlets than more easily satisfiable ones.

The kindness of nature has made sexual activity pleasurable, not just to encourage reproduction but to promote bonding and, plausibly, health also. Our closest primate relatives, bonobo chimpanzees, enjoy frequent sexual encounters as a means of bonding and recreation, just as with humans. Among other primates mating activity is governed by the oestrus cycle, which renders female sexual interest periodic. Otherwise chimpanzees, gorillas, and ourang-outangs do not moralize, still less agonize, about sex, but simply get on with it when hormones prompt.

Matters are greatly more complex with humans, of course, and there is no clear answer to the question: what is the 'natural place' of sex in human life? A woman's potential investment in sexual activity, with its possible sequels of pregnancy and childcare, is so heavy that it seems natural to expect her to be more circumspect than a man about engaging in sex – at very least, when contraception is unavailable or unreliable. If some characteristic kinds of male homosexual activity are any guide to male sexuality in general, men are rather like bonobos in being apt to engage in frequent casual sexual encounters, with little emotional commitment. On this view, the argument might be that heterosexual males differ from their homosexual brothers only in having, as a rule, less opportunity for sex, owing to conventions and the restraints imposed by potential partners.

Studies suggest that, if women's potential investment in sex is reduced by effective contraception and greater economic independence, their behaviour changes. In particular, wherever women attain equal status in business and the professions, their sexual behaviour comes increasingly to resemble that of men – even in such respects as employing prostitutes while on business trips (often female prostitutes, it seems), and in having more casual sexual encounters generally. (The similarities do not end there; it also appears that increasingly many women business executives suffer stress-induced hair-loss.)

There is mildly surprising evidence from a different quarter: that over 30 per cent of children are fathered by someone other than their mother's husband or resident partner. (This information comes from two recent studies in Britain.) Parallel studies show the same pattern among birds. This obviously makes good genetic sense; it appears that among humans nature remains stronger than convention.

These points suggest that men and women differ in sexual behaviour only when the latter are obliged to consider consequences. The advance of science has made these factors contingent, not essential; anatomy is no longer destiny. So everything one wishes to say about sexual morality applies equally to both sexes.

Sex and Society

Sexual activity is not morally neutral in itself; it is – when consensual – a good, because it can be pleasurable and establishes bonds between people. But in some societies, chiefly Judaeo-Christian ones, it is complicated by the influence of ancient beliefs and practices. People are more interested in sex than informed about it, and, while ignorance remains, its urgencies and ecstasies make it equally tempting and threatening. Sexual pleasure, said Aristotle, subverts rationality, and his remark is the premise for persistent anxiety in certain religions: if sex is irrational it is a threat to order and therefore authority. In consequence sexuality has been constrained by laws and customs in many cultures throughout history, with Christianity among the worst offenders. In 1800AD more people were hanged in England for sodomy than for murder; in the Middle East adulterers are still stoned to death; in most countries censorship of art continues on 'obscenity' grounds. As a further consequence, sex is shrouded in hypocrisy, guilt, exploitation, anxiety and perversion, adding fuel to its fires and making it a real rather than merely a perceived problem.

Despite the increased openness which has permitted objective research into human sexuality, there is still no widely accepted theory about it upon which personal decision or public policy-making can rely. Yet there has never existed greater need for such a theory, because sex-related dilemmas currently offer Western society dramatic challenges: AIDS, venereal diseases, abortion, contraception, surrogate motherhood, artificial fertilization, homosexual demands for the right to marry and adopt children, teenage sex and pregnancy, sexual harassment, marital and 'date' rape, child abuse, pornography – the list of concerns is long, and even so omits the fact that 'ordinary' sexual relations are themselves still subject to repressive and muddled thinking.

One attempt to understand the place of sex in social life applies to it the theory of rational choice, where 'rational' means the appropriate fitting, conscious or otherwise, of means to ends. It may seem quixotic to apply such a theory to sex, given assumptions about the latter's irrationality, but although sexual instincts are indeed at least non-rational, the strategies people adopt to satisfy them are otherwise. Consider the analogy of hunger: we do not will hunger, but we take thought about appeasing it.

Such theorists offer analyses in cost-benefit terms. Among the benefits of sex are pleasure and progeny; among the costs, the effort of finding a mate, defeating rivals and tending offspring. A simple example is afforded by 'opportunistic homosexuality' among prisoners who, usually heterosexual, behave homosexually because in the circumstances benefits outweigh cost. So stated, the theory seems simplistic, but studies employing the model are surprisingly powerful in explaining differences in, for example, styles of marriage and prostitution in different societies. One unsurprising conclusion is that the status of women is a principal determinant. In societies where wives are uneducated and much younger than husbands, companionate marriage does not exist, so sex is formal and occasional. Women are sequestered to 'protect their virtue', but men are freely permitted extra-marital sex. In societies where women have high status, as in the contemporary West, companionate marriage is the norm, so that courtesan services are no longer in demand, and prostitution becomes a source of variety or specialist sex supplementing (even, on some views, protecting) marriage.

Such theories provide useful perspectives, but they have not freed sexual attitudes from ancient taboos and restrictions. Public nudity is a crime; public exposure of genitals by a live human male is regarded with peculiar horror; elaborate social and legal barriers control how, when, where and with whom sexual activity is permissible. People are taught to be offended by public displays of sex; a person who might be shocked to see copulation at the roadside will watch it in a film, shielded by the relative unreality of celluloid. These attitudes, as a result not least of religious moral teaching over centuries, are deeply ingrained.

Relationships

Sex both creates relationships and – because of the taboos and anxieties that surround it – destroys them. In Western societies marriage and marriage-like partnerships are based on mutual attraction; what we call romance is, in prosaic dress, sexual infatuation prompted more by biochemistry than by conscious choice. Infatuation is the hot torch that first welds people together; but passion is temporary, and the interesting question is: what conjunction remains when the alloy has cooled? If infatuation matures into friendship, the basis of the settled domestic affections is to hand. But lovers not infrequently find that, when the blaze of desire dies, only ashes remain; and they sensibly move on.

But what of sex and the domestic affections? As noted above in connection with 'family values', the monogamous principle in Judaeo-Christian societies is an attempt to preserve the family, but because of its restrictive view of sex it often achieves the opposite. Monogamy entails 'sexual fidelity', which means restriction of one's sexual expression exclusively to one other person.

Historically, women were the main target of this restriction, to ensure that their offspring genetically belonged to their husbands; but it is chiefly in Christianity that it applies also to men. For both men and women it is an unnatural and unkind arrangement, especially after initial sexual infatuation quietens and normal interest in the wider world returns. By linking sexuality with the domestic emotions and the social institution of monogamous marriage – along with expectations of mutual lifelong romance, which infidelity is believed to destroy – the settled domestic relationships become a trade-off: if you desire to form and pre-serve such a relationship, you must cramp or deny your normal sexual expression.

This is an absurd, often a destructive, and sometimes a tragic confusion of two quite different matters. In practice this Judaeo-Christian attempt to restrict sex is largely unsuccessful: most parties to marriage-like relationships have affairs, commit adul-tery, visit prostitutes, or somehow circumvent the restriction, having to be deceitful and hypocritical in the process – thereby risking damage to their domestic relationships, which is what few of them desire. So in a 'family values' dispensation the choices for combining nature's kindly gift of sex with the great pleasures and benefits of domestic relationships are: (a) marriage breakdown, or (b) deceit and hypocrisy, or (c) an unnatural self-denial.

The principal solutions are so-called 'open marriage', or a sec-ond partner (a lover). It is claimed that the former does not work; we certainly hear of the failures, but the successes only become apparent when we read biographies. In the monogamous Western tradition, where sexual attitudes are so ingrained that few can think differently, such arrangements are little tolerated. Accord-ingly, one has to suppose that the best alternative to hypocrisy is discretion and good manners – of the kind that civilized couples have anyway always practised.

But obviously it would be best if, first, it were recognized that domestic relations do not essentially depend on (keeping up the pretence of) sexual fidelity, and secondly, if society was rescued from the view that one person is entitled to exclusive ownership of another's sexual expression. The painful choice – the tragic conflict – that this view forces is an evil. The desideratum is to live in a dispensation of things where the settled domestic affections are not inconsistent with normal human sexuality.

None of this denies the importance of fidelity in domestic relationships, in the sense of commitment to a partnership of shared life and goals, and of deep mutual private loyalties. Much of the value in domestic affection rests on the security thus provided. But fidelity in this sense is not the same thing as exclusive ownership of another's sexual expression. This essential point is, at great cost, almost universally overlooked.

In most other cultures in the world the problem is solved – except in very few cases, for men only – by polygamy, concubinage or the social acceptability of extra-marital sex. If saner attitudes were to prevail in the West, it would have to be equitably between the sexes; the removal of anatomy from destiny, as remarked above, makes this possible. And as implied by the opening remarks, taking the pressure off sex would undoubtedly make it loom less large in general. Moral conservatives of course think the opposite; they think they would be stepping over writhing couples in every street, which is why they keep the motors of our present unsatisfactory dispensation running.

Homosexuality and Prostitution

Two of the largest margins of sexual life, homosexuality and prostitution, have always been targets for moral conservatives, who for millennia have succeeded in turning the weight not just of custom but of law against both. In the Judaeo-Christian tradition prostitutes were sometimes stoned to death. No single method for killing homosexuals regularly established itself, although hanging later became usual. It is a profound anomaly that classical Greece, a civilization admired by the West and claimed as its cultural ancestor, permitted – indeed encouraged – not merely homosexuality but pederasty. There are contemporary non-Western cultures where similar views remain; in one Papuan society, for example, it is the practice for men to 'supply seed' to boys entrusted to their tutelage, so that they can father children in their turn. This is a literal version of what the Greeks saw in more educational terms (although the relationship between men and boys in Greece was usually physical).

These are customs many will think well superseded. It is a pity history is so selective, though; for just one example of something infinitely more vile which, nevertheless, contemporary moral conservatives tolerate with equanimity – some indeed regularly practise it – consider the genital mutilation of millions of boys and girls which flourishes today in religious practices of circumcision.

The case against homosexuality is that it is 'unnatural'. The argument is simple: male and female sex organs are mutually adapted anatomically for the purpose of reproduction. Since the organs of two men or two women are not thus adapted, and cannot result in reproduction, congress of any kind between them is 'unnatural'. The same reasoning prohibits heterosexual practices which do not have reproduction as a possible outcome.

If this argument were generalized, it would be disgusting – and by parity of reasoning ought therefore to be illegal – to ride a bicycle or blow a whistle, since these activities are not what legs or lips are biologically 'for'.

But the best analogy is eating. We eat to nourish our bodies; but also to enjoy tastes and textures, to relax, to meet friends, to converse. One needs just so many calories and vitamins each day, but one also enjoys sampling Indian and Chinese and Italian cuisines. One may discover a taste for Chinese, and a distaste for Indian, food. So it is with sex. It is natural to enjoy sexual pleasure, as it is to enjoy food; and the purpose of sex, as with eating, is not exclusively the minimum which either is 'for'.

These points show that appeals to 'nature' provide no ground for hostility to homosexuality. The real source of hostility is religious and social, and, as we have seen, only *some* religions and societies are hostile. In them the result is, or has frequently been, persecution of individuals on the mere ground of their difference from the majority in regard to taste or choice.

Hostility to homosexuality has a number of sources, but one of them is that it threatens the model of interpersonal relations at the core of the 'family values' ethos. Hostility to prostitution (chiefly in the realms of Anglophone Protestant Christianity) has the same roots. Yet the irony is that prostitution at least in part flourishes precisely because of 'family values' – as suggested above, by providing one way of releasing the pressures caused by nuclear-family life under a restrictive sexual morality.

In some American states, and in Britain, prostitution remains legally circumscribed, the legal sanctions expressing the opposition and disgust of moral conservatives. As a result it is riper for the hands of organized crime. Except for its financial aspects, the casual, uncommitted nature of interaction between prostitutes and their clients mirrors the cottaging experience of homosexual men, which, as noted, perhaps says something about the nature of male sexuality in general. This appears to be recognized by society, which implicitly accepts what is sometimes described as the 'hygienic' function of prostitution; but it does so in secret and shame, which means that the question is not sensibly addressed, but fudged. It is obvious on the least reflection that prostitution should be legal, not only to enhance the health and safety of both practitioners and clients, but also to end waste of police time and burdening of the legal system. All the reasons moral conservatives have for wishing to control prostitution legally – the supposed threat to family life, the supposed threat to minors, and the fact that girls might be forced into sex work by economic conditions or exploitative pimps – will remain whether or not prostitution is legal, with the one difference that the third of these will always be much worse if it is illegal.

It must be supposed that some of those who work in the sex industry do so by choice. They provide a service which will always be in demand, and, because they might wish to work together with colleagues in safe and comfortable surroundings, it seems only sensible to allow brothels. In societies where prostitution is legal there has been no social collapse of the kind moral conservatives fear. States with restrictive laws might take that fact alone as a reason to reconsider.

Pornography

The same considerations apply to pornography, defined as 'sexually explicit material designed to cause sexual arousal'. In countries with liberal laws on pornography there has been no social implosion, so one main argument against it collapses. There are other and better arguments against it: that it conveys abusive images of women, and involves exploitation of the people who produce it. These points are important, for abuse and exploitation are evils. But they are evils because they are abuse and exploitation, not because they involve sex. If there were sexually explicit material made by happy people who grew rich providing a service to contented clients, it would on this reasoning be unexceptionable. If pornography were legal, the likelihood of its being produced in an exploitative way diminishes.

Some feminists, in unaccustomed alliance with conservatives and the Churches, oppose liberalization of pornography on the ground not just that it involves a denigrating portrayal of women, but that this promotes rape and violence against them. Here again what is objectionable is the denigration and the violence, rather than the sexual content of either. One can make a case against any group being portrayed in any such way; and one can and should resolutely combat incitements to harm. At the same time, it has to be possible that there should be sexually explicit material which does not incite to hatred or violence. The facts again speak for themselves; in countries where restrictions on pornography have been lifted – for example Denmark – violent sexual crime has diminished.

There is a struggle within feminism itself over the nature and legitimacy of attitudes to pornography, and by association to female heterosexuality in general. A premise of one strand in radical feminism has been that heterosexuality is a vehicle of male exploitation and is therefore intrinsically wrong, like a modern version of original sin. To be properly free, this argument goes, women must free themselves from heterosexuality. In urging their sisters to deny access to their bodies – allegedly regarded by men as mere receptacles for their secretions and desires – feminists taught their sisters to think of their own bodies as dustbins and betrayers: dustbins, because of what men variously wish to deposit in them; and betrayers, because women's bodies desire those deposits.

But increasingly there are women who want what feminists want for womankind – justice, equality, respect – who also wish to enjoy their heterosexuality without guilt. One way to do so is to accept the nature, and assert the value, of female heterosexuality as part of repudiating ill-based, harmful, outdated attitudes to human sexuality in general. One source of the oppressive nature of relations between the sexes is the traditional morality of a social arrangement that feminist thinkers have correctly identified as 'patriarchal' – that is, as serving the interests of a male-oriented perspective on relations between the sexes, justified and defended by conservative morality.

Consent and Reform

Everything so far amounts to saying that sex is an amenity of life which we handle badly and should allow to go free, whereupon we will soon find it less of a preoccupation. But the subject cannot be left without registering the point, obvious but important, that sex is only a good when it is consensual.

The worst examples of non-consensual sex are rape and what might be called constructive rape, which occurs when the consent given is not properly informed or free. Into this second category fall many cases of child abuse, because it cannot be plausible to think that children – depending on age or level of understanding – are in as good a position as normally placed older people to reflect on the choices involved. This degree of paternalism is justified by the fact that, even if some children are in fact so placed, it is better to start with the reverse assumption as a way of protecting interests prospectively.

Rape and sexual abuse are peculiarly horrible because they violate physical and psychological privacy, and in the latter case trust also. If the one great sin is harm to others, these crimes are close to murder.

It is painfully obvious that legal and social attitudes to consensual sexual activity need reform. Given the way law has been called in aid by moral conservatives over the centuries to restrict or prohibit human sexuality or steer it in the direction of their own tastes and prejudices, reform is especially needed in all those jurisdictions still influenced by their legacy. These are chiefly the Anglophone Western jurisdictions.

Consider the fact that sodomy between consenting males over the age of twenty-one is legal in Britain, but between men and women is punishable by life imprisonment. (Matters are still worse for offenders in Georgia USA; they can be executed.) This is not the only anomaly in the law relating to sexual matters, but since it is in effect a dead letter it is far from the most serious. The age of consent for homosexuals, their rights to marry one another and to adopt children, are far more pressing questions; and so is the confusion over marital and date rape, pornography, obscenity, and prostitution. In each of these areas reform is required to liberate attitudes as much as practices, and to alleviate the tensions that make them problematic.

One of the barriers to reform is the existence of the tabloid press. Its rabid attitudes and the hypocritical way it titillates readers about what it pretends to condemn – 'Vicar in sex romp with choirboys' – mean that politicians, not a notably courageous race, are reluctant to institute reform, having no wish to prompt such headlines as 'government opens floodgates to vice'. The tabloid press subverts discussion of important public questions, a fact we have had to learn to live with; but on the question of bringing sanity and humanity into the law there can be no temporizing.

The tabloid formula of salaciousness masquerading as moral outrage is not however the main barrier to reform. The main barrier is that queer beast 'public opinion', which the media half follow and half form. 'Public opinion' is in reality the opinion of a decided and emphatic minority, whose claim to the moral high ground, usually staked in the name of religion and organized into effective lobbies – as in the United States – makes it formidable. Moral conservatives succeed in giving enough of the rest of us an uneasy feeling that *perhaps* such-and-such is wrong; and a seed of doubt is sufficient for inaction, because few are courageous in matters they have not much pondered, and it always seems easier to follow what appears to be majority opinion than to be isolated. For this reason, liberal reform has to be not just generous but bold.

Drugs

This is an appropriate point to comment on another topic that exercises moral conservatives, because it affords a good illustration of the way conservatism creates rather than solves problems. The topic is drugs. Actually, neither the use nor the abuse of drugs,

legal or otherwise, is a moral problem; it is, rather, a practical one
– although in a quite different way one might regard the *abuse* of
drugs as an ethical problem.

By 'drugs' I mean opium and its derivatives, cocaine and such
substances as LSD, 'Ecstasy', amphetamines, solvents, tranquilliz-
ers and anything else people use to alter their states of mind and
mood, whether they become addicted to them or not; and so the
list includes alcohol, nicotine and caffeine. Drugs fall into three
classes depending upon whether they are narcotic, stimulant or
hallucinogenic in effect. There are many other substances in what
we eat and drink that have such effects, but they are generally
much milder.

The distinction drawn between substances now controlled by
law and those that are not is the result not of principle but of
history, and is otherwise arbitrary. Alcohol and nicotine are arguably more dangerous to health than marijuana, and the latter has
been found to have medicinal value – as have the opium derivatives and cocaine for analgesia and anaesthesia. So the reason
alcohol and nicotine are legal (for adults) while the latter are not
is simply that they have been used more widely and for longer in
Western societies, and efforts to ban them have proved unacceptable to the populace. The distinction is therefore not a well-based
one, so already the rationality of public policy on drug use and
misuse is questionable.

Drugs first came under legal control in Britain in 1868, not to
regulate their use but to protect the professional status of pharmacists, who desired the sole right to dispense them. Opium was
widely used in the form of laudanum, and heroin was developed
from opium towards the end of the century. During the First
World War soldiers in the trenches of Flanders and Picardy tempered the horrors they faced by using opiates and – as did Freud
in fact and Sherlock Holmes in fiction – cocaine. This prompted a
Defence of the Realm Act banning the public sale of these drugs
for the first time. Anti-drug legislation thus began as a means of
ensuring that young men would be fit to murder one another. For
several decades prior to 1914 moral conservatives had been cam-
paigning in Britain and America for prohibition – principally of
alcohol, but there also existed a British society for the suppression
of cocaine. The war gave them their chance; their time had at last

come. In the United States the great folly of Prohibition was enacted almost immediately after the war, and in the same mood laws began to be passed in most Western countries against opiates, cocaine and marijuana.

Since then many substances have joined the list. When these laws were first enacted in the 1920s the incidence of drug use and abuse was relatively small, and in the case of addiction was regarded rather as a medical than a legal problem. One result of the prohibition of drugs has been more rapid growth in their use, by the familiar mechanisms of marketing by criminal organizations, and the attractiveness of the forbidden.

The disaster of Prohibition in America should have taught the world lessons enough on this score. Not only does prohibition lay the foundations of a massive criminal industry, but it turns millions of ordinary people into law-breakers also, and imposes high costs in money and human life.

In the case of alcohol prohibition these developments were rapid; when Prohibition was lifted, the criminal gangs it created turned to other activities, including drug-running. Here development was slower, but as sure. The business practice of creating and fostering a market for commodities is followed by illegitimate just as by legitimate businesses. Selling all kinds of drugs – alcohol and cigarettes as well as cocaine and marijuana – includes focus on the young, making their use fashionable and desirable. All these substances provide relief from the pressures and complexities of life, and induce states that are intrinsically pleasant. Add a garnish of social disapproval, and their attractions are complete.

The criminalization of drugs thus creates an enormous problem where a far lesser one previously existed. By providing opportunities for organized crime, and turning many users into criminals – principally those who become addicted and who therefore have to work hard at mugging or theft to pay for their habit – it entangles the police, courts and customs authorities in mighty and expensive labours.

All these problems would be abolished at a stroke by decriminalization. What would follow? Would the entire populace suddenly become addicted to heroin? Of course not. Most people who wish to take drugs already do so; most people who regularly consume currently legal drugs – alcohol, nicotine, caffeine – do so sensibly, and manage to lead normal lives despite their addictions and the health problems that follow. Just as one encourages people not to smoke or drink excessively, so one would encourage people not to take heroin or cocaine; and just as one prosecutes people for driving a motor-car or causing a public nuisance under the influence of alcohol, so one would prosecute those who misbehaved under the influence of cocaine or LSD.

I suggested that drug *ab*use is not a moral problem, but an ethical one. By this I mean that people who depend upon (rather than occasionally employ for recreational purposes) exogenous chemical means of attaining well-being or fulfilment, or to escape from difficulties, are in a sad case, either because they genuinely need the support of the community in some respect, or because they lack the intelligence or courage to attain life's satisfactions under their own steam. Dependence on readily ingestible sources of life's amenities, at least in any regular way, therefore strikes me as either pitiable or contemptible. But neither is a reason for making it illegal.

Forbidding people to eat or drink what they wish, or to seek certain pleasures, is a gross form of interference. One must suggest limits, exactly as one does with alcohol: on the age at which people might be supposed capable of informed choices, and on the acceptable degree of the public consequence of making those choices, under the ever-present condition that what anyone does must not interfere with or harm others. But, although there can be justification for regulating matters in these minimal ways, there can be none for forbidding them.

This discussion illustrates two points. The first is that prohibition is a creator of problems, not their solution. This insight applies almost universally. To lift prohibitions is not to deregulate entirely; any group of people who discussed their joint and several interests reasonably among themselves would conclude that certain minimum rules are required. But the presumption has to be on the side of permission, not prohibition; every limitation has to be exceedingly well justified.

The second point expands the ethical remark already made. It is that we may not wish, and in the clearest picture of ourselves ought not to wish, to be people fundamentally dependent on quick outside fixes for our reliefs and satisfactions. This is a point about autonomy: if you are a heroin addict, your well-being is at the mercy of a powder; you are in a heteronymous state, governed by something external. The good life for an individual must include self-government to the maximum degree consistent with its community setting. A life of dependency on drugs, whether alcohol or heroin, is not such a life, and seems a peculiarly feeble and contemptible way to live.

Death, Life and Dogma

The problems so far discussed are problems about life and living. Problems about death and dying seem even more vexed, not least because they are more influenced by religious attitudes. The lack of clarity in discussion of the ethics of death reflects the subject's emotional significance; it is no surprise that the liberal-conservative disagreement here is especially sharp.

Euthanasia and Assisted Suicide

Although there are some accidents and diseases that kill people quickly, and although the mechanisms of senescence can bring gentle endings to life, it is also and often the case that dying is protracted, difficult and painful, sometimes involving unendurable physical and psychological distress. In such cases it is not only the victims who suffer, but the loving witnesses.

Contrast the case in which a person has elected to die before some paralysing disease has made speech or swallowing impossible, or before age has leached away the mind so that the remaindered husk trembles and drools, perhaps fractionally aware of its indignities. In this case the subject is able to say farewell, to share the parting, and to go with the painless ease that medical science can so simply provide. It is a devoutly wishable consummation.

Here is an actual such case. A woman in her seventies, agonizingly crippled but alert despite reliance on drugs, considered her predicament, balanced it with the pleasures that life still afforded – and chose to die before these last were gone too. After discussion, her family and closest friends accepted her decision. In the week before the chosen day they came to see her, and wrote affectionate letters; on the day itself there was a gathering, with reminiscences and poetry, and farewells. Then she was left with friends who had agreed to administer the barbiturates and sit with her. As she slipped into unconsciousness they read aloud and held her hands; within an hour she stopped breathing.

This is a case of assisted suicide, which is the best form of euthanasia in that it has the conscious elective participation of the subject. Involuntary euthanasia occurs when someone is unable to express the desire to die, but is in such a terrible state that a quick means of ending life is administered. There are many cases where both forms of euthanasia are completely justified. In jurisdictions where, nevertheless, euthanasia is illegal (even if widely practised; which is almost everywhere – for human pity is stronger than the law), many people are needlessly condemned to suffering by the chief anti-euthanasia argument: that legalized euthanasia might be abused.

And so indeed it might. Is that a reason for letting unrelievable suffering continue or increase? Or is it a reason for so arranging matters that abuse (everything, legal or otherwise, is open to at least some abuse: humans are endlessly ingenious) is minimized?

Opponents of euthanasia imagine that inconveniently ageing parents will be destroyed like unwanted kittens; that hard-pressed hospitals will routinely increase morphine dosages not just in clearly terminal cases but in long-drawn, doubtful, expensive ones too; that the ill, in a temporary fit of gloom, will make a mistakenly permanent decision; that someone will ask for a last injection just weeks before a medical breakthrough. These anxieties increase the sum of human agony throughout the tender-minded West. In poor countries, where there is not the technology to prolong life, the dilemma arises less often. What makes the euthanasia debate more acute is precisely the fact that we are technically able both to kill and to keep alive with relative facility. It is the endless medical dilemma: should we do or not do what we can do? Does 'can' ever mean 'must', and if so, when?

The rule here should be that, when we are satisfied that euthanasia is the right, merciful, humane course, we should do it. It is not beyond human wit to devise thoughtful controls. There will be difficult cases; there could be mistakes; abuse might occur. But that is par for the course in human affairs. The belief that it is mere quantity of life that matters blinds us to the recognition that we can and must accept defeasibility in the euthanasia case as we do everywhere else. One act of genuine mercy, in which we help a person escape agony or indignity or both, will justify us.

Abortion

At the other end of life matters are complicated by our instinctive tenderness towards babies. 'Pro-lifers' make frank use of emotive appeals in describing abortion as slaughter of the innocent. The truth is that abortion is always difficult and unpleasant, for it does indeed involve the ending of a form of human life. But this fact does not make it invariably wrong. There are many hard things we have to do that are necessary or justified – in the name of compassion too, for a foetus always competes with established human interests and goals. Cases of deformed foetuses or endangered mothers seem most clear. Cases of (for example) pregnant schoolgirls seem more difficult; but here the rule should surely be to protect the actual commitments and projects of a present person, in balance with which the multiplying cells within her at most represent a potentiality. Of course this does not make the potentiality null; we accord rights of a kind even to the not-yet-conceived when we give future generations a claim on us to protect the environment in their interest. So *a fortiori* the conceived have claims too. This means that abortion can never be taken lightly, as when it is used for tidying up irresponsibilities in contraception.

But very few women take abortion lightly, and many are hurt by the experience; yet most of them maintain, on sober reflection, that in the circumstances they made the right choice between continuing their lives as then situated, or undergoing the dramatic alteration that parenthood involves – even when the child is adopted, for the psychological burden of that can be massive.

Opposition to abortion is not exclusively religious, but religion is one of its chief sources. Life is regarded as sacred because God-given, so ending it is a sin. This view does not allow that to create a lifetime of suffering is a far greater sin, as it is – say – to require a woman already overburdened with caring for other children to add to their number. It is not the sanctity of life (whatever that means: for it is not invoked in the conservative view on capital punishment and legitimate war) but the quality of life that really matters; and this last figures centrally among the justifications for abortion.

Religion

Because so much of the moral outlook labelled 'conservative' in preceding sections has its root in religious tradition – in particular the Judaeo-Christian – a comment on it is appropriate. There are no doubt sincere believers who find solace and inspiration in their faith, and who do good because of it. To them the spectacle of religion's terrible record of bloodshed, cruelty and intolerance – throughout history, and still in this present day – must be painful. But religious beliefs do not rely upon rationality for their acceptance; so it is not surprising that faith visits violence upon its heretics and opponents, for its roots lie in emotion. These roots lie especially in ignorance and fear; religion began as the science and technology of earliest man, who, surrounded by fearsome nature, devised explanations of the universe ('it was made by an agency like us, only invisible and much stronger'), and a means of controlling (by prayer and sacrifice) its phenomena – especially the weather, so vital to life. The moralities that exist to ease human relationships came to be enshrined as divine commands, disobedience to which was seen as a threat to the precarious abeyance of storm and earthquake which, as God's anger, always impended.

Thus the source of much contemporary moral conservatism. But religion is in fact either irrelevant to questions of morality, or it is positively immoral. This claim undoubtedly seems contradictory at first, but a little reflection shows otherwise.

In an individualistic society, where personal wealth is the chief if not the sole measure of achievement, a morality that tells you to give all your possessions to the poor, that says it is easier for a camel to go through a needle's eye than for the rich to enter heaven, that preaches selflessness towards one's neighbour and complete obedience to a deity – such a morality is wholly opposed to the norms and practices not just accepted but extolled in Western society. Most people therefore simply ignore the staring contrast between such views and today's comfortable materialism, and pursue the latter. In this way religious morality is an irrelevance.

But when fundamentalists add preparedness to incarcerate women, mutilate genitals, amputate hands, murder, bomb and terrorize in the name of their faiths, religion becomes positively immoral.

Much religious energy seems to be devoted to controlling our sexual behaviour, either by disallowing it (or thoughts or representations of it) other than in strictly limited circumstances, or by preventing the amelioration of its consequences once it has happened. Thus, the righteous write complaining letters about televised nudity, while tons of armaments are exported from the factory next door to their homes to regions of the world gripped by poverty and civil war. With such examples and contrasts, religion has little to offer moral debate.

Some think that a deity is required to provide grounds for morality: 'such and such is good (or bad) because God says so'. But as Bertrand Russell succinctly argued, 'Theologians have always taught that God's decrees are good, and that this is not a mere tautology: it follows that goodness is logically independent of God's decrees.' It might be added that if the will of God is the ground of morality, one's reason for being moral is merely prudential; it consists in a desire to escape punishment. But this, though sensible enough, is hardly a satisfactory basis for the ethical life – and threats are never logically compelling premises for any argument.

Blasphemy

If it were argued that religions set moral examples unparalleled by secular faiths such as political movements, the claim would be easily refuted; as noted, religions fare no better than most secular outlooks, and much worse than some – humanism, for example, has killed no one for disagreeing with it. One might quote 'by their fruits ye shall know them': one of the chief threats posed by religious militants is their use of the concept of blasphemy, even to the extent of justifying murder.

If I impugn your gods, in your view I blaspheme. So if a missionary alien comes to a Christian country and tells its devout citizens that their belief in virgin birth, miracles and resurrection is childish nonsense, and that they should instead worship (say) the horned toad, he would be branded a blasphemer. The alien, of course, would retort the charge on his accusers' heads. And so it would continue, until either he or they were reduced to cinders at some convenient stake.

Blasphemy comes into existence when someone's utterances give a special kind of offence to others, the offence typically consisting in a perceived insult to something cherished as divine. But it depends on cases; and it always takes two – a giver and a receiver of offence – to make blasphemy possible. It is, in essentials, a product of conflicts between perceptions. The perceptions are subjective, shaped by tradition and often associated with cultural identity.

Because what counts as blasphemous depends so heavily on relativities and (non-rational) subjective commitments of faith, blasphemy is not a fit matter for law. Blasphemy laws, like those relating to obscenity and censorship, are instruments for controlling ideas; which implies, if anything, that blasphemy is healthy because it is an expression of free speech, and demonstrates the maturing of an intellectual community from one level of belief and practice to another.

Solutions: Education and Society

The Loss of Civility

The foregoing merely samples the contrast, from a liberal point of view, between attitudes to some familiar moral concerns. Earlier it was claimed that the real question is not one of morality, but of ethics: a question of how we can live flourishingly as whole persons, and in ways that respect the choices of others and their differences from us. To consider this point a different angle of approach is required, one that takes into account the medium in which ethical lives can be lived: the medium of an ethical society.

Consider the following suggestion. Despite appearances, the Western world is not undergoing a new immoral age: rather, it is suffering a different phenomenon, namely, a loss of civility, an arrears of good manners. What is often regarded as moral collapse or decay is no such thing; Western societies at the opening of the twenty-first century are no worse, and by many measures better, in 'moral' respects than a hundred or so years earlier: compare (say) Victorian London's sweatshops, swarms of child prostitutes and violent street muggers. Rather, what has happened is a threatened collapse of what makes the social machine function – a breakdown of the mutual tolerance and respect that allows room and opportunity in a complex plural society for individuals to choose their own way.

This is an important point. Civility is a matter of mores, enshrining ways for us to treat each other with respect and consideration, giving us rituals that facilitate our interactions. Youths spitting on the pavement and swearing on buses offer merely superficial symptoms of the loss of civility; more serious are such things as invasion of privacy by tabloid newspapers, and irruptions into areas of personal life irrelevant to public concerns

– for example, exposés of the sex lives of political figures. If anything, although our age is a moralistic one, it is not an age comfortable with itself, for it suffers problems in both the cohesion and the latitude that makes society work. The consequence is division, and abrasion between the resulting fragments.

Of course, civility, in its most obvious manifestation of politeness, can be a mask; it has always been open to abuse, and if we relearned our manners it would continue so; but that does not change the good it does. It helps foster a society that behaves well in itself, whose members respect and take seriously the intrinsic value of the individual and the rights of people different from themselves.

Civil Society

The point of civil society is best understood by contrasting it with a situation in which there are deliberately no institutions for governing relations between individuals and groups: namely, anarchy, defined as an absence of structures maintaining a social and legal order, by compulsory means if necessary. One might, in brief and collectively, call such structures the 'state'. On a typical anarchist view, the state is to be replaced by a network of voluntary associations, unconstrained and unregulated by anything beyond good will between individuals.

The central weakness in the anarchist view is that individuals are to some degree self-interested, and not all self-interest is indefensible or irrational. The same applies to groups, such as families or tribes. Sympathies are limited, and so are resources; competition between individuals and groups is therefore inevitable. Competition can, and often does, lead to conflict. So unless there are rules to ensure fair competition and a just resolution of conflicts, the strong will trample the weak and injustice will prevail.

The anarchist's belief that people can live in unregulated mutual harmony is touching but naive. To his inadequate moral psychology he adds pieties about 'freedom' as the aim of the anarchic dispensation; but he fails to see that freedoms worth having require protection because of their vulnerability, and that it is precisely in pursuit of genuine liberties that people congregate into civil society and agree rules. The anarchist's mistake is to think that because tyranny is hateful the state should be abolished. A more rational idea is to abolish not the state but tyranny, by making the state fairer and freer, thus protecting its members from the depredations of the greedy and the vile, who are too numerous among us to make anarchy even a remotely serious option.

This is not to say that the liberal civil polity just envisaged is easy to devise or to run, because the very reasons that make it desirable also threaten its existence. Such a society is by definition pluralist, and pluralism means the coexistence of often irreconcilable and conflicting values. We might believe or hope that such can be resolved by the exercise of reasoned tolerance, thus achieving harmony. But conflict and the damage that results from it is almost certainly unavoidable.

Enlightenment thinkers believed that, by the use of reason, mankind can identify universal goals for itself, and both discover and apply the means of achieving them. They believed that science and rationality can overcome superstition, depotism, inequality and war. This faith was strongly opposed by critics who argued that different peoples have different needs and aims, and that there are no universal standards of reason and therefore no ultimate solutions for the dilemmas faced by humanity. If one accepted this latter opinion, one would have to accept that a liberal society is only one form of human possibility, with no special status *vis-à-vis* others; whereas what our earlier thoughts suggested was that such a society provides the best opportunity for the ethical life.

Here therefore one has to take a stand (as with human rights) and argue that although conflicts and difficulties are endemic to the human condition, it remains worthwhile quietly to push the claims of reasoned tolerance as a means of solving or at least managing them. Even if the critics of Enlightenment values are right – even if the relativist view that certain values are mutually irreconcilable is true, and even if there is no clear answer to how a given present dilemma should be resolved – still we can say that tolerance and reason are our best hopes for maintaining that subtle and constantly renegotiated equilibrium upon which the existence of civil society depends.

Liberal Education

To achieve a civil society, as the appropriate medium of ethical life, requires liberal education. By 'liberal education' I mean one that includes literature, history and appreciation of the arts, and gives them equal weight with scientific and practical subjects. Education in these pursuits opens the possibility for us to live more reflectively and knowledgeably, especially about the range of human experience and sentiment, as it exists now and here, and in the past and elsewhere. That, in turn, makes us better understand the interests, needs and desires of others, so that we can treat them with respect and sympathy, however different the choices they make or the experiences that have shaped their lives. When respect and sympathy is returned, rendering it mutual, the result is that the gaps which can prompt friction, even war, come to be bridged or at least tolerated. The latter is enough.

The vision is utopian; no doubt there were SS officers who read Goethe and listened to Beethoven, and then went to work in the gas chambers; so liberal education does not automatically produce better people. But it does so far more often than the stupidity and selfishness which arises from lack of knowledge and impoverishment of insight.

Liberal education is a vanishing ideal in the contemporary West, most notably in its Anglophone regions. Education is mainly restricted to the young, and it is no longer *liberal* education as such but something less ambitious and too exclusively geared to the specific aims – otherwise of course very important – of employability. This is a loss; for the aim of liberal education is to produce people who *go on* learning after their formal education has ceased; who think, and question, and know how to find answers when they need them. This is especially significant in the case of political and moral dilemmas in society, which will always occur and will always have to be negotiated afresh every time; so members of a community need to be reflective and informed.

Educating at a high level is expensive, and demands major investment by a society. But attaining the goal of high-quality education offers glittering prizes. It promises to produce a greater proportion of people who are more than mere foot-solders in the economic struggle, by helping them both to get and to give more in their social and cultural experience, to have lives more fulfilling and participatory both in work and outside it – especially in the amenities of social intercourse, and in the responsibilities of civic and political engagement. (Recall Aristotle's remark that education is important because it helps us to make noble use of our leisure.) People who are better informed and more reflective are more likely to be considerate than those who are – and who are allowed to remain – ignorant, narrow-minded, selfish and *uncivil* in the profound sense that characterizes so much human experience now.

The Medium of Ethical Life

One thing such a society needs to be is an equitable one, in which the distribution of social benefits reflects the worth of individuals' contributions. In Western society the head of a large corporation earns the same in a year as fifty nurses together do. It is possible that this strange fact is consistent with the idea of a good and just society, where the climate of expectations about relationships between people results in recognition of genuine merit, mutual respect for rights and willing fulfilment of obligations. But it does not give confidence that Western society is such a society, nor even that it is developing into one; rather the contrary.

The aim of ethics is to identify conceptions of lives worth living – whole lives, well lived, satisfying and rounded. This needs the right setting: a society that tolerates diversity, allows opportunities, agrees – in a rational, generous and enlightened manner – where the limits are; and is just. It is hopelessly utopian to expect that, even if an ideal medium came into existence, all those living in it would be transformed. The workings of social institutions cannot replace the ethical endeavours individuals have to make on their own account; indeed, by making choices and controlling activities on behalf of its members a society negates the very basis of ethics: the great tyrannies of recent history demonstrate this point with painful clarity. But in fostering a climate of aspiration towards ethical goals, a society can produce a current in the general drift, which draws along some of those afloat in it. It can educate and encourage; and where what it encourages is the willed insistence on values of reason, tolerance and fulfilment, it offers a beacon to some, and a standard for all.

Prediction Again

An optimist might say that the liberal case sketched in this essay has a better chance of winning in future because increased literacy and global communications will overcome the narrow and backward-looking sentiments from which conservatism draws its nourishment. A pessimist might say that as the world grows more complex, beset by too much information and too rapid change, people will wish to retreat into certainties, and to seek stability in moral austerity. Only the ancient dogmas of religion provide certainties, and they also provide satisfying and (to believers) compelling reasons for restricting and controlling whole ranges of human behaviour.

I think both will happen; the age-old conflict between the liberal and conservative impulses will continue. The reasons for these historical oscillations are complicated, having much to do with social organization and economics, in which religious moral doctrines have long played a powerful role on the side of infusing discipline into social arrangements. (Belief in an invisible and ubiquitous policeman who sees what you do even when you are alone in the dark, and who will punish you without fail one day, is an immensely useful instrument for governing people; which is why Plato said that ordinary people should be encouraged in religious beliefs because, even though they are false, they induce better behaviour.) But these past oscillations do not make impossible the idea of an enlightened society; there have indeed been, and are, such: chiefly, sub-societies within society, where more rational dispensations have flourished, sometimes at odds with the law and often vilified – because feared – by the conservative institutions around them.

I know that both the optimist and pessimist are right in their predictions; but I hope that the former is more right, and that reason and tolerance will eventually prevail, so that – in the words of an earlier moralist of the same general temper – we can become, and can flourish as, people who are 'vital, courageous, sensitive and intelligent, all to the highest degree'.

8 Manipulative Reproduction

ROBERT WINSTON

Laban's Sheep

When Jacob had completed more than sixteen years' work as Laban's farm manager, Laban finally asked him what payment he wanted. Genesis (chapter 30) recounts Jacob as saying that he wanted no payment but asked if, as a reward, he might have from Laban's huge flock of sheep those which were speckled black and white or ring-straked. These sheep were a small minority of Laban's flocks and not as well regarded as the apparently pure-bred whites. Jacob clearly knew that his father-in-law, Laban, was a fraudster and untrustworthy. His track record in his dealings with others was poor. Indeed, his name in Hebrew, 'Laban', means 'exceedingly white' because he was regarded as shining with wickedness. Nine years earlier Jacob himself had suffered from Laban's deceit on his wedding day. Then he was hoodwinked into a marriage with Laban's unloved and ugly elder daughter Leah, who was disguised under a thick veil. Jacob must have had a rude shock later that night as he expected to see the pretty younger daughter Rachel in his bed.

In fact, as soon as Laban agreed to let Jacob have the defective sheep, he had his other shepherds remove all the spotted and speckled ones to a remote and inaccessible place, a feeding ground three days' journey away from where Jacob was. Undaunted, Jacob then selectively bred speckled sheep from the remainder of Laban's herd, to which he had full access during his work. Ancient people believed that preconception and antenatal stimuli could influence the developing characteristics of a child. It is a familiar notion, and is still believed by many people around the world. While Laban's animals were drinking at the trough of water or copulating, Jacob showed them speckled whitish sticks at which he had whittled. The Bible reports that these sheep then gave birth to mottled offspring.

What is this story all about? Jacob was certainly no fool; moreover he was a highly skilled husbandry man, having worked with breeding sheep for fifteen or more years. He certainly must have known, from personal observation, that a visual influence at the moment of conception could have no bearing on the outcome of the pregnancy. The speckled sticks were simply a smokescreen to deceive Laban's sons and servants about what he was really doing.

Speckling is a recessive genetic characteristic. Carriers of recessive genes for a particular trait do not show the recessive features of that trait, unless they inherit that recessive gene from both their father and their mother. A single copy of the gene from one or other parent merely makes them a carrier of the trait, but they look externally in every way normal just as a non-carrier. In technical language they have a normal phenotype, but an abnormal genotype. Jacob had recognized, from his years of making Laban rich with his experience of sheep breeding, that the pure whites occasionally gave birth to sheep with abnormal speckling. By identifying the animals which gave rise to the speckled offspring, he could identify carriers (see Figure 1).

These he then selectively bred – the Bible tells us he segregated the animals which showed the most reproductive strength – and soon had a massive flock of speckled but entirely healthy sheep. Genesis records how he soon became richer than Laban with the flock he accumulated.

So humans have been manipulating reproductive processes since recorded time. This manipulation extended beyond animal husbandry to human reproduction. Ancient Egyptians used a variety of substances, including pessaries of crocodile dung, for contraception. Vedic literature is full of references to sex selection, a theme which carries on through ancient Greece, through Talmudic literature and more recently through medieval times. Although we think of eugenics as essentially a twentieth-century 'solution' for purifying the racial and mental health of society, the manipulation of populations started in the depths of history. The destruction of female babies on the hills of Sparta is relatively recent, but the ancient Hebrews attempts to exterminate all the Amalekites, and to prevent their reproduction, reflects a human compulsion since Biblical times. Indeed, the Bible is one of the richest sources of examples of manipulation of human conception. Onan 'spilt his seed' to avoid the obligation of marrying and having a baby by his childless sister-in-law – the earliest Biblical example of contraception. No fewer than three out of four of the matriarchs, Sarah, Rebecca and Rachel, were infertile, and various remedies from surrogacy to mandrakes were tried.

Modern ambivalence about our ability to influence the next generation therefore seems surprising. There is a popular notion that, at the turn of this millennium, mankind stands on a precipice. All our technology, it is frequently claimed, has overtaken us and now threatens us and our planet. Advances in nuclear physics, deforestation and expansion of the use of the internal combustion engine are all seen as frightening enough, but the new developments in reproductive technology are held to be the most dangerous. Presumably this is because they are so personal and question our very nature. Fertility treatments undermine conventional family structures; the selection of children for desirable characteristics such as gender menaces the economy of nations; cloning research imperils our species, yet contraception has failed to check the exponential growth of the world's population.

In this monograph I try to analyse where reproductive advances are taking us. Too frequently, attempts to make predictions are based on poor scientific understanding and inadequate assessment of the kind of technology likely to be available. I hope that the scientific indicators are both encouraging and reassuring. I do not share the alarm and pessimism which is often declared and I hope my analysis may persuade readers of the essential value and relative safety of the development of these advances.

Manipulating Fertility

Perhaps the greatest developments in human reproduction in the last two decades have been in the field of infertility treatments. Until very recently indeed, it was virtually impossible to treat most male infertility effectively, and after treatments for female infertility at least two-thirds of women remained childless. Moreover, probably half of those conceiving after treatment did so spontaneously. That is to say, the treatment itself probably played little part in the successful outcome.

The first major breakthrough came in the 1960s, when scientists managed to measure the hormones secreted by the ovary using techniques such as radioimmune assay. This meant that it was possible to see if a woman was not ovulating – the commonest cause of female infertility. Improvements in biochemistry also led to the isolation or synthesis of hormone preparations capable of stimulating ovulation, given either in tablet form (clomiphene) or by injection (menopausal gonadotrophins). Another very significant advance was the ability to pinpoint when ovulation was occurring. In this respect, ultrasound detection was revolutionary. Using ultrasound, doctors in the early 1980s could image the ovary and detect when the follicle containing the egg was about to rupture resulting in ovulation. This led to better timing of insemination or intercourse.

While improvements were rapidly happening in hormone therapy, laparoscopy was also being developed. Although it was possible to put a telescope into the abdomen and inspect the contents of the pelvic cavity before the Second World War, laparoscopy only really became established with the improvements in optics and the development of powerful halogen light sources which generated little heat. This revolutionary technique gave remarkably clear views of the uterus, tubes and ovaries and enabled surgeons reliably to detect the second commonest cause of female infertility, namely blocked fallopian tubes. Before the development of laparoscopy, very often the only way a fertility specialist could identify tubal disease was by performing a laparotomy, a major operation to open the abdomen and inspect the contents of the pelvis. Apart from the relatively huge trauma involved, and the long convalescence needed, this kind of exploratory procedure itself carried risks to a woman's fertility by sometimes causing adhesions to form between the tubes or ovaries and other tissues such as the bowel. Occasionally such surgical scarring could block or damage fallopian tubes which had previously been entirely healthy. So laparoscopy was an undoubted breakthrough. By 1976, some more adventurous surgeons were even starting to use the laparoscope to conduct simpler surgical procedures (keyhole surgery) to repair tubes which were blocked and divide adhesions. Such minimal invasive surgery became more popular with the development of medical lasers and fine electrosurgical instruments. Another significant advance was in microsurgery. The human fallopian tube is small and delicate – at its narrowest part, where it is frequently blocked by infection or other disease, it measures no more than 0.5 millimetres in diameter. The use of the operating microscope provided the only accurate means of removal of pathological tissue and rejoining blocked tubes reliably.

Treatments for male infertility – when low sperm count was the cause – lagged behind. By 1980, there were over 200 drugs which were in more or less frequent use to try to stimulate the testis to produce more sperm. The fact that so many different preparations were developed argues that none was very effective. Indeed, drug treatments for male infertility have now almost been completely abandoned because they were virtually useless except in a tiny proportion of men.

In Vitro Fertilization

The greatest breakthrough was the birth of Louise Brown in 1978 after *in vitro* fertilization (IVF). IVF was initially developed to bypass hopelessly damaged tubes when surgical reconstruction was a forlorn procedure. IVF using natural ovulation was limited because humans normally only produce one egg at a time. Thus drugs are given to stimulate the ovary to produce a large number of eggs simultaneously – perhaps ten or even twenty. These are then collected by sucking them from their follicles in the ovary when they are matured. As immature eggs are not capable of being normally fertilized, much research went into working out precisely when ovulation was about to occur, so that only eggs which were fertilizable were collected. These eggs are then exposed to sperm in dishes, and, once fertilization has occurred, the resulting embryos are grown in culture fluid, in an incubator. The incubator and the culture media allow an environment which loosely mimics conditions inside the body, so that normally some viable embryos are produced. After seventy-two hours in culture, two or three healthy-looking embryos can be selected for transfer back to the uterus.

Although IVF was originally used for patients with diseased tubes, it soon became clear that it could also be used in some cases of male infertility. This is because fertilization is facilitated in these artificial conditions when there are not enough sperm produced for natural fertilization. By the late 1980s, IVF was also being used for many other causes of infertility, including those patients for whom there was no clear-cut cause for the infertility.

Currently IVF is demanding. It requires quite massive stimulation to the ovaries with drugs, and this can cause considerable ovarian enlargement. The hyperstimulation which sometimes inadvertently happens can make a woman ill. Moreover, considerable monitoring for up to two weeks with daily hormone blood tests and regular ultrasound is needed to ensure that only mature eggs are collected. Such testing is emotionally tiring for the woman. Even with all this intervention, IVF has a relatively low success rate and in the best clinics only 20 per cent of treatment cycles results in pregnancy. Moreover, the need to transfer more than one embryo simultaneously to improve the success rate means that many IVF treatments have the unpredictable result of multiple pregnancy – twins, triplets or even quadruplets. This means that the risks of losing the entire pregnancy are greatly increased – humans were not designed biologically to produce a litter.

In the last five years, there has been a major advance in the treatment of male infertility. Even with IVF, many men producing poor sperm samples are unlikely to ejaculate sufficient normal sperm to provide a good chance of fertilization. There has been a genuine revolution with the advent of micromanipulation. Using sophisticated instruments and specially designed optics on microscopes, it has been possible to select an individual spermatozoon and inject it directly into the egg. This treatment, called Intracytoplasmic Sperm Injection, or ICSI, has been remarkably successful. Even those men producing very few sperm – perhaps less than 1 per cent of normal numbers – are now treatable. At the time of writing, some 4,000 babies have been born using this approach.

IVF still has a poor success rate – although treatments can be repeated – admittedly, with considerable expense and inconvenience. The latest statistics show that only about 14 per cent of treatments result in a live birth. There are several reasons for this. Firstly, it is clear that humans produce very few embryos which are capable of normal further development. This is why the average fertile couple tend to require several months of regular sexual activity before successful conception occurs. In Britain, it seems that about 18 per cent of couples will conceive in each menstrual cycle. Published reports suggest that American couples are slightly more fertile, with about 20 per cent conceiving each month. The most fertile are Australian women, with a cumulative conception rate of around 22 per cent per month. This may be because American and Australian citizens are more sexually active. In spite of their national reputation, the French do not do so well.

On average, only one in every five embryos produced by IVF results in a pregnancy after embryo transfer. All available evidence suggests that this is because many, if not most, human embryos have defects incompatible with viability. It is true that the uterine environment into which they are placed could be hostile, or incapable of providing proper support for implantation, but there is very little evidence for this. Detailed microscopic examination of human embryos shows that about 20–25 per cent have an abnormal number of chromosomes. In general, an abnormal complement of chromosomes means a major restructuring or deficiency of genetic material, incompatible with life. One exception is trisomy 21, three copies of chromosome 21, causing Down's syndrome. Although some Down's babies survive after birth, probably far more trisomy 21 embryos do not implant, or miscarry early. It seems that failure to allow survival *in utero* is a kind of natural safety-valve, guarding against large numbers of abnormal babies being born.

Chromosomal defects represent a fairly massive abnormality, affecting a whole number of different genes along the entire length of a chromosome. Many human embryos show other more subtle imperfections. For example, a majority of embryos contain some dead or dying cells. In some cases this cell death is probably programmed – the phenomenon is called apoptosis. Apoptosis occurs in all tissues and accounts for the constant remodelling that happens during development. This is how the web between the fetal fingers gradually disappears during growth; it is also how a tadpole loses its tail as it grows. But some embryos show excessive cell death during the very earliest stages of development, or just abnormalities of cell division. It is quite common for some embryos, for example, to have cells which contain more than one nucleus – or no nuclei at all. Many of these imperfections are not detectable with an ordinary light microscope when embryologists make their routine inspection of an embryo before its transfer to the uterus after IVF.

It is also likely that a number of human embryos do not develop because of as yet undetectable gene defects. For example, there are many genes which control early embryonic growth, implantation and development. If for some reason these genes are not properly expressed during early development, progression to the next stages of fetal life may be prevented.

The Future of IVF

Improved Hormone Treatments

The first development in the next few years will be improved methods of stimulating the ovary to obtain more fully mature eggs with greater efficiency. The hormones currently used are derived from the pituitary gland. This gland secretes follicle stimulating hormone (FSH) which stimulates the ovary *in vivo* to produce a mature follicle. Until recently this hormone was obtained by extracting it from the urine of menopausal women. After the menopause, very large amounts of this hormone are naturally made by the pituitary. It is an attempt by the pituitary to stimulate the failing ovary. During normal reproductive life relatively small amounts of this hormone are secreted. Once the menopause has commenced, the ovary is incapable of responding to stimuli, so the pituitary compensates by pouring out more hormone. The excess spills over into the urine, from where it can be concentrated chemically and extracted for therapeutic purposes. However, the body treats FSH extracted from urine as a foreign intrusion, and, when it is given to another woman by injection, antibodies can be formed. Also, biologically derived drugs produced like this often have varying strength, which means their effectiveness varies considerably from batch to batch.

One of the advances in modern therapeutics has been to synthesize these, and similar protein hormones by genetic engineering. It is now possible to produce hormones normally made in the pituitary gland entirely artificially. Cells taken from the ovary of Chinese hamsters are grown in culture vats, and these cells multiply vigorously in a kind of soup. Before commencing active growth, the cells have been modified with the human gene which makes FSH. Once the 'soup' is really brewing vigorously, massive amounts of hormone are produced relatively economically and very reliably. Moreover the process of production can be tailored, so that the active principle can be altered by changing its molecular structure. The 'designer drug' recombinant (see Glossary) FSH is likely to be more potent than biologically produced hormones and over the next five years there will be a new class of more effective drugs. It will be possible to stimulate the ovary more precisely and with few side-effects, and less chance of hyperstimulation with its unpleasant and dangerous side-effects.

In Vitro *Maturation of Eggs*

A much more important advance is also under way. It may be possible to dispense with the use of expensive stimulatory drugs altogether, using immature eggs recovered from the ovary. There are, apart from any other consideration, good commercial reasons why this would be helpful. IVF is an expensive treatment, and generally costs £1,500 to £2,000 per treatment cycle. This cost includes monitoring the time of ovulation, the removal of the eggs and the laboratory expenses. It does not include the cost of

FSH, which is itself expensive. In young women, the added cost of the drugs for a single course of treatment is typically £200–£500. Women in their thirties or early forties usually require a much more hefty stimulus and the extra cost of drugs can be more than £1,000. These factors make IVF a privileged treatment, affordable only by the relatively well-off, or those fortunate few who are able to obtain public funding (such as National Health Service support) for their treatment.

Using immature eggs recovered from the ovary could revolutionize the whole of reproductive medicine within the next ten years. It is feasible because a woman is born with her entire complement of eggs already formed in her ovaries. Very early in intrauterine life, a female fetus has about five million eggs formed in her ovaries. Each of these eggs is genetically unique, containing the individual mix of genes from mother and father. Remarkably, most of these eggs start to atrophy even before birth so that, by the time a baby girl is born, she is left with about two million eggs. By puberty, there are possibly between 200,000 and 300,000 left. Thereafter, only one egg each month will actually be ovulated. Over a thirty-year period therefore, some 400 will reach normal maturity and, given the average-sized family, two or three will develop into babies. This extraordinary redundancy seems all the more remarkable when one considers that, as each egg is genetically unique, the inherited characteristics of our children are left purely to chance.

All these eggs are contained in tiny primordial follicles in the surface of the ovary, called the cortex. This is a skin, just a few millimetres thick, surrounding the ovary. In any average young woman, one square millimetre of this cortical tissue will contain between 200 and 400 eggs. Being on the surface of the ovary, it is extremely accessible to a surgeon. A simple needle stab under local anaesthetic will collect a small sliver of tissue containing several hundred eggs. This tissue can then be frozen in liquid nitrogen and stored. Methods are being developed for the successful thawing of this tissue and for separating from it individual follicles containing eggs. Work now in progress will eventually allow such follicles to be matured in artificially produced culture media (maturation *in vitro*) to the stage where the egg can be fertilized. The hope is that embryos formed in this way will be normal and have a chance of survival.

The main problem facing researchers studying maturation of follicles *in vitro* is that we are uncertain which genes and which growth factors are essential. It has already been possible to mature follicles to the early antral stage, the stage at which the egg prepares for subsequent fertilization. This has been achieved by dosing the culture media with minute quantities of the hormone FSH, together with other factors which are guessed to be important. It is likely to be only a matter of time before scientists will be able to collect fully mature eggs in such systems.

This would be a major breakthrough in fertility medicine. Eggs could be produced cheaply and there could be a plentiful supply. It could provide a source of donor eggs for those women with no eggs of their own, having suffered a premature menopause. It would also be highly useful for cancer victims. Many cancers are quite common in relatively young women, such as leukaemia, lymphatic cancers and some forms of breast cancer. One problem that these young women face is that the chemotherapy and the radiotherapy needed to cure their cancers make them sterile by destroying egg cells in the ovary. In future, before undergoing treatment for cancer, such patients could have small amounts of their ovarian tissue stored. Once the cancer has been cured, they could have IVF with their stored, matured eggs and a genetically related child. But the biggest opportunity will undoubtedly be the possibility of replacing the cumbersome treatment that women now experience during routine IVF.

The continuous process of egg loss from the ovary during reproductive life means that women become increasingly infertile by a process of attrition. A woman's fertility halves during her early thirties, and women over forty are likely to be severely infertile. In most of Western society, women are delaying pregnancy for many good social reasons. Sadly, many women find that by the time they are in a position to conceive they have left things too late. A substantial number of women attending infertility clinics are infertile simply because of this natural ageing process. Nothing at present can be done for them beyond offering them donated eggs from another individual. The future could bring extraordinary procreative liberty. Is it too far-fetched to envisage the time when more mature women use eggs kept in the deep freeze for twenty years? I like to think of the example of the young law student, who may take her final examinations and obtain her university qualification at twenty-one years old. Having had some ovarian tissue stored, she could read for the bar, find chambers and develop a career as a barrister. Once she has taken silk in her early forties, she could return to have her eggs matured in the laboratory. After fertilization with her husband's spermatozoa, the embryos could be transferred with a simple ten-minute procedure. Such a process would require less monitoring and drug use, and would be cheaper and much less emotionally demanding than are current IVF treatment methods.

Genetic Diagnosis

One of the most challenging developments in IVF has been methods to screen human embryos for genetic defects. There are about 5,000 single gene defects. They frequently cause death in young children and those gene defects which are not fatal generally cause severe disability.

Gene defects can be divided into three groups. The most common are the recessive genetic defects. These cause a problem only if both parents carry the same defective gene and both pass that gene to the child. In such families, with both parents carriers, there is a 25 per cent chance of any child being affected. Typical common recessive defects include cystic fibrosis, which causes severe lung and digestive disease, and thalassaemia, a blood disorder causing severe anaemia. About 500,000 babies worldwide die from thalassaemia each year. It is common in Britain in many immigrant populations, particularly some Asian families and those from the Mediterranean – for example, Cyprus.

The second group of gene disorders are those caused by dominant genes. Any person inheriting one copy of such a gene from either parent will suffer from the disease. It therefore follows that the parent carrying that gene will also have the disorder. Consequently, most dominant defects die out because gene defects tend to affect people from childhood onwards, and carriers rarely live to mature life. The dominant gene defects which are prevalent are mostly those which only express in older adults. The commonest is Huntingdon's chorea, a crippling neurological disorder which only starts to take effect normally when a person is over forty. By that time they may have had several children without realizing they have inherited this defect.

The last group of gene defects are those which are sex-linked. These are defects produced by genes on the X chromosome. Every female has two X chromosomes, males have only one. A woman may carry one of these defects on one of her X chromosomes, but because she has another normal X chromosome, she will not suffer the disease. A man is less fortunate if he inherits the 'wrong' X chromosome from his mother. Having only one X chromosome will mean that this defective gene, if present, will be expressed, and he will suffer from the disease. The chances of any man inheriting an X-linked disorder from a carrier mother are 50 per cent. There are about 300 known X-linked disorders. Among the commonest is Duchenne muscular dystrophy, which causes slowly developing paralysis in young boys – most dying from suffocation by their teens. Another is haemophilia, the famous disorder affecting members of the Russian Royal Family, which causes severe haemorrhage or bruising after slight injury because of the failure of the blood to clot.

Families generally only know they carry a gene defect if there is a family history. Most frequently, the majority of couples find they may be carriers when they have a child who turns out to have one of these horrible diseases. In the long-distant future more and more people may undergo routine genetic screening for the commoner disorders and therefore will know whether they are at risk. It seems extremely unlikely that there will ever be adequate screening for the rare disorders and most individual gene disorders are not very common. It is just that there are so many different ones that collectively they present a significant medical problem. Until recently, the only practical way of dealing with these defects has been to screen pregnancies, once the pregnancy is well established. This requires amniocentesis or removal of a piece of tissue from the placenta, and both procedures are not entirely without hazard to the pregnancy. Once a diagnosis has been made, the couple may face the heartrending decision of whether to have an abortion.

A major development occurred in 1990 with the technique of preimplantation diagnosis at the Hammersmith Hospital in London. Using IVF, embryos were obtained from couples who had already had a child die of a genetic disorder. Three days after fertilization, when the embryos comprised just eight cells, micro-surgery was used to remove a single embryonic cell. This cell was frozen and immediately thawed to release the DNA contained in the cell's nucleus. The DNA was then examined to see if the embryo from which the cell came carried the specific defect in that family. Initially, when the technique was first started, it was decided to concentrate on diagnosing just the sex of the embryo when the woman was a carrier of a sex-linked disease. Determina-tion of DNA associated with genes for sex was thought at the time to be easier than looking for a specific gene disorder. The strategy was to transfer female embryos only to those mothers who had lost a male child with muscular dystrophy, adreno-eukodystrophy or severe X-linked mental with physical retardation. Three women were initially treated and each had two female embryos trans-ferred. Two became pregnant and both had twin girls. By 1992, the technology was extended to make specific diagnosis of an individual gene defect. Cystic fibrosis was chosen as being the most important because it is so common – about one in 2,000 babies are born with this disorder. Since that time about seven or eight different genetic disorders have been detected in embryos by these methods. A number of healthy babies have been born to parents who had previously watched a child tragically die. These families chose preimplantation diagnosis after IVF, with all the rigours involved, because they were reluctant to consider termi-nation of an established pregnancy. Their decision was often based on their moral views about the abortion of an established pregnancy.

Preimplantation diagnosis has now expanded to include chro-mosomal disorders. The breakthrough became possible when sci-entists learnt how to stain the DNA in individual chromosomes, or parts of chromosomes, with brightly coloured fluorescent dyes. Gene defects are not the only problems which cause genetic disease. Less than half of 1 per cent of all babies born have a single gene defect, but a defect of one or more chromosomes is much more common. Indeed, at least 20–30 per cent of human embryos have abnormal chromosomes, one of the commonest causes of failure to conceive or of miscarriage. Down's syndrome, three copies of chromosome 21, is one of the few disorders compatible with viable life. Nonetheless, most of these children are severely handicapped usually with profound mental retardation and other defects such as an abnormal heart.

Chromosome staining (or painting as it is frequently called) is now being used to detect these severe abnormalities in embryos, from those women who have had repeated embryonic loss or early pregnancy failure, or who have merely repeatedly failed IVF. One prospect for the relatively near future is that, because many older women have eggs which are likely to be more prone to chromosomal abnormality, this technique can be used for older women having IVF treatment. It may just be possible to improve the success rate of IVF in these women quite dramatically. Biopsy and screening of cells taken from the embryo during the first five days after fertilization may ensure that doctors select healthy embryos for transfer.

However, at present, chromosomal detection of this kind is limited. This is because it requires the complexities of operating on the embryo to remove cells first. Microsurgery of this sort can damage embryos and prevent subsequent development. Moreover, the technique is time-consuming, labour intensive and consequently expensive. Because it is difficult to see how it could be automated, it is unlikely to be suitable for the routine screening of large numbers of human embryos.

In the next few years, preimplantation genetic diagnosis will almost certainly be applied to screen those embryos from women who are at risk of having disorders which only express themselves in later life. Typical of these are the cancer genes. Familial breast and ovarian cancer, polyposis coli (which causes bowel cancer) and some forms of brain cancer such as retinoblastoma are diseases which are inherited. A carrier of one of these genes is highly likely to develop the cancer at a young age. Moreover, many of these cancers are hard to treat because they grow so rapidly and spread to other organs. For example, even if a breast cancer from one of these victims is successfully treated by radiotherapy or surgery of one breast, there is a likelihood of another similar cancer developing in the other breast at a later date because of the overall genetic predisposition.

This approach to preventing cancer raises increasingly interesting ethical problems. Perhaps the main one is that people who carry these genes will be perfectly capable of conducting full and useful lives up until the time when the cancer strikes. Should we therefore be destroying embryos who may survive until the age of forty or even fifty years old? Franz Schubert was thirty-one when he died of syphilis, Wolfgang Amadeus Mozart died at thirty-six, and the poet Keats contracted tuberculosis as a teenager, dying from lung haemorrhage at twenty-five. All contributed immeasurably to human culture and happiness. Who is to know that we might not be selecting out another Schubert by discarding a particular embryo? This argument seems a poor one. It could equally be true that the embryo free of the gene defect could be the one with the talent of Schubert, or indeed a Picasso, who lived until his eighties. The characteristics which contribute the nature of an individual are always likely to be undetectable by these methods and therefore such selection would always be random.

Currently preimplantation diagnosis can be done by examining individual genes, or by staining all or part of some of the chromosomes. As already mentioned, both methods are complex. There is potentially a third option. It is now clearly established that many of the genes which contribute to the general function and health of an adult are already 'switched on' and working during very early development. These genes are often producing proteins which may be detectable without necessarily making a biopsy of the embryo.

A good example of this is the enzyme HPRT, or Hypoxanthine Phosphoribosyl Transferase. Absence of this vital enzyme is caused by mutations in the gene responsible for its manufacture. Children who are born with deficiency of the HPRT enzyme suffer from the terrible disease Lesch-Nyhan syndrome (see Glossary). The enzyme deficiency causes, among other things, mild mental retardation and very severe cerebral palsy. Such children suffer from constant writhing movements and are spastic – for example, they cannot walk. Most horrific is their compulsive desire to self-mutilate and consequently they have to be restrained, strapped in a wheelchair. Without such restraint, these children sometimes bite off the tips of their fingers, for example. Even with restraint, many of these children mutilate themselves by biting off their lips or tongue. In spite of the most thorough care, it is rare for these affected children to live beyond the age of about twelve.

It may just be possible to treat these children by gene therapy. There have been a number of attempts to introduce the unmutated gene into the child's white blood cells, so that sufficient HPRT is made to alleviate this horrible disease. A discussion of somatic cell (see Glossary) gene therapy is beyond the scope of this book, but suffice it to say that, given our current state of knowledge, such gene therapy is really only possible once the disease is firmly established, by which time the severe neurological damage is irreversible. In the absence of effective treatment, techniques such as preimplantation diagnosis seem worth exploring.

In a very few cases, preimplantation diagnosis has been used to prevent Lesch-Nyhan by screening embryos for the specific gene mutation and then transferring only healthy embryos to the uterus. But this, of course, has involved a biopsy. To avoid this invasion, attempts to try to detect the presence or absence of the gene product HPRT have been made. The hope was to examine the fluids in which the embryo is grown in culture to see whether this enzyme has been secreted by embryos from carrier mothers. Such a technique has the beauty of being entirely non-invasive – that is, it involves no surgery. Theoretically it is also likely in time that measurements of such enzymes could be done using automated machinery. This would eliminate much of the intensive work that is currently needed both for embryo biopsy and for detection of specific segments of DNA, or of parts of chromosomes.

Unfortunately, this non-invasive approach – a general strategy which could be applied to a good number of different hereditary diseases – is not yet possible. The major problem is that most of the gene products of interest are already present in the substance of the egg before fertilization. This is because the mother, being unaffected, has normal genes. Some of the products of maternal genes linger in the embryonic cells which are formed from the cytoplasm of the egg, and they may last for several days. However, preimplantation diagnosis using chemical screening in this way may be feasible eventually. One strong possibility is that embryos will be grown for longer in culture until the blastocyst stage, just before implantation. The human embryo becomes a blastocyst on about the fifth day after fertilization and normally comprises well over fifty cells. Examination of the blastocyst and the secretions in fluids around it would be advantageous; because there are more cells by this stage, there is more metabolic activity and consequently there should be more of the specific gene product available for testing. This would mean that the diagnosis could be made with more security. Secondly, by this stage of development, it is much less likely that any genetic 'residue' from the mother would still be present to confuse the diagnosis.

The current drawback to testing embryos in culture is that it has been surprisingly difficult to grow human embryos outside the womb for more than the first two or three days of life. Blastocyst culture is currently problematic because, as yet, we do not fully understand the ideal milieu needed for the embryo once it starts to grow to later stages. This is a problem which, as we shall see later, is almost certainly soluble and which when solved will produce substantial other benefits.

Selection of the Best Embryos for Transfer

In vitro fertilization has a very low success rate unless more than one embryo is transferred to the uterus simultaneously. This is because, as has been previously described, most human embryos seem incapable of advanced development, possibly due to a variety of defects. It is this essentially biological problem which has led doctors to transfer several embryos to the uterus simultaneously. While this practice increases the chance of a pregnancy with at least one embryo implanting, it does risk multiple implantation – which carries risks of miscarriage and multiple births. Since the advent of IVF, the incidence of multiple birth has more than doubled in Britain. Most triplets, and nearly all quadruplets, that are born have been conceived following assisted reproductive treatments of one sort or another. Although high-order multiple birth has often been seen as a triumph in the lay press and by some of the public, it is little short of disastrous in the majority of cases. Apart from the difficulty that parents have in coping with many babies after birth, there are significant medical problems. Firstly, triplets virtually never go to term; indeed, most are born six to eight weeks prematurely, if they survive pregnancy at all.

Having three or four babies develop simultaneously in the womb greatly increases the hazards of pregnancy, with high blood pressure, toxaemia, diabetes and blood clots being much more likely. Delivery by Caesarean section is nearly always needed and most babies born this premature require intensive nursing in incubators, often for several weeks. It costs the National Health Service approximately £500 to £1,000 each day to care for a very small baby intensively, and therefore the cost of supporting premature quadruplets can be very substantial. Moreover, surviving premature babies are far more likely to have developmental and health problems later. For all these reasons it is hardly surprising that *in vitro* fertilization has not always been a very popular treatment with paediatricians and health service managers.

Unfortunately the current imperfect technology puts much pressure on infertility specialists to continue transferring several embryos simultaneously, in order to increase chances of pregnancy. IVF is a costly process and most patients simply cannot afford to go through endless cycles of treatment. In Britain the regulatory authority (HFEA) has placed a limit of three embryos at once, but even this carries quite a risk of multiple birth. In most other countries there is no statutory limit and it is not uncommon for practitioners to transfer five, six or even seven embryos.

A major advance will clearly be tests on embryos in culture to ascertain which are most likely to be viable and to implant. The eventual aim is to give IVF a high chance of success with just single-embryo transfers. So far a number of tests have been devised, but none is very reliable.

One of the best of these tests has been non-invasive assessment of metabolism. Remarkably, it is actually possible to measure how much energy an embryo is using. The idea behind such measurement is the assumption that the more energy used, the more likely the embryo is to be growing actively and therefore to be viable. The technique is relatively simple. Each fertilized egg, invisible to the naked eye, is placed in a tiny droplet of culture medium so small that if spilt on one's finger one would hardly feel wetness. To remove the droplet from outside influences, it is placed under a globule of sterile inert oil. The medium in which the embryo is allowed to grow contains a measured amount of sugar. After twenty-four hours, the embryo can be removed from its droplet and placed in a new, freshly prepared one. The original droplet can then be analysed to see how much sugar has been taken up, and thus the amount consumed by the embryo in twenty-four hours can be estimated.

Measurements on several hundred embryos have consistently shown that embryos more likely to be viable consume more sugar and are more metabolically active. Of particular interest is the finding that male embryos are, on average, 18 per cent more active than female embryos. It seems that we men are more aggressive from the moment of conception. Unfortunately, sugar consumption is not reliable as a discriminatory test. There is so much variation in metabolic activity of this sort from embryo to embryo, irrespective of sex, that the test is insufficient to determine which embryos are most likely to become a baby if transferred. One problem is that sugar metabolism is a very basic process, and even cells which are about to die may consume considerable amounts of sugar.

In the near future, however, there are likely to be significant advances. Although sugar metabolism is a very basic function, there are other forms of metabolic measurement which may reveal more. A promising area is to see what amino acids are taken up into the embryo during growth, using similar culture techniques. Amino acids are the vital components of proteins. Proteins are the essential building blocks during growth and are needed for cell division. Many amino acids are needed for embryo culture and it should be possible to measure their depletion from culture media over a fixed period of time, thus gauging an individual embryo's growth potential. Continued research in this area should make it possible to select viable embryos with rather more accuracy, and it is likely that this approach may be applicable within the next five years.

Metabolic measurement is not the only refined, non-invasive assessment likely to give information about embryonic viability. Cells that are actively dividing need substances called growth factors. Growth factors are chemical messengers which attach themselves to receptors on the cell wall. Attachment to receptors leads to the generation of further messages within the cell which tell it to grow and divide. It is already known that embryos require growth factors of various sorts to stimulate their growth and researchers are assessing which growth factors are most important, and which may be needed to provide the best culture environment. It is also true that the embryo itself may produce different growth factors as its own genes are switched on. These growth factors are messengers which tell the lining cells of the uterine cavity that the embryo is present. It is likely that these messages are important in preparing the endometrium (see Glossary) for implantation. Consequently the most viable embryos, the ones most likely to implant, are most likely to produce good amounts of growth factors. In due course, their measurement is likely to be quite simple even though they are present only in low concentrations. It is more than probable that, within the next ten years, these measurements may help pick the embryos most likely to be healthily viable.

Improvements in Culture Media

It is clearly established that embryos of different species require different conditions for the best growth. For example, most embryo culture media have traditionally contained glucose. This is, on the face of it, hardly surprising as glucose has always been regarded as a basic energy provider for most mammalian cells. It now turns out that glucose, even in moderate amounts, actually tends to prevent growth in mice embryos in the first two days after fertilization. The evidence that glucose is 'poisonous' to early human embryos is not nearly so convincing. However, it is clear that the human embryo culture media in which embryos are currently grown after IVF are less than ideal. The evidence for this is that human IVF embryos grow more slowly than after natural fertilization and normal incubation in the fallopian tube. Secondly, they tend not to survive very well if grown more than three days in culture media outside the body. Thirdly, embryos which do survive usually have fewer cells than embryos at an equivalent stage after natural fertilization and growth inside the body. It is also true that, in most IVF units, any single embryo transferred to the uterus after IVF on or around the second day after fertilization only has around a 10 per cent chance of becoming a baby. In units which take a great deal of trouble over their laboratory techniques, the chances of a single embryo going on to further development is better than 10 per cent, reaching a maximum of around 20 per cent. All these observations lead to the conclusion that the artifical conditions in which embryos are kept in culture laboratories are not optimal.

The gaps in our knowledge about the best environment for human embryo growth will undoubtedly be filled within the next five to ten years. This is one of the most reassuring developments in IVF because, once we know the best solutions in which to nurture human embryos, there is likely to be a substantial improvement in treatment. Currently, embryos kept in culture in most laboratories seem to deteriorate. There would be a great advantage in being able to culture the embryo to the fifth day, when it becomes a blastocyst, because available knowledge suggests that any single normal blastocyst transferred to the uterus would have at least an even chance of developing into a healthy fetus. Given that a three-day embryo only has a 10 to 20 per cent chance of viability, the availability of good blastocysts could give massive improvement to current results.

There are several promising ideas already being explored. It is now clear that the right concentration of carbohydrate can promote human embryonic development and the wrong concentration can inhibit it. We do not yet know what is ideal for the human embryo, but its requirements are likely to change during development. It seems that pyruvate is the essential carbohydrate needed for the first two days, but thereafter the human embryo needs glucose. It may well be that the culture media in which embryos are grown need to be changed depending on the precise stage of development.

While there has been quite a lot of research on the energy requirements of embryos, much less is known about their need for amino acids, the building blocks making essential proteins. There are twenty common different amino acids and their relative importance to developing embryos is a mystery. One of the most interesting, and possibly important, is the substance glutamine. Some embryos require glutamine for best growth. This requirement varies not merely between different animal species, but even between different strains of the same species. Most mouse embryos, for example, need it, but there are some strains of laboratory mice whose embryos can develop normally in media which contain very little or no glutamine at all. New research in the human suggests that the presence of glutamine in the culture media may greatly enhance growth in the early stages. Currently, as conventionally used media in human IVF laboratories do not have this substance, there is a very strong case for adding it – but in the right proportions. Too much, of course, may inhibit growth. I use glutamine as an example, but there is a whole range of other compounds, including inorganic metals and various salts, which when added to media may possibly make a considerable difference to the clinical outcome of IVF.

One very new and exciting area is that of growth factors. We now have evidence that embryos almost certainly need these compounds for best development. They are present in varying quantities in the fallopian tubes and uterus, and seem to have a most important influence. So far no laboratory has tried adding these substances systematically to embryos in culture. Some preliminary work in our own unit suggests that the addition of one particular factor, from the family of insulin-like growth factors, may actually enhance development by as much as 30 per cent. Undoubtedly, therefore, further research in this area will yield rich rewards for infertile patients.

Sex Selection

Since time immemorial, humans have tried to influence the sex of their babies. It seems males were preferred to females in most ancient societies. An exception to this is possibly the dilemma of the Hebrew slaves in captivity in ancient Egypt. The Bible reports that Pharaoh ruled that all male children born to them should be drowned, so that only females would survive, thus reducing the chance that the Hebrews would rise in revolution. This is why Moses' mother hid him and floated him down-river in a reed basket.

The ancients tended to believe that boys were generated from the right side, girls from the left. Coital position was therefore considered important to influence the humours forming the fetus. Timing of intercourse during the menstrual cycle, delaying orgasm, changing the amount of salt in the diet or the acidity of the vagina, taking up less stressful living, have all at times been favoured methods of influencing the sex of the fetus. There is little evidence for the efficacy of any of these remedies. While the remedies themselves are not particularly notable, the fact that they have been employed in ancient Egypt, ancient Greece, Roman times and many other civilizations in almost all parts of the world ever since records began argues that most peoples found little moral objection to the notion of sex selection.

The sex of a baby is determined by the sperm fertilizing the egg. Sperm carrying the Y chromosome produce males. The Y chromosome is physically smaller than the X chromosome, and there is therefore a minuscule difference in the weight of male- or female-bearing sperm. Some authors have argued that male sperm swim faster and are also smaller. In spite of various scientific papers still published on the subject, there is no convincing evidence for the agility or increased speed of Y-bearing sperm.

Nevertheless, this has not prevented commercially minded doctors and scientists attempting to devise methods to separate X- and Y-bearing sperm. These methods have the object of producing enriched sperm samples for artificial insemination into the female partner.

Sperm separation generally involves passing sperm through a fluid of relatively high density, and/or spinning samples in a centrifuge to isolate those of a particular weight. One popular method devised by a Dr Ronald Ericsson, and used at various times by one rather notorious clinic in London, employs these basic techniques, and the service is sold to quite large numbers of people who may give a preference for having boys. Without going into detail, there is little or no genuinely independent evidence that this – or indeed any other related method – actually works. There is therefore the possibility that a number of patients who come to such clinics could be hoodwinked or exploited.

At the present time, the only method of sex selection which definitely has a high chance of working is the one devised at Hammersmith Hospital, used for preimplantation diagnosis (see pp. 345–6). This is very reliable, but it is complex – involving, as it does, IVF. Moreover, it is expensive and requires the biopsy of, and possibly damage to, an embryo. For this reason, the UK regulatory authority has, probably justifiably, sanctioned its use only for those patients at risk of having a baby with a severe sex-linked disorder.

There is no doubt that in the near future, perhaps by the year 2000 or 2002, there will be a very reliable way of sex selection which will not involve the complexities of IVF, let alone embryo biopsy. Work in Cambridge in cattle clearly indicates that it is possible to enrich sperm samples with X- or Y-bearing sperm by using the method of flow cytometry. This involves placing a fluorescent dye on the X or Y chromosome, following which the sperm are sorted in a laser beam. There is doubt whether the fluorescent 'tagging' of sperm might carry genetic hazards, with damage to the DNA. It is possible that it does not and it seems that, with refinements, this kind of approach is likely to be used eventually in humans. While the apparatus and the technical back-up needed to do this are expensive, it is bound in time to be very much less involved than IVF. This is because, once the sample is enriched, only artificial insemination is needed, the simplest of reproductive treatments.

This technology will open up a huge ethical debate. While it is feasible to regulate sex selection using IVF methods – existing legislation, together with the difficulty of treatment, ensures that – a simplified method involving sperm separation and insemination will be almost impossible to police. This will be particularly true in developing countries which have relatively sophisticated technology and where couples are under considerable social pressure to have a child of a specific gender – usually a boy. The lid may be kept on the technique for a while in Europe, but people in countries like India and China may well provide the impetus for the regular use of these treatments.

There are reasonably clear arguments against the widespread implementation of sex selection. Firstly, there is the concern that there would be a risk of changing the balance of the population, probably by increasing the ratio of boys to girls. Although this in itself seems highly undesirable, there is little clear evidence that it would bring about deleterious social pressures. A society filled with males may be more aggressive, but this is doubtful. Moreover, there is a strong possibility that, if males predominated, females may become more 'valuable' – and there would be pressure, both natural and social, to restore balance. Another argument against sex selection is that it would be likely to increase inequality in society, by 'benefiting' the better-off families. Should there be a preference for males, females may find a reduction in their status. Sadly, given that this is probably true of many contemporary societies, there is little evidence to suggest that sex selection would make matters any worse. One prevalent argument is that this kind of social engineering is ripe for state exploitation. Governments may use it to further interests not necessarily to the advantage of all members of that society, or countries beyond – for instance selecting in favour of males in order to create armies, or females in order to increase population.

Introducing New Genes

The most fundamental advance in reproduction this century has almost certainly been the development of transgenic technology. Using the access to embryos that IVF provides means that new genes can be introduced into them, thus changing their genetic expression as they grow older. 'Foreign' genes (or transgenes) were first injected into mouse eggs in the early 1980s. Among the early mouse experiments were those by Dr Marston Wagner and colleagues, who introduced the human gene which makes part of the haemoglobin molecules in red blood cells. At about the same time Drs Richard Palmiter and Ralph L. Brinster were introducing growth human genes into mice embryos – making the so-called giant mouse. The mention of a giant mouse may conjure up surreal images, but it was in reality just a slightly larger-than-average mouse, which grew faster and made more efficient use of foodstuffs. Mice remain the most common species for scientists studying the effects of transgenes, and such animals have become very important models for human diseases with a genetic component, and for new therapies. They have been very valuable for studying cancer-causing genes and are used for the study of DNA and its function.

Making transgenic animals is not easy at all. It is now most frequently done by injecting a solution containing a number of copies of the gene of interest into the fertilized egg, shortly after the sperm has entered it, and before it starts to divide for the first time into two separate cells. While there are other stages of development when transgenic animals can be made, this is the stage when researchers have had the most success. Once the gene has been injected, the fertilized egg is returned to the tube or uterus of a foster female animal previously prepared for pregnancy by giving hormones. The process is technically demanding – for example, the glass needle which is used to inject the gene solution into the microscopic egg is so fine that its tip cannot be seen with the naked eye. The slightest untoward pressure on it breaks it, rendering it useless.

Normally genes injected into embryos this early in life will tend to enter all tissues, including the newly formed eggs or sperm of the fetus. Consequently, transgenic animals, when they become mature, will give rise to offspring which will also be transgenic. This potentially offers scientists a number of animals suitable for scientific study.

Injecting new genes is difficult enough, but, at present, even after successful injection the results are extremely unpredictable. Very often the fertilized egg is destroyed by the injection process. Hardly less frequently, the embryo develops lethal damage and does not develop. Most injected embryos that do develop and are subsequently born show no evidence of the injected DNA and are therefore not transgenic. Those that are transgenic may not express the gene of interest – that is, the DNA may be present in the animal's chromosomes, but it is not working. Some animals show expression, but only for a short period and, most frequently, the expression varies so that the DNA does not produce its full normal effect. Many transgenic animals are mosaic – that is, the gene is present and expressing in some cells or tissues, for example the liver, but not others, such as the brain. This can be very frustrating if the tissue of interest to the scientific team is nervous tissue, but not the liver. Injecting new genes in this way can sometimes unpredictably cause problems with other genes, perhaps by displacing them or altering their function. Moreover, transgenic animals may show serious congenital abnormalities. One expert scientist, Dr Carol Readhead, who has spent years making transgenic mice, tells how in one particular transgenic experiment she needed to inject and transfer around 1,600 mouse embryos to get a single young animal clearly expressing the gene that she needed to study.

There may be a number of ways of improving the poor success rates involved in making transgenic animals. One exciting idea which is being tested, and which would revolutionize transgenic technology, involves targeting sperm cells with new genes rather than embryos. The testis is making new sperm cells all the time during reproductive life. These sperm cells are derived from primitive stem cells, called spermatogonia. It is possible to remove spermatogonia from the testis and place them in culture. Once in culture, there are a number of ways in which new genes can be encouraged to enter these cells. One method involves attaching the transgene of interest to a suitable virus. Once in culture, the viruses infect the spermatogonia cells and release their own DNA and the DNA which has been piggy-backed with them. These new genes may then become incorporated into the spermatogonia. In any culture, only a certain number of cells will become invaded (or transfected) by the new gene, but there are various ways of assessing which cells are transgenic and sorting them away from the unsuccessfully transfected cells. These modified spermatogonia can then be returned to the testis. To prepare the testis for receipt of these new cells, it will have first been depopulated of all non-transgenic sperm, possibly by X-radiation or by the use of chemotherapeutic drugs which destroy growing sperm cells. Consequently, after transfer of the new spermatogonia, that animal will only produce sperm which have been modified. The beauty of this technique would be that transgenic animals would be much easier and far cheaper to produce, simply by natural mating – rather than by complicated embryo manipulation. This technique would also have the advantage that it could be applied to large animals. Currently, transgenic technology using embryos is so cumbersome that really only mice are generally used. For example, it costs over £25,000 to make a transgenic pig, suitable for one human cardiac transplant. This technology could be applied cheaply to a whole range of large animals such as cattle, sheep, pigs and monkeys.

However, manipulation of embryos is still likely to be the main way of producing transgenic animals for a considerable time. There will be progress in our ability to insert new genes into any animal embryo. Advances in molecular biology will also increasingly ensure that any gene inserted will work normally and express, and that this expression will be permanent. Great strides are already being made in the field of gene insertion for gene disorders and for the treatment of cancers. In humans, so-called gene therapy has been limited to inserting genes into somatic cells – cells in tissues such as liver, muscle, nerve cells and the cells which circulate in the bloodstream. Somatic cell therapy only has implications for the patient treated, and not for any offspring, because these inserted genes do not enter sperm or egg. Germ-line therapy – insertion of genes into embryos or germ cells (that is, eggs or sperm) so that these genes are inherited – is likely to be feasible in future. If it is possible to make transgenic mice, it is surely possible to make transgenic humans.

There are essentially two reasons for wishing to introduce new genes into human embryos. The first would be to correct gene defects which occur in that family, so that future generations would not suffer the particular disease carried in the family. Ultimately there is the notion that specific gene defects could be permanently eradicated. A second objective, perhaps further into the future, would be to introduce genes giving specific characteristics which are regarded as desirable. This concept leads to the idea of the 'designer baby'.

Not surprisingly, the idea of genetic engineering has provoked many expressions of horror and alarm. Indeed, the fear of such genetic manipulation has been so great that this was probably one of the most frequently used arguments in recent years against the development and use of IVF as a fertility therapy. For example, in the 1980s many Parliamentarians, theologians and journalists saw this as the main reason to ban embryo research completely. It is therefore worth analysing carefully the advantages, disadvantages and dangers of human genetic manipulation in embryos.

The potential advantages of germ-line therapy for disease treatment are not inconsiderable. Even though the technique is difficult, insertion of genes into embryos is likely to be easier than insertion into somatic cells. To date, numerous attempts have been made to insert 'corrected' genes into the tissues of sufferers from inherited diseases such as cystic fibrosis, but results are poor and few workers have been able to get these inserted genes to work for more than a few weeks. Moreover, because somatic gene therapy is potentially dangerous because it may induce cancers and cause other unexpected effects, it is really only considered once the disease is advanced; there are much safer and gentler treatments in the early stages of such genetic diseases. Correction of the cystic fibrosis gene in an embryo would have the huge theoretical benefit of treating the disease before it appears –

consequently there would be no suffering. Secondly, the effects are more likely to be permanent, as experience with transgenic animals has shown. It is possible to get complete integration and normal function of inserted genes in some cases. Thirdly, of course, gene insertion into the embryo does not only prevent that individual from getting the inherited disease, but prevents future generations in that family from suffering its ravages. Lastly, some people have moral objections to destroying embryos simply because they carry a defect, but feel it is perfectly permissible, indeed potentially laudable, to treat the embryo by gene insertion to make it healthy.

In spite of the instant horror with which human genetic engineering is greeted, there may, after all, be substantial and real benefit. Moreover, if treatment of genetic disease by embryonic gene injection becomes feasible, why should we not go one step further and give our children a better start in life? There are many characteristics that people might think desirable, given the ability to implement genetic enhancement. They would almost certainly include beauty, intelligence, strength, aggression, prevention of ageing, and protection against disease. As it happens we already manipulate all of these in our children and young people in varying ways. In order to make our offspring more attractive we ensure they have orthodontic treatment for unsightly teeth, and we employ the best education possible, often on a selective basis at university and secondary school, to increase their mental capacity. Strength is encouraged by physical education and young sportsmen train vigorously to ensure they are as competitive as possible. Aggression is undoubtedly encouraged in young fighting men; the training for example in the marines or the infantry is largely designed to ensure this important fighting quality. We attempt to delay ageing in numerous ways, not least by taking hormone replacement therapy even before the menopause commences. Prevention of disease is a high priority in the welfare of children in nearly all societies, with the use of vaccination and vitamins on a regular basis.

What is ethically wrong with doing the same job more simply and permanently by inserting genes and creating 'designer babies'? The objections are manifold. Firstly, such treatment may produce an inherited elite, leading to increased tensions in society, such as racial prejudice. Because such treatments are likely to be the prerogative of the privileged, they might inevitably increase the poverty gap and class distinctions. There would also be a real risk of children not meeting the expectations of their parents after genetic manipulation – with consequent fragmentation of family and society. This is already a key issue with regard to screening the fetus during pregnancy. Western society has tended to screen for inherited disorders or handicap. When an abnormality is diagnosed, there is often said to be pressure to have a pregnancy terminated. Opponents of screening claim that it leads to the devaluation of handicapped people and possibly the same would be true in a society regarding genetic enhancement as being the desirable norm. A most important argument against genetic engineering to enhance our children's attributes is that we would be choosing on a contemporary and subjective basis what is regarded as being desirable. It may well be advantageous to be tall and blond in 1997, but in a different society in years to come, perhaps when the ideal is to be short and dark, such a blond descendant might be undesirable. He or she would have inherited a given characteristic that is not only unwelcome, but disadvantageous and permanent in all future generations.

Some philosophers have argued that allowing genetic enhancement to the potential offspring of interested couples is simply an extension of procreational liberties. This respects the autonomy of prospective parents. However, what is surely ethically unacceptable is to remove the autonomy of a future generation from choosing what it sees as in its best interests.

But, above all, the real ethical argument against introducing new genes into human embryos is the recognition that the effects of gene insertion are at present unpredictable. We could cause severe congenital handicap or disability. Mouse experiments have now been continued for about twenty years, but transgenic animals still frequently turn out to express unwanted or unpredictable traits than they do those desired by the scientists. There is no absolute guarantee that the DNA will be inserted into the correct part of the animal's chromosomes, the genome, or any certainty that other essential 'natural' genes may not be displaced or altered. This unpredictability is a cogent reason why transgenic technology is unlikely to be applied to humans in the near future.

Leaving aside any considerations of morality or medical duty, no physician could afford to risk the medico-legal consequences. Not only can parents sue for a genetic mistake, but nowadays any deformed or disadvantaged child that results from such an experiment could successfully pursue a genetic engineering doctor through the law courts.

As it happens germ-line gene therapy to correct genetic disorders is a largely unnecessary technology. In order to treat an embryo by gene insertion, doctors would first need to know that it carried the defect needing treatment. With virtually all gene disorders only some of the embryos from a carrier couple will be affected. In order to confirm that an embryo is affected with a gene defect, preimplantation diagnosis would be needed. Given that access to embryos for gene manipulation is always likely to be by IVF and that several embryos will be available, it will be simpler – as well as safer – simply to transfer those embryos diagnosed free of the particular defect.

The notion of genetic manipulation of embryos for desired characteristics cannot, however, simply be dismissed on the basis of the availability of preimplantation diagnosis. Enhancement certainly would require the addition or altering of genes. Nevertheless, this too is extremely unlikely in the foreseeable future. Even if scientists in the long-distant future are able clearly to verify the complete safety of gene transfer in embryos, there would still be huge problems. Popular notions of genetic inheritance obfuscate the real issue. Beauty, intelligence, aggression and so on are not produced by the interaction of one or even a few genes. The genetic component of these traits is extremely complex but probably all the components need to be present. Take, as an example, the disease diabetes. Like height or strength, it has a strong genetic basis. Diabetes is a relatively simple disease, basically an intolerance to sugar which is caused by lack of insulin secretion from the pancreatic gland – unlike the trait of height or strength, a very simple but invariable mechanism. Yet diabetes is a multigenic disorder; we know of at least twenty separate genes on several different chromosomes which are likely to predispose to it. Consider how many different genetic interactions must have to take place for the creation of such 'desirable' qualities as beauty or intelligence. It is very unlikely that in the foreseeable future geneticists could unravel such complex knots and give us the DNA keys to enhancing our inheritance.

So much for what can be foreseen. Yet in the longer term, I think it very likely that germ-line gene therapy will be applied in humans because of its huge potential. The problem of its unpredictability will eventually be capable of solution by improved understanding of molecular biology and repeated, meticulous experimentation in various animal species. Paradoxically, the greatest value of germ-line gene therapy is likely to be in preventing multigenic diseases. Fifty per cent of us in the western world currently die of heart disease and the risk of developing coronary artery disease is highest in those people whose parents or grandparents suffered from it. Children of a diabetic parent have approximately between a 25 to 50 per cent chance of being diabetic themselves. Which of us carrying genes which predispose to these diseases, or diseases like Alzheimer's, would not prefer to see that our children have a reduced risk? By repairing or removing some of the genes in our germ cells which may induce these disorders, we may diminish these risks substantially.

The key could be to target sperm cells. Eventually, with merely a little local anaesthetic, it may be possible to inject protective genes directly into the testicle, where they could, with suitable chemical help, be incorporated into the developing sperms. With disorders which are multigenic, it will be possible to identify the best gene sequence to introduce to give at least partial protection. This would lower the risk of a susceptible family suffering, for example, from heart disease or diabetes. This technique would avoid all the complexities, expense and inconvenience of *in vitro* fertilization. It would be rather like vaccination but it would not only protect our children, but generations beyond. As well as reducing suffering, such an approach will have phenomenal economic advantages. The rising cost of health care – a major concern to all governments – could be controlled in future times. Such powerful technology will need the most stringent care if it is not to be abused, but its carefully regulated use seems eventually inevitable.

Cloning Humans

A clone is an individual, or a group of individuals, genetically indentical to another individual. Thus, identical twins – coming from one egg after spontaneous splitting following fertilization with a single sperm – are natural clones containing identical genes. Artificial cloning is not new. Humans have used plant clones for centuries, certainly since ancient Greece. MacIntosh apple trees, for example, are all a clone, having been produced from a single mutated plant, and all share identical genes. One of the first researchers to work seriously with animal clones was Dr Gurdon, who in 1968 published details of making a clone of a frog. He transplanted the nucleus from a tadpole's intestine into the egg of another frog. The egg had been previously prepared by destroying its own nucleus. Once the new nucleus took over function, the egg divided and grew into a mature frog – without any sperm being involved in fertilization. With the transfer of more nuclei from the same tadpole into more frogs' eggs, many identical frogs could be produced. Initially it was impossible to use the nucleus of a mature mammal for cloning, and until recently all experiments with cloning were done using a nucleus taken from an embryo. Amphibians such as frogs are a good deal easier to clone and it is only in the last fifteen years or so that scientists have found ways of making mammal clones of, for example, pigs and sheep. A major development occurred in 1997 when Dr Ian Wilmut and his colleagues from Edinburgh announced that it had finally been possible to use the nucleus taken from an adult animal and transfer it to an enucleated egg. Thus Dolly the sheep was born.

The most exciting aspect of Dr Wilmut's work is that the nucleus from an adult cell is capable of being reprogrammed, being returned to 'infancy', where it can start to initiate the action of genes which only express in the earliest stages of development. Study of these and related phenomena will give us great insight into how cells are normally controlled and what goes wrong with this control – for example, in the genesis of cancers.

The ability to clone a mammal from an adult cell raised a spectre which still haunts the mind of the public. There was an immediate outcry when Wilmut and colleagues published their work. Quite serious and mature journalists argued that it was now merely a matter of time before some rich, elderly or powerful man, possibly an American – or, worse still, Saddam Hussein of Iraq – invested in this technology to reinvent himself. There was much talk of grieving people 'stealing' skin cells from some recently deceased relative and having the cells frozen for later cloning technology. Others suggested that misguided parents might want to clone children prematurely dead, possibly after being killed in an accident.

It is not easy to see a clear ethical objection to cloning a single individual on an isolated basis, not least because twins naturally occur already and their existence presents no obvious ethical problem. However, the thought of large numbers of clones from a single individual seems very different. But it is doubtful whether there could ever be any point in such an enterprise, unless it be to pander to some authoritarian dictator. It is, as we shall see, extremely unlikely that the authoritarian dictator would get much satisfaction from the fruits of his enterprise.

Much of the recent debate over cloning seems rather superficial and ill-judged. While there is a perfectly understandable objection to making 'carbon copies' of people, I do not believe that the technology behind cloning is nearly as threatening as it first appeared. Firstly, there is no chance at all that any individual created by nuclear transfer would be identical to the parent from whom the nucleus was taken. Although nearly all our DNA is held in the nucleus, a much smaller part of it is in the mitochondria – small organelles present in the cytoplasm of the egg. Consequently, the egg as well as the parent nucleus would contribute DNA to that individual. In genetic terms, that individual would be less similar to his or her parent than would identical twins be to each other. Moreover, we are undoubtedly a product of our nurture as much as our genetic nature. Even twins brought up together are entirely separate individuals with their own personality. In the case of a clone, the parent being an adult would inevitably have been brought up in entirely different circumstances from the cloned offspring. Who knows how a clone of a skin cell of an individual like Adolf Hitler might grow up given a warm and sustaining environment. He could be loving and gentle, and even contribute greatly to society.

There is a clear need to continue research into cloning. These technologies will have very significant applications for both human and animal well-being in the twenty-first century. There will be immense clinical value in being able to clone human tissues and organs, rather than whole people. Over the next decade or so there will be much research into the control of how cells differentiate. The embryo starts with just a few cells, each of which as we have seen, is totipotential – that is, capable of generating into a complete organism. The exciting challenge will be to manipulate embryonic cells so that they grow into just skin, or just muscle – or whatever tissue is needed. At present, when an individual contracts leukaemia there is a desperate search to find a compatible bone-marrow donor. Even if one is found, and a bone-marrow graft is successful, there follows a life of immune suppression with unpleasant and expensive drug therapy to ensure that the vital graft is not rejected. In the very far future, leukaemia could potentially be treated by taking the nucleus from one of the cells of the patient and then growing new bone-marrow cells which would be immunologically compatible; consequently there would be no rejection and no need to take immune suppressive drugs afterwards. This kind of approach, with modification, could be used for skin cells to provide skin banks for burns victims and other patients undergoing plastic surgery for various disfiguring lesions. It could be used to produce nervous tissue cells for transplantation into patients suffering from Parkinson's disease and other degenerative conditions. We could provide banks of muscle cells to treat the muscles of children weakened by various incurable forms of muscular dystrophy.

Cloning would also be of potential value for men suffering from intractable infertility. Some men cannot produce sperm because their testes are depleted of spermatogonia. One solution might be to make a clone. For many married couples, this would be ethically much more justifiable than using donor semen from, say, an anonymous donor. But refinements of cloning could allow for new cells which would effectively replace sperm. Sperm and eggs are different from all other cells in the body in having one copy of each of the normally paired chromosomes. This state prepares them for fertilization, so that the egg, when it develops, has paired chromosomes with one copy from the father and one from the mother. In time it may be possible to remove the nucleus of an adult cell having manipulated it to lose one set of chromosomes. This nucleus could then be injected into a normal egg which contains its own nucleus. This could then potentially develop like any fertilized embryo, with half its genes maternally derived and half paternally.

Another benefit of cloning would be in producing transgenic animals. Some scientists are presently claiming that the cloning of cattle might be used to produce whole herds with desirable traits – for example, very good milk yields, or excellent muscle for beef. This seems unlikely and I believe dangerous. Cloning a herd would result in loss of genetic diversity, which is a useful protective mechanism. A genetically engineered herd which turned out to have little resistance to foot-and-mouth disease would be a liability, not an asset. Cloning might have much more use to produce transgenic animals, raised for medical purposes – such as organ transplantation. Recently there has been much interest in the use of transgenic pigs for transplantation. There is an acute shortage of spare hearts and other tissues, such as heart valves. Once a genetically engineered pig has been raised with the appropriate human genes, cloning would provide a convenient way of expanding the herd without loss of the unique genetic make-up needed for medical purposes. Cloning could also have important implications for the preservation and breeding of endangered species. Once initial clones had been obtained, they could subsequently be allowed to breed naturally so as to encourage normal genetic diversity.

Cloning, then, is unlikely to be used to produce multiple copies of similar or identical human beings. Although powerful technologies like this may cause considerable anxiety, there is little doubt that the benefits that could be derived from this research are really very significant. It should be perfectly possible to regulate these techniques in future, possibly by international agreement, so that they are used for the good, not to the detriment, of mankind.

Ectogenesis

In Aldous Huxley's novel *Brave New World*, human embryos were kept in vats, where they developed into fetuses. Birth was achieved by a process of decanting.

It is possible to keep rodent embryos outside the body for the early stages of development, and this has been applied experimentally in studies of placental development and in studies on toxicology. However, all mammalian embryos rapidly become too big to allow them to survive without a placenta supplying oxygen, nutriments and foodstuffs. There has never been the slightest success in developing an artificial placenta, which grows and adapts rapidly to the changing needs of the growing fetus. The development of an artificial placenta would be of great theoretical benefit in treating a number of congenital disorders. It would also help the understanding of the genesis of a number of diseases specific to pregnancy, for example toxaemia, and the causes of birth defects. However, given the complexity of placental function, and the extraordinary nature of its rapid growth and development, it seems most unlikely that scientists will be able to reproduce even a crude copy of this organ in the foreseeable future. For the time being, it seems, women will continue to give birth in the old-fashioned manner.

Contraception and the Population Explosion

Although humans are, relatively speaking, a very infertile species, they are extraordinarily prolific. Our intelligence and our ability to use tools means we protect ourselves from adverse environmental conditions. Consequently our fecundity now threatens the planet.

The issue of population growth and its control is certainly not new. As observed earlier, the ancient Egyptians used the expedient of infanticide to reduce the effects of the fertility of their Hebrew slaves. Much more recently, in the 1790s, Thomas Malthus proposed that Britain was heading for disaster. Continued expansion of the population from the then figure of around eight million meant that Britain would run out of food by 1900, when he miscalculated that there would be 112 million people to feed. As it happens, a number of unpredictable events such as improved hygiene and changing demography slowed population growth.

It is true that effective contraception is a very recent development and has already had profound social consequences in the improvement of our society. It has, above all, empowered women. Until this century, most women who were not prepared merely to accept menial or domestic activity had to choose between a career or marriage. Women who wanted a productive profession simply did not get married. Marie Curie, the pioneer physicist who isolated and purified radium, was one of the rare exceptions. This was because she was most unusually supported by her husband Pierre.

Unfortunately, world over-population is now a very genuine threat. In the years to 2010 we may face a population increase of around 15 to 25 per cent, around a thousand million people – more than the total population of India. Moreover most of these people will be born in the parts of the world least able to provide the resources needed for such an increase. There will be need for increased food, health services, employment, social security, sewage, maintenance of law and order, and education of course, on an unprecedented scale. Given that the world is already starting to see the effects of deforestation and global warming; that more pollution on a massive scale is almost inevitable; that social instability, both nationally and internationally is at risk; and, above all, that the population may continue to grow almost exponentially, these are very serious reproductive issues indeed. Under these circumstances, the manipulation of reproduction becomes one of the most important scientific issues of our time.

Contraceptive technology is clearly going to be one way of dealing with this burgeoning population. However, experience suggests that contraceptive technology is likely to be less important than improvements in health and education, because birth rates are invariably highest in the most underprivileged parts of the world. Unfortunately high birth rates contribute to social deprivation, so much of the developing world is caught in a vicious circle. Perhaps help to break this circle will come to a considerable degree from improved contraceptive methods.

The existing problems with current contraception are well known. Natural methods, such as breast feeding after pregnancy, and timing intercourse, are helpful but unpredictable and unreliable. The barrier methods need considerable commitment by couples, and are frequently felt to interfere with sex and its spontaneity. Moreover, many religious groups frown on their use. Hormone preparations avoid these problems but may have a number of side-effects which worry couples; they require considerable education and compliance from couples if taken orally. Intrauterine devices are associated with bleeding and menstrual cramping in a number of women. Sterilization has been increasingly used, but its irreversible nature and the fact that an operative manoeuvre is needed limit its applicability.

Over the next decade there will be continuing attempts to improve contraception. Various developments are likely. One area in which there has been more scientific investment is vaccination. It is likely to be possible to vaccinate women against certain proteins held in the envelope surrounding the egg, the *zona pellucida*. Because the *zona* is composed of protein and because there are several different proteins on the surface of the egg, it should be possible to derive a vaccine which would block the interaction of the sperm with the egg's surface. One of the problems with this approach, as with any immunological method to control conception, is that vaccination may result in irreversible contraception. However, it is likely that a vaccine with a short duration – perhaps of a year or so – could be developed. However, it is difficult to be precise about such factors, and people in poorer countries may not know whether they are still protected. Another concern about immunization against proteins in the *zona pellucida* is that the vaccine could result in an antibody reaction to all the eggs in the ovary, causing a premature menopause. This has been found by scientists working in Edinburgh to be a problem in experimental monkeys. It may be impossible to prevent this, in which case, of course, this technology will have little future.

Another approach, using vaccines, is to immunize a woman against sperm. Sperm antibodies are a well-known cause of infertility; women having them produce a reaction from their white cells which sees the sperm as 'foreign' and destroys them. Sperm antibodies immobilize any sperm which are not destroyed, and this is therefore potentially quite an effective method of birth control. The problem here is that sperm antibodies, once formed, are extremely difficult to get rid of. Vaccination may therefore be long-lasting, and perhaps the trick may be to find the best sperm protein to limit the length of immunity. So far it has proved surprisingly difficult in animal work to produce effective immunity against sperm at all.

One of the more promising approaches to immunization is to produce a vaccine against the hormones which are produced by the developing embryo. These hormones are proteins. The main pregnancy hormone is called human chorionic gonadotrophin (HCG). HCG is the hormone which can be detected in the bloodstream and urine about ten days after conception, and is the basis of the modern pregnancy test. It is a molecule composed effectively of two parts, a so-called alpha unit and a beta unit. If a large foreign protein is attached to the beta unit, it rejects. Preliminary vaccines have been developed and have been tested by the World Health Organization. Problems with the method include variability of immune response, variable duration, possible interference with other hormones in the body which have a rather similar structure, and the risk of causing miscarriages in later pregnancy. The last problem would be particularly serious in developing countries with poor economic and health resources.

One area which was thought promising, but in which too little research is currently proceeding, is the area of drugs which interfere with pituitary gland function in the brain. It is possible to block the production of FSH by giving so-called gonadotrophin-releasing hormone antagonists (GnRH). These drugs, which are used sometimes during IVF treatment and for the treatment of endometriosis, make a woman semi-menopausal by damping down ovarian activity. They can be given by depot injection once every month, or even every three months. As these drugs are particularly safe, the approach is rather attractive. The current problem is the temporary menopausal symptoms they cause, and also occasional irregular vaginal bleeding. It is possible in future that these drugs could be mixed with a small amount of oestrogen – as a kind of hormone replacement therapy – to provide a safe and symptom-free balance.

Envoi

It is a pretty foolish scientist who goes out on a limb and attempts to predict the future. In the 1830s members of the establishment predicted that it would be completely unsafe for humans to travel faster than thirty miles an hour. One is reminded of Leonardo da Vinci in the Court of Francesco Sforza of Milan in 1495. There he drew a heavier-than-air machine which was designed to fly, to the amusement and incredulity of the courtiers. Five hundred years later (a tiny space in man's history on this planet), a view of flight paths and schedules in and out of Milan International Airport might give those same courtiers pause for greater thought.

What is very clear, however, is that whatever happens in the future, human reproduction and its manipulation are going to pose some impressive and threatening challenges both scientifically and, more particularly, ethically. I do not share the horror of those people who are often illiterate about technology and who claim we have started to open a Pandora's box which threatens human welfare. It is fashionable in a society threatened by environmental deterioration and the visions of nuclear destruction to say that technology has gone too far. Yet we do not ban the modern methods of travel because of the greenhouse effect, nor the computer because of its possible use by belligerents. What we do is to regulate, modify and control the technology. Who is to decry Prometheus' gift of fire, simply because of the destruction of London in 1666, or the holocaust of Dresden in 1944? Whatever the future brings, we have to ensure that reproductive technology is used for human happiness and welfare, and to promote and protect human life and its dignity. That is a challenge which is worth taking and, I believe, achievable.

Glossary

Amino acid There are around twenty or so different amino acids. They are essentially the building blocks which combined together make the larger molecule, a protein. Proteins will all be different depending on which amino acids they contain.

Amniocentesis The investigation done at around twelve to seventeen weeks of pregnancy to assess the normality of the developing fetus. Fluid sucked from the sac surrounding the baby is analysed in the laboratory.

Antral stage Late stage of follicle (q.v.) development in the ovary when the egg starts to mature.

Apoptosis Cell death. Cells in all organs are continuously dying and being replaced. Apoptosis is the phenomenon of programmed or 'planned' cell death which is controlled by genetic influences. This is different from cell death from disease or injury.

Biopsy Removal of tissue or cells from the body or from an embryo for analysis.

Blastocyst Stage of embryonic development at around five days.

Chorionic tissue Cells from the developing placenta, sometimes biopsied for antenatal diagnosis of defects.

Chromosomes Structures on which the genes are placed. The human genome (q.v.) is essential to our genetic library, and each chromosome is a volume in that library. In humans there are twenty-three pairs of chromosomes, one-half of the pair inherited from the father, one from the mother. In addition there are two sex chromosomes, two copies of the X giving femaleness, and an X and Y forming a male.

Dominant genetic defect A genetic defect which, when inherited from either parent, invariably expresses and causes the disease. Consequently only one copy of the genetic mutation is required, on either chromosome, for expression (see also Recessive genetic defect).

Ectogenesis Development of the baby artificially, outside the uterus.

Endometrium The uterine lining into which the developing embryo implants.

Follicle The cystic structure in which an egg develops in the ovary. Initially about a millimetre in diameter, it grows to around 20 millimetres before rupturing at the time of ovulation.

FSH Insertion of genes into cells to combat genetic defects, or diseases such as cancer with a genetic component.

Genome The total composition of DNA in the body. The genome is effectively the blueprint of body function. The human genome project is the attempt to analyse the complete sequence of DNA in the genome.

Germ cell Either sperm or egg, or precursor cells which go to make these cells.

Glutamine An essential amino acid, required for normal life.

HCG Human chorionic gonadotrophin, the pregnancy hormone produced by cells in the placental tissue in the developing embryo.

HFEA Human Fertilization and Embryology Authority. The government regulatory authority set up in the UK to monitor and police all aspects of human IVF and donor insemination.

Hyperstimulation A serious condition caused by over-stimulation by the drugs given to induce ovulation. On very rare occasions it has even been known to be fatal.

In vitro Biological processes (e.g. fertilization of an embryo) which are activated outside the living body.

In vivo Biological processes which occur within the living body.

Intracytoplasmic Injection of a single sperm into the substance of an egg to induce fertilization in cases of severe male infertility.

Laparoscopy The insertion of a telescope into the abdomen to inspect the pelvic organs.

Laparotomy Surgical exploration of the abdominal contents through an open incision.

Lesch-Nyhan A crippling genetic sex-linked disorder affecting boys. The syndrome causes severe metabolic disturbances including kidney failure, and is one cause of physical handicap.

Mitochondria Small organelles present in every cell which contain a small part of our DNA. This DNA is mainly concerned with the genes which are responsible for some key metabolic processes.

Multigenic disease A disease caused by several genes interacting, or predisposing to it.

Nucleus The command structure of the cell which contains the great majority of the DNA.

Parthenogenesis Production of an embryo without sperm, that is without the process of fertilization.

Phenotype The physical characteristics of any organism which are largely determined by its genes (or genotype) but also influenced by environmental factors. Thus a child suffering from limb deformities caused by thalidomide will have a normal genotype – with normal genes – but an abnormal phenotype.

Preimplantation The diagnosis of defects, usually genetic or chromosomal, in embryos before the embryo has implanted in the mother's uterus.

Recessive genetic defect A genetic defect which causes disease only if the gene responsible is present on both the maternal and paternal chromosome. People having the gene defect merely on one of the chromosomes are said to be carriers, that is they can pass the gene on but are not affected themselves.

Recombinant Genetically engineered, i.e. produced by altering the composition of the DNA.

Sex-linked genetic defect A genetic defect inherited on the X chromosome. In affected cases, only males express the disease, while females may be carriers.

Somatic cell Any cell in the body which is differentiated for a particular function – such as skin, liver, gut – and therefore not a germ cell (q.v.).

Spermatogonia Primitive or precursor cells which in turn give rise to sperm.

Transgenic animal Any animal which has had new 'foreign' genes incorporated into it during early development. Because its germ cells will also be transgenic its offspring will inherit the same genes.

Zona pellucida The glycoprotein 'shell' or coat that surrounds and protects the unfertilized egg, and subsequently the embryo during the first five days after fertilization. At around five days, the zona pellucida ruptures and the embryo hatches, ready for implantation.

9 Disease

MATT RIDLEY

A Tale of Two Viruses

In 1972, a woman – we'll call her by her medical name, Patient 3 – left her home in the district of Yambuku in central Zaire and made the long journey to the city of Kinshasa. She lived there as a *femme libre* for four years, making ends meet by prostitution. In 1976 she returned to Yambuku at the age of thirty-six. Shortly after her arrival, but through no fault of hers, the place became a vision of hell. Inexplicably and suddenly people began to die. They did not die peacefully; they disintegrated. One day they felt aches in their joints and a sore throat. Three days of feverish, delirious vomiting later, covered in skin pustules, bleeding from nose, mouth and rectum, they went into fatal shock. Within a month, forty people had died in Patient 3's village – a place of just 300 souls. They were the first recorded victims of possibly the most deadly strain of virus ever discovered: Ebola Zaire.

But Patient 3 did not die of Ebola virus. Perhaps she stayed away from the mission hospital where most victims caught the disease, from hypodermic needles used and reused by the well-meaning nuns of the Soeurs du Saint Coeur Marie. Perhaps she had no close relatives to bury so she did not evacuate the bowels of a corpse by hand in the traditional pre-funereal ritual. Certainly she was alive when Belgian and American doctors flew into the area in search of clues to the cause of the outbreak; they took a blood sample from her.

Or perhaps she was already unwell for a different reason. A few months after the Ebola plague, as she counted her luck at having survived it, she began to suffer from diarrhoea. She could not shake off her cough. She frequently felt feverish. She began to lose weight. Her health went from bad to terrible. By the middle of the next year, she was dead. She is buried in Yambuku beneath a simple gravestone. The blood sample, held in a freezer in Atlanta,

Georgia, holds a clue to her premature death. In 1976 she was HIV-positive. Her sample is the oldest blood sample in the world with the AIDS virus in it.

Where she contracted HIV remains a mystery, but she did so many years before it was known to science and a decade before people began to die of AIDS all across Central Africa. She was not alone: four other people in the Yambuku area carried antibodies to the virus at the same time; three are dead. Chances are, HIV was a rare but ancient infection of people in the basin of the Congo river. Patient 3 may even have been the first person to carry it to the brothels of Kinshasa, whence it spread to so much of the rest of the world. More likely, somebody had already carried it there and she brought it back east into the forest. Whatever the truth, Patient 3 dodged one plague new to the human race, but not a second. The rest of humankind would soon do the same. In the twenty-one years since then, Ebola virus has turned out to be a paper tiger, incapable of sustaining a major epidemic for long – too lethal for its own good.

HIV, far less easy to catch but much better at keeping its victims healthy enough to infect others, is rapidly joining the great plagues of history. It is less contagious than bubonic plague, smallpox or measles. It spreads more slowly than influenza or cholera. It kills more gradually than typhus or yellow fever. But like those diseases in their heydays it is global, frequently fatal and cruelly hard to cure. In 1976 the medical world was celebrating the imminent extinction of smallpox, which would officially happen a year later with the recovery of Ali Maow Maalin in Somalia – the last man to catch the disease in the wild. Yet all we had achieved was to swap one plague for another. We enter the third millennium with as many dangerous parasites on board as ever.

The conventional wisdom about infectious disease has swung from one extreme to another. From the hubristic optimism of the 1960s, when the United States Surgeon-General said we could 'close the book on infectious disease', we have plunged into alarmism. Publishers and film producers have reopened the book with lucrative results. *The Hot Zone, Outbreak, Plagues, Virus X, The Coming Plague, Plagues and Progress, The Virus Hunters*: the titles of recent books screech their pessimism. All argue, to a greater or lesser extent, that we are doomed unless we take urgent action. Infectious death is on the way back into our lives, part of the planet's ecological revenge for our despoliation of it. It has happened to other successful species. Irish potato blight altered world history. Dutch elm disease spared hardly an elm tree in Britain. Myxomatosis killed 99 per cent of southern Australia's rabbits in its first wave. Could it be our turn next?

This book makes two predictions in answer to that question. The first is that there is no end to the struggle with disease. Infection is never going to be entirely defeated, however well we organize our governments, however ingeniously we invent new cures and however much we stop interfering with nature. The ten or eleven billion people that will inhabit this globe at the peak of world population midway through the next century present too tempting a target to the microbial world, too gigantic an ecological niche to be left vacant. It is not in the nature of the war of attrition between a parasite and its host for either side to declare victory or accept defeat. There is no such thing as surrender.

Yet, second, much pessimism is misplaced. Some fatal, epidemic and chronic diseases will persist for ever. But most of the successful ones will be mild, like colds, or relatively hard to catch, like AIDS. And, far from living near the end of a brief golden age of drugs – after penicillin and before too many drug-resistant diseases – we are on the threshold of a new age of technology. DNA vaccines, molecular-designed drugs and genetically engineered resistance are only part of this. The other part is that played by ordinary technology. Our rat-free, mosquito-free, suburban houses, in which we live atomized, sanitized lives with purified water and little physical contact with strangers, offer handholds only to diseases that are among the mildest and most contagious. In other words, the common cold may get commoner, but mass epidemics of typhus, plague and Ebola virus are probably a thing of the past – for most of us at least. It is no accident that the common cold is actually an umbrella term covering more than 200 kinds of virus – rhinoviruses, coronaviruses, adenoviruses and others – yet none of them is life-threatening. Easy contagion and high virulence do not go together.

Plagues of the Past

The plague came down the Nile from 'Ethiopia', according to Thucydides. From Egypt it spread to Libya and then appeared suddenly in Piraeus, the port of Athens, in 430BC. It soon reached Athens itself. In a single year, it killed a quarter of the Athenian army, shattered the morale of the city and in due course handed military supremacy to Sparta.

The plague of Athens is the first well-documented epidemic. It is probably futile to speculate about what it was, because, although the symptoms were well described by Thucydides, symptoms can change, especially when a disease first reaches a virgin population. It sounds, to modern ears, remarkably like Ebola virus: sore, red throat, aching and discomfort, skin pustules, retching and bleeding. If it came down the Nile as Thucydides said, maybe it was. One of the first known outbreaks of Ebola virus occurred in Sudan in 1976 on a tributary of the Nile. We will never know.

But from that date (or probably an earlier, unrecorded one – Egypt and Babylon were visited by frequent plagues, to judge by ancient texts), the human race became afflicted by a series of epidemic plagues, nearly all of which found their main opportunity to turn virulent in cities and armies. Some of these diseases, like Shigella dysentery, mumps, diphtheria and chicken pox, were simply old human pathogens that had taken the opportunity of denser human populations to turn virulent. Others may have recently jumped into the human species from their domesticated animals – measles from dogs and smallpox from cattle in India. Yet others were simply taking the opportunity to invade new areas where virgin immune systems awaited them.

Empires are good at spreading plagues because they send soldiers into distant lands and bring them back to mix in the empire's core. By the third century BC China was embarked on a history of sporadic plagues that continued until the present century. Empires also infected each other. In 162AD, a Chinese plague of unprecedented ferocity killed one-third of some armies fighting in the west of the empire. Just three years later, the Rome of Marcus Aurelius was devastated by a plague brought back by soldiers from the east. Outbreaks continued for fifteen years, weakening the empire and inviting barbarian invasions: in repulsing one of which, Marcus Aurelius himself died of the fever. This may have been the first appearance of measles in the Mediterranean. A century later in 251AD an even more vicious disease appeared, possibly smallpox. Rome was brought to its knees, never to recover its pre-eminence.

Constantinople's turn came in 542, at just the moment when Belisarius was on the brink of reuniting the Roman empire. This, the great plague of Justinian, announced the arrival in Europe, perhaps for the first time, of bubonic plague. According to one calculation, 48 per cent of the city's population died. Plague's main effect over the next two centuries was to shift the centre of civilization from the depopulated Mediterranean to Christendom and Islamic Arabia. The plague reached China a century later, probably by sea.

For Europe, there then came a long pause. Disease continued to kill and disable during the Dark Ages and medieval period, but sudden and widespread epidemics seemed to peter out. Even during the Crusades, the worst mortality among besieging soldiers came from the non-infectious scurvy. The reason may be the feudal system, which encouraged a more even spread of the population, less trade and smaller cities. In China, too, there is a hint that the terrible plagues of the seventh century were not repeated with such intensity for 500 years. When an epidemic returned, it was not a new disease, but bubonic plague again.

Bubonic plague is a bacterial disease carried by fleas that will find a reservoir in any wild burrowing rodent. It is probably indigenous only in India, the original home of the black rat. But at some point it reached the rodents of the steppes of Central Asia and was delivered afresh by the Mongols to various parts of their empire. It reached Europe in 1346 aboard a ship from the Crimea, and found cities with thatched roofs teeming with black rats that dropped their fleas upon human backs. How many people died in this, the worst of all the epidemics? A third, says Froissart, half or more of those in some cities, say modern historians. A quarter even of rural peasants, say the demographers. Population continued to fall for nearly a century as waves of plague returned with diminishing severity.

As it recovered, Europe began to open up to the world, its trading and colonizing tentacles reaching around Africa to India and China, as well as across the Atlantic. This process brought Europeans three new epidemic diseases, one probably from America, one probably from Arabia and one probably from China. Syphilis, the virulent and sexually transmitted form of yaws, was almost certainly unknown in the Old World. To this day, despite frequent reports to the contrary, older skeletons showing syphilitic deformities have failed to appear on the eastern shore of the Atlantic, whereas they are common in the Americas. Syphilis reached Spain soon after Columbus' voyage, a coincidence too good to ignore, and by 1495 it was epidemic in a French army retreating from Naples. For nearly a century, the 'pox' would trouble Europe, ushering in a new religious abhorrence of sex.

Also making its European debut in Spain, and also playing its part in a siege of Naples (in 1528) was typhus, a louse-carried bacterium that would henceforth be the scourge of armies, jails and poor houses right into the twentieth century. Typhus probably came with the Moors from the Middle East, where it was known already; it first killed Europeans in 1489 in the wars between Spaniards and Arabs over the kingdom of Granada. If syphilis helped spark the religious purification that led to the Reformation, typhus took advantage of the religious wars that followed. In 1632 at Gustavus Adolphus' siege of Nuremberg, 29,000 of the besieged died in seven weeks while the typhus, showing no impartiality, forced the besiegers to retreat, leaving heaps of corpses behind them.

From China, meanwhile, came influenza, a strangely evanescent virus of wild ducks, new strains of which are still transmitted to man through domesticated Chinese ducks and pigs. Although it may have existed in Europe at an earlier date, the first great epidemic of influenza in Europe occurred in the 1550s. To this day new Chinese strains of influenza soon spread to Europe, though none has ever achieved the virulence of the strain that found its niche in the armies of the First World War.

But Europeans gave more than they got. In 1506, nine years after Vasco da Gama rounded the Cape of Good Hope, there was a devastating plague all across the Chinese empire. Was it some European speciality such as measles or smallpox? The Spaniards gave to the natives of America not only their home-grown scourges – smallpox reached Mexico in 1520, the year after Cortez, and measles in 1531 – but also their newly acquired ones: typhus in 1545 and influenza in the 1560s. The natives of the Americas, made vulnerable by their passage through a cold and narrow genetic bottleneck on the Bering isthmus 11,000 years before, were not only free of most diseases but were immunologically monotonous, which rendered them easy prey to the European germs. Germs adapt to the defences of their hosts; if an adaptation works in one individual, it will work in others that have similar genes. North, South and Central America suffered a population collapse unprecedented in history. Mexico's population shrank from twenty-five million to three million; Inca Peru's from eight million to one million. From being the most populous city in the world, Mexico City declined to a little town.

Meanwhile an old European disease, leprosy, was on the wane. Its decline, however, was probably caused by the resurgence of another, closely related disease, tuberculosis. Leprosy was prob-ably originally a disease caught from water buffalo. Tuberculosis, like smallpox, jumped from cattle. They competed for the same niche, because immunity to one gives cross-immunity to the other. By the end of the Middle Ages, leprosy was almost extinct, but tuberculosis was rampant. It soon acquired an ability to infect human beings that would make it – even today – the most effective killer of all the infectious diseases. Every year it infects eight million new victims and takes maybe two million lives.

Tuberculosis thrived in post-medieval Europe for two principal reasons: the close proximity of strangers, in towns and cities, gave it the opportunity to spread; and the monotonous diet of the urban poor provided victims with weak immune systems in which the bacterium could get a beachhead. It was the archetypal symp-tom of the industrial age. When conditions began gradually to improve for the poor, tuberculosis began a long retreat – many decades before effective antibiotics became available. But its reappearance in multidrug-resistant form in recent years alongside AIDS and intravenous drug abuse is a symptom of how far we are from defeating it. The number of new cases diagnosed each year worldwide rose from seven and a half million in 1990 to nearly ten million in 1996.

The large cities of the industrial age gave an unprecedented opportunity to water-borne epidemic diseases, especially typhoid, dysentery and cholera. Cholera, as far as we can judge, was an endemic disease of the heavily populated Ganges delta until Calcutta became a large city under British rule. Then, quite suddenly in 1817, cholera consumed Calcutta, spread to other parts of Asia and thence to Arabia and East Africa, killing a large proportion of its many victims. In 1830, cholera reached Russia and Western Europe. Since it killed so many of its hosts and flushed itself so effectively from their bodies in diarrhoea, cholera was a disease that could sustain only brief epidemics in crowded cities where people drank water freely contaminated with sewage. As soon as sewers were separated from sources of drinking water, the pandemics of cholera ceased.

By 1960, infectious disease seemed to be on the retreat all over the world. Sanitation had defeated cholera, typhoid and dysentery. Hygiene had defeated typhus and bubonic plague. Better hospital practice had defeated scarlet fever. Nutrition was defeating tuberculosis. Vaccination was defeating smallpox and would soon defeat polio. DDT had defeated yellow fever and malaria. Antibiotics were defeating syphilis and gonorrhoea. There was no reason to be pessimistic about any germ in the world. According to the conventional wisdom of the age, the rising population of the world threatened a Malthusian crisis of starvation, not of disease.

Since then, there has been a retreat on almost all fronts. Cholera has achieved another epidemic, in Latin America. Bubonic plague broke out in India in the 1990s. Hospitals have encouraged the spread of hepatitis and drug-resistant staphylococcus. Tuberculosis is on the increase. Measles, rubella and whooping cough all mounted minor epidemics as vaccination rates began to fall. Smallpox is gone, thank goodness, and polio will be gone by 2000 (there were only about 100 cases last year), but other vaccines have failed to provide sufficient herd immunity to eradicate diseases. DDT has been defeated by resistant mosquitoes and by public alarm over the effects of the chemical on wildlife: malaria is back with a vengeance. Antibiotics are increasingly powerless in the face of drug-resistant strains of bacteria, including syphilis and gonorrhoea. And, to cap it all, a brand-new disease with high mortality has entered our species, thus far defeating all attempts to cure it or even to prevent its spread: AIDS.

The Meaning of AIDS

If I had written this book before the AIDS epidemic, I would have been unflaggingly optimistic. The setbacks in the war against disease were no more than temporary retreats. Victory was still inevitable and the chance of a new disease threatening our species in the era of vaccines, antibiotics and public health measures was remote. But AIDS drives a coach and horses through such optimism. A virus appeared that killed people. We quickly recognized it, identified its method of attack, defined its biology, read its genes, deciphered the structure of its proteins and warned the world about it. We put our best brains on to defeating it. We made it a household word. All in vain. It spread through Africa and the Americas, crossed the seas to Europe and Asia and became so entrenched in our population that it is now the leading cause of death in young adults in many parts of the world. Twelve years after its first identification, there are some glimmers of hope: drugs that seemed to delay or reverse the onset of disease in those carrying the virus. But the fact remains that we have been well and truly humiliated by this little package of proteins and genes.

We may never know for sure where the human AIDS virus came from. Its closest relative is found not in monkeys, which carry a slightly different virus, but in apes: chimpanzees in particular. Chimps are ideally suited to carrying sexually transmitted diseases, because their social lives involve promiscuous sex among most members of each troop, and regular exchange of young females between troops. In them HIV seems to be only mildly harmful, which suggests that it may have been with them for ever. But it probably crossed the species barrier many times in the past. Blood samples preserved from various parts of Central Africa suggest that it was present at low levels during the 1970s in rural areas – indeed, at levels similar to its prevalence in such rural areas today. Like cholera in Bengal, or typhus before the siege of Naples, AIDS's opportunity came with a change in human habits.

Central Africa before the 1970s was a place where people rarely travelled far from their home towns. Held in traditional and nosy communities, HIV-infected people were very unlikely to infect more than one person before they died, so the virus could not spread outside small closed circles. But then transport routes opened up across the continent and with them came prostitution. All the evidence suggests that it was in the trucks, barges and armies using these routes that HIV first reached the cities. It was at first a disease of roadside and riverside brothels. Men were travelling in unprecedented numbers and single women were selling their bodies. From the cities it quickly spread to the Caribbean and North America. In America, the newly liberated gay movement provided an ideal amplifier for the virus. With a typically male affection for casual sex uninhibited by women, gay men in the United States had begun to invent a lifestyle unprecedented in its promiscuity. Some claimed hundreds or even thousands of sexual partners in their lives. Having rid themselves of prejudice about their sexual orientation, they were not about to heed warnings of disease. Chancroid, gonorrhoea, cytomegalovirus, herpes, chlamydia and other sexually transmitted diseases began to rise rapidly: by 12 per cent a year among American gay men in the late 1970s. One gay pop singer who had had 3,000 sexual partners admitted that he had also contracted hepatitis A and B, herpes, warts, Giardia, syphilis, gonorrhoea, chlamydia, cytomegalovirus and Epstein-Barr virus, not to mention various undiagnosed infections. AIDS merely joined the queue.

As the epidemic continued, AIDS changed little. Aside from the shared needles of heroin addicts and the shared blood products of haemophiliacs, it did not invent new means of spreading and it penetrated traditional, rural, monogamous societies very little. Only in parts of Central Africa torn apart by war did the disease become common outside big cities. In this there was an important lesson for the future. In retrospect, if you had been asked to predict how a new disease would strike the modern world, you would have to conclude that it would be sexual. In the twentieth century we made it harder for diseases to spread by insect, by water and (perhaps) by sneezing and direct contact. But we made it easier for them to spread by sex. We have, you might almost say, been lucky that only one lethal virus has appeared to exploit this opportunity.

The Haemorrhagic Fevers

AIDS raised the prospect that the threat from infectious disease might come not from the reappearance of old diseases, but from the sudden emergence of new ones, or at least unrecognized ones. Hence the excitement over Lassa fever, Ebola virus and Hanta virus – an excitement which suddenly exploded after the AIDS epidemic, although each had first appeared long before AIDS. These three groups of viruses between them fuelled much of the alarmism of the 'diseases are coming' publishing boom of the mid-1990s. They are in essence very similar.

Each of these haemorrhagic fevers was as lethal as bubonic plague, at least at first. One Ebola outbreak killed more than 90 per cent of those infected. They all kill in much the same way: by causing the leakage of blood or fluid from the damaged blood vessels. Each spreads by aerosols (infected droplets from the lungs) or by direct contact with the infected blood and fluids of the victim. And each had gone unrecognized until the advent of modern microbiological techniques, when the viruses could at last be isolated.

Hanta virus and Lassa fever, like the Bolivian (Machupo) and Argentine (Junin) haemorrhagic fevers, are diseases of rodents, especially mice and voles. They are caught directly from the excreta of these animals by people living in rural areas and then spread person to person. Terrifying as they are, they have never managed to turn into major epidemics. Lassa fever causes frequent but limited outbreaks in West Africa, Machupo burned fiercely through the Bolivian town of San Joaquin in 1962, a Hanta virus killed 121 American soldiers in the Korean War and another caused a rapid epidemic that struck eighty people in the western United States in 1993.

It is unknown what would happen if an epidemic of one of

these diseases occurred in a large city (although in 1989 a Lassa fever victim did spend some weeks seeking diagnosis and treatment in Chicago hospitals without infecting anybody before he died), but the chances of any of them developing the infectivity of flu are remote. First, they incapacitate their victims quickly, which is a big mistake for diseases that wish to be spread. Only if you can be sure that mosquitoes (in the case of malaria) or sewage pipes (in the case of cholera) will carry you away does it pay to lay your victims low. All aerosol-transmitted diseases have an interest in keeping their victims active – as colds do. Second, the haemorrhagic fevers kill too quickly. This facilitates the doctors' task of tracking down the victim's contacts. Asymptomatic carriers are an essential element of many diseases – Typhoid Mary being a good example. Mary Mallon was a New York cook who did not wash her hands and infected seven families in 1906 with the typhoid of which she was an asymptomatic carrier.

Ebola virus deserves special consideration. Together with Marburg virus, which killed some monkey handlers and their contacts in Germany in 1967, it comes from a family called the filoviruses. There have been almost annual outbreaks, the latest being those in Kikwit, Zaire (1995) and Gabon (1994–6). More than 200 people died in the Kikwit outbreak, which started with a forest charcoal worker. But antibodies in the blood of pygmies shows that the disease has probably been endemic in Central Africa for a long time. The animal reservoir remains unknown for certain, but all indications point at the bats. When artificially infected with the virus, all animals and plants so far tried either die or kill the virus – except bats. Bats infected with Ebola remain healthy but reproduce the virus in large quantities. Moreover, the only locations where known index cases probably caught the virus (on two occasions in both cases) were bat-infested: the Kitum cave on Mount Elgon and the Nzara cotton factory in Sudan.

Quite how the virus spreads from bats to human beings is uncertain, but in several cases it has come via monkeys or apes. Ebola is as lethal to other primates as it is to people, but it is from infected and dying primates that people have usually caught the disease. Perhaps the primates catch the disease from fruit licked by fruit bats during the previous night. In the latest outbreak, in

Gabon in 1994, the epidemic began with a man who hunted and ate a chimpanzee.

So why, after centuries of slow-burn in the rainforest, did Ebola suddenly mount eight brief epidemics in twenty years? Is it, as some have suggested, a sort of ecological revenge by the wounded ecosystem of a ravished planet, a punishment for our transgression upon nature? No. The answer is simple, disturbing and deeply ironic. The cause of Ebola virus's new ability to break out is modern medicine. What happened in Yambuku is typical. A man walked into a mission hospital complaining of fever. The sisters gave him an injection of quinine. He was one of hundreds of patients injected that day. In a part of Zaire with no access to medical care at all, the mission hospital was overwhelmed with requests which the sisters were loath to refuse. But they had few hypodermic needles, and time was short so the needles were sterilized only once a day. In the queue behind the man, there was perhaps a pregnant woman who had come for a regular jab with B vitamins. The same needle was used for both. Three-quarters of those who caught the Ebola virus caught it from the nuns' needles: 92 per cent of those who caught it this way died.

In Sudan, it was a similar hospital that amplified the disease, and again in Kikwit more recently. In Marburg and Reston it was the trade in monkeys for medical research that brought the virus to the West. Modern medicine, not ecological disturbance, gave us Ebola epidemics. With this lesson learnt, the future of Ebola virus is clear. It will be like the Mount Elgon cases: single victims will walk into hospitals to die in agony, but, treated with care and caution, they will infect nobody else. A global pandemic of Ebola virus is highly unlikely.

Plagues of the Future

So, if not Ebola, where is the next plague to come from? A coherent guess must identify a type of pathogen, an animal species from which it would jump, a method of transmission, and a new human habit that makes it possible for the epidemic to gain an unprecedented foothold in our species. There can be no doubt that we are a tempting target. Six billion individuals, many of them constantly jetting backwards and forwards between continents, constitute a single herd of vast proportions. The rewards for a germ that colonized us would be immense. It would quickly become one of the most successful microbes in history.

First, the type of pathogen. By and large, we have found large parasites easier to deal with than small ones (and, to extend the point, we have also found predators easier to deal with than parasites). This is perhaps because of their complex life cycles. Tape worms, round worms and hook worms – the really big parasites – have been fairly easily defeated in most countries. Smaller invertebrate parasites, like the flukes that cause schistosomiasis and the worms that cause river blindness (onchocerciasis), are more problematic, but are generally retreating in more areas than they are advancing. They have rarely caused epidemic plagues. Fungi and yeasts, too, are not much of a threat and never really have been. Protozoa are more intractable enemies: malaria, sleeping sickness, Chagas' disease, Leishmaniasis and amoebic dysentery in particular. They are not usually difficult to treat, but they are hard to prevent. Until very recently they evaded all attempts to vaccinate. A malaria vaccine may at last have been minted. Called the 'Columbian' vaccine it has shown promise in field trials in Tanzania.

Serious as they are, most protozoan diseases are not new. With the exception of Leishmaniasis, which first appeared in India in

1824, they are 'heirlooms' that have been with us for aeons. Much the same can be said of bacterial diseases, on the next step down in size (most bacteria are about one-tenth the length of most protozoa). Although bacteria have mounted some remarkable insect-borne and aerosol-spread epidemics – bubonic plague and tuberculosis, for example – their speciality is the water-borne disease: cholera, typhoid and shigella dysentery. We have on the whole found ways to close that niche. Emerging bacterial diseases tend to be newly virulent forms of old diseases (such as E[scherichia] coli 0157:H7, which first kidnapped virulent genes from shigella dysentery in about 1982) or bacteria exploiting highly specialized new niches such as Legionella. Moreover, antibiotics have given us a formidable armoury against bacteria. Some are hard to treat, others quickly devise resistance to many or all antibiotics, but it would be very surprising if a brand-new human bacterial epidemic appeared and was as incurable as AIDS, for instance.

By far the greatest new source of threat to our species comes from the smallest of all our enemies, the viruses (a virus is one-hundredth the length of a typical bacterium). Not only do viruses specialize in causing the rapid epidemics of aerosol crowd disease that we are ideally suited to entertaining (things like measles, influenza, colds), but viruses are also peculiarly intractable. They do not have a biochemistry set of their own which we can attack: they use ours instead. To attack their metabolism is therefore to attack our own. This is why antivirals have never rivalled antibiotics in their efficiency, and medicine has truly cured very few viral diseases. The list of antiviral chemicals is short – interferon, gangcyclovir, ribavirin, acyclovir, AZT, DDI and protease inhibitors – and most are only partly effective. Viruses also seem to have less trouble jumping species than larger parasites do. A catalogue of the emerging diseases that keep epidemiologists awake at night is dominated by viruses: AIDS, influenza, Ebola, Lassa, Hanta, monkeypox, rabies, dengue, Rift Valley and so on.

So it will be a virus. Which animal species will be the reservoir? Virtually all new diseases begin as zoonoses: infections caught directly from other animals. We may have already acquired diseases from or exchanged diseases with dogs (measles), cows (smallpox, tuberculosis), pigs (which refracted duck influenza), ducks (influenza), rats (plague, typhus), horses (some colds, equine encephalitis), mice (Lassa fever, Hanta viruses), monkeys (yellow fever, monkeypox) and bats (rabies, Ebola). There is an obvious bias in this list towards domesticated creatures, and one estimate places the total number of diseases we have acquired from our domesticated animals at 300, with another 100 caught from wild species. Because of the biochemical similarities, closely related species are a greater risk than distant relatives, which is why so few poultry diseases spread to human beings and why mammals are the most frequent source. Gregarious species such as bats and cattle are also more apt to supply us with germs suited to exploiting our crowded cities. Solitary habits, like those of cats, militate against contagious epidemics. And, finally, tropical species are more dangerous reservoirs than cold-climate or (especially) mountain species such as sheep.

I see little risk from domesticated animals; our contact with them was far more intimate and frequent in classical and medieval times. We have harvested what we can from cattle and pigs in the way of pathogens and parasites (though food-poisoning from industrial abattoirs is a special case). Our contact with wild animals also was more intimate in the Stone Age, when hunting was a staple means of earning a living. But in those days we lived in scattered rural communities. Perhaps today a disease that could not sustain an epidemic in a village will reach a city instead.

So we can narrow the search for a source of new disease to the following description: it will be a mammal, living in the tropics, that gathers in large flocks and has until now had little contact with our species. My money is on bats. Nearly one in every four mammal species is a bat, so probably one-quarter of all mammal diseases are in bats. Rabies and Ebola are not the only diseases to have jumped from bats to humans. Australia has encountered two brand-new bat viruses in two years, both of which originated with flying foxes (fruit bats) in sub-tropical Queensland. One was equine morbilivirus, which killed fourteen horses and one human being in 1994. Two years later, a woman who cared for sick bats at an animal sanctuary died from a virus of the same family as rabies: a lyssavirus. If I were writing a screenplay for a scary new film about a disease, I would set the opening scene in an animal sanctuary. Such places did not exist a generation ago. They are ideal marketplaces for wild animals to give their diseases to human beings.

Contagion in the Third Millennium

This new disease would be a virus whose mode of transmission would have to be precisely right to work in the modern world. Insect vectors are one possibility. In the 1960s and 1970s, new 'arboviruses' – arthropod-borne viruses – were appearing (or at least being identified) at an astonishing rate: over 500 have now been recognized, of which 120 can cause human disease. For instance, mosquitoes transmit various forms of potentially lethal viral encephalitis from mammals to people. There have been recent outbreaks of such encephalitis in every continent except Antarctica.

Some of these encephalitis viruses are highly virulent. Rift Valley fever is spread by *Aedes* mosquitoes from new lakes created by dams. The Aswan dam in Egypt and the Diama dam in Mauretania each caused epidemics of Rift Valley fever when they were completed – though the epidemics quickly declined as fish populations expanded and reduced the numbers of mosquitoes in the lakes. Eastern Equine encephalitis, caught from horses in America, kills up to 80 per cent of its human victims. Borna disease virus, also caught from horses (though not necessarily via mosquitoes) in Germany and Japan has been associated with severe depression and mental illness (see p. 417). It homes in on the limbic system of the brain, where mood is determined. Viruses love infecting the nervous system, because nerves form such easy paths along which to spread, bypassing the blood with its patrolling immune cells.

But other arboviruses have developed a special ability to attack the blood, causing haemorrhagic fever. Oropouche virus, which has afflicted 200,000 people in Amazonia, is spread by midges that breed in the tiny puddles inside cacao bean husks. Heaps of these husks outside villages caused a population explosion of the biting midges near human habitation. They brought the virus from the blood of sloths, their more usual source of meals. In Australia there are other mosquito-borne diseases, transmitted from kangaroos: Ross River and Barmah forest viruses in particular. They cause a form of virulent arthritis, which has turned epidemic in parts of the Pacific to which its vector has been introduced.

Mosquitoes and midges are not the only arthropods to carry viral fevers. Crimean-Congo haemorrhagic fever, which is caught from infected ticks mostly in desert parts of Western Asia, has a habit of infecting surgeons who operate on patients thinking their haemorrhages can be repaired. Lyme disease, a rickettsia (small bacterium) that causes fever and arthritis which can be fatal, also spreads by means of ticks from deer in Europe and Asia. Its sudden resurgence in recent years has been caused by the recovery of deer numbers. It is now the commonest arthropod-borne disease in America.

Yet, because so few people now harbour, let alone share, fleas and lice and because ticks and mosquitoes are mostly a rural or seasonal problem, this long list of horrible afflictions probably contains none that can sustain a major human plague. It is doubtful if any of them are even new, though some, such as Lyme and Ross River, have certainly become commoner.

It is true that malaria thrives in the tropics and once thrived in temperate countries. Indeed, certain kinds of malaria are equipped with a feature specially designed to enable them to survive during northern winters when no mosquitoes are about – a long dormant period in the liver of their host. But malaria died out in the temperate world long before effective drugs were used against it. The reason is that people gradually improved their defences against mosquito invasion. First, they drained the marshes where the mosquitoes bred. To this day in tropical countries there is a clear correlation between population density and malaria: the denser human populations become, the fewer malaria cases there are, because the mosquitoes' breeding sites are built on, cultivated or drained. Population growth is the enemy of malaria. Moreover, malaria died out in Northern Europe because the *Anopheles* mosquitoes found cattle in barns a more easy source of blood than people, and switched their habits. This was a disaster for the malaria plasmodium, because it cannot survive in cattle, and the mosquitoes, replete with cow blood, stopped biting people.

This illustrates the real problem for diseases with using mosquitoes to ferry you about. You have to infect the animal that the mosquito bites most. If you do not, then you will eventually lose out in competition to another strain of pathogen that does infect that species. There is room in each genus of mosquito for only one kind of malaria. This is why the bite of by far the commonest kind of mosquito, *Culex*, is mostly harmless. *Culex* mosquitoes carry avian malaria, which they transmit to birds. *Anopheles*, which at some point in the past must have found itself biting monkeys and apes more often than birds, carries primate malaria. *Aedes*, another genus, is almost a domesticated mosquito, which prefers to breed in man-made receptacles like water butts, old tyres and tanks. This made it almost inevitable that it would carry human diseases and sure enough different *Aedes* species carry yellow fever and dengue fever. They crossed the Atlantic with their insect vector in the slave trade and became the curse of the Caribbean and Central America. In the nineteenth century, thousands died in epidemics that afflicted cities as far north as Memphis and Philadelphia. Yellow fever defeated the first attempts at building the Panama canal, where it was eventually quelled by rigorous control of man-made mosquito breeding sites. But yellow fever has resisted efforts to eradicate it in the New World by taking refuge in wild monkeys, from where mosquito-bitten rainforest loggers still bring it back to cities. Epidemics continue in the Old World, as well: 30,000 died in Ethiopia in the 1960s.

Dengue fever uses the same *Aedes* mosquitoes, a new and aggressive species of which, called the Asian tiger, has been spreading in North America. This has led some to prognosticate a new epidemic, and a far more dangerous form of dengue has appeared and spread from the Philippines. In 1981, this form of dengue infected nearly 400,000 people in Cuba; in 1995, it infected 30,000 in Venezuela. This disease is actually an immune overreaction to infection with two successive strains of dengue.

Despite these problems, I still say there is little prospect of a new mosquito-borne disease spilling out of the developing world and into the West. The scarcity of mosquitoes in densely populated, urban centres, the ease with which new insecticides could be deployed in an emergency (notwithstanding the problems of mosquito resistance to some older insecticides) and the general precautions that most town people now take against being frequently bitten, make it unlikely that such a new virus could take off in American or European towns in the way that yellow fever did in the past. And it is a prerequisite of an emerging plague that it must be a crowd disease capable of spreading in urban areas.

Insect-borne diseases are often highly virulent. They do not get 'tamer' as the years go by. Malaria, yellow fever, bubonic plague and typhus are among the most lethal of all infections and have shown no signs of declining virulence over the centuries. There is a good reason for this: laying low the victim, sending him to a flea-ridden bed or into a mosquito-indifferent delirium, is actually to the pathogen's advantage. It increases the chance he will be bitten again. The victim's death in the process has no consequence for the germ. It does not need him to be healthy in order to spread the infection – though it does need the insect to be healthy, which is why malaria kills or incapacitates people, but does not hurt mosquitoes.

For much the same reasons, water-borne diseases are also virulent. They spread not in the bodies of their victims, but in their sewage. An immobilized and dying victim is no drawback. But water-borne plagues are now equally unlikely and for similar reasons. On the whole sanitation is improving, even in the poorest parts of the world, and those diseases that could go pandemic like cholera, typhoid and dysentery have long since sung their best arias. Isolated bursts of cholera are still possible and new crises caused by creatures that specialize in public water systems, such as cryptosporidium, are even likely. But we must look elsewhere for the true danger.

Aerosol diseases are enjoying the modern world immensely. Frequent, rapid travel has vastly multiplied the number of strangers we each meet in our daily lives. Cities are constantly exchanging bodies with other cities all across the world. By the year 2000, there will be 600 million person-trips on international flights every year. It is, in theory, a paradise for air-transmitted infections. Colds, in particular, can cross oceans and continents in a matter of hours, infecting the whole globe in weeks. Flu strains can do the same. On one flight, grounded in Alaska for three hours while repairs were carried out, nearly three-quarters of the passengers caught influenza from one person. The possibility therefore remains that a new disease, with the characteristic contagion of a cold or a flu, could sweep the planet in a month. If it were lethal, the death toll can be imagined.

That is roughly what happened in 1918. A new strain of an old disease, influenza, arose in Chinese pigs who had caught it from ducks. Called H1N1, it had mutated its surface protein genes in such a way as to escape existing immune defence and simultaneously attack in a much more virulent way than normal. For the first time influenza could kill not just the old, the very young and the weak but healthy adults as well. It ravaged the troops in the trenches, spread to cities all around the world and killed more people in six months than the worst war the world had ever known had claimed in four years. As it spread, so did herd immunity, with the result that it became harder and harder for viruses to find new susceptible hosts. The epidemic died gradually away.

Two new varieties of flu have since come out of China: H2N2 in 1957 and H3N2 in 1968. In 1977 H1N1 reappeared, presaging, or so it seemed, another virulent pandemic. But nothing happened. America's health establishment cried Wolf! and lost face. The harmlessness of the new 'swine fever' flu epidemic of 1977 remains as great a puzzle as the virulence of it in 1918. To this day many health professionals are extremely nervous of new strains of flu. There is nothing to stop another virulent one sweeping the world even more rapidly than it did in 1918. In wild waterfowl that migrate north through China, there are scores of strains. The marshy areas where they rest on their long flights are epicentres of such unnumbered H and N types. These areas are fairly far from human habitation, almost by definition. But it would take little for domestic ducks to pick up a new strain, mix and reassort it with domestic pigs and pass on to human beings a more than usually virulent strain.

Is it just luck that none of the emerging diseases to threaten us in recent years have been as casually contagious as influenza? I suspect not. Highly contagious epidemics with high mortality are rare. Only smallpox, measles and flu meet the criteria. Two of those showed rapid evolution to lower virulence and the third, smallpox, also decreased in virulence, though less rapidly. There is a tendency for highly contagious diseases to be tame, for the same reasons that insect-borne diseases refuse to be tamed: the more they keep their victims healthy, the better they spread. Our species is now so full of mild, contagious infections, which we call colds, bugs, flus and 'dreaded lurgis', that there may be relatively little room for other, more vicious ones to catch on. Diseases, after all, are in competition with each other for the scarce resource of our bodies' fluids.

The Virulence Enigma

It is worth looking at disease from the germ's point of view. Living inside the human body is a hard enough challenge. The body has formidable weapons at its disposal. It can raise its own temperature to a level at which the germ's own fragile proteins start to fall apart. This, we now know, is the point of fever: it is a defence, rather than just a symptom. Studies show that trying to lower people's temperatures during infections merely prolongs and may even worsen the infection. The body can also sequester the blood's free iron into a form that the germ cannot get at. Infectious bacteria are dependent on finding iron. Thus the fact that the dissolved-iron content of blood falls during an infection is again a defence, not an effect of the disease. Studies show that giving patients iron supplements is counterproductive.

These are just the first line of defence. Then the germ must dodge the immune system, which has three strong lines of fortification. Its first is the mucosal immune cells: patrolling squads of cells in the mucus of throat, gut and other surfaces, intent on keeping these vulnerable areas sterile. Then comes the antibody system: a whole chemical assembly line producing whatever highly specific protein designs best smother the proteins on the surfaces of bacteria and viruses. Finally, if the germ beats that, there is the cellular immune system, a poorly understood array of bug-eating white blood cells, carefully distinguishing self from non-self.

This is all very ingenious – and it begins to become clear why new diseases do not appear every week – but having gained entry, survived the fever, found a secure refuge and avoided alerting an immune response, the germ still has its hardest task to do. Its whole future, and that of its offspring, depends on being able to come out of hiding at just the right time and in just the right place to jump into a new individual. Thus certain kinds of malaria take care to emerge from their refuge in the liver after a year's wait, the better to be around when the summer and mosquitoes are back. Typhoid in the temperate regions has invented the ability to lurk, symptomless, in the gall bladder, so as to re-emerge later when the chance of infecting another host might be greater. Herpes takes care to migrate to the surface along nerves that serve the mouth and the genitals – places where contact with other people is likely. In every case, the germ's most important adaptation is that which enables it to cross the inhospitable space between the bodies of its victims.

The answer would seem to be easy: the germ should evolve the ability to survive in the air or on the ground at all temperatures and in all conditions of humidity and despite the best efforts of chemical companies to disinfect it. Yet this does not happen. Germs are amazingly fastidious. Some can survive only in genital mucus yet cannot even live on a toilet seat for a few moments. Some require a mosquito of exactly the right genus. Some spread by droplets sneezed from the nose and mouth yet last no more than a few minutes in the open before dying. Why is this? Why do colds not have the durability of anthrax, or malaria the ability to be sneezed? The answer is wonderfully elegant when it dawns on you. For most pathogens the closest thing they have to an enemy is other pathogens of the same species. Just like rabbits or mosquitoes they compete with each other to become ancestors. Those that are best at it eventually crowd out those that are less effective. Suppose two tuberculosis bacteria have equal ability to spread in sneezes, but one of them also has the ability to survive for several years if it falls on barren ground. This ability comes at a price: it requires some extra machinery which takes a little time and energy to make. So it will actually spread more slowly than its more vulnerable cousin, because the short-lived bacterium can reproduce faster. Nature is a ruthless economist, stripping away all unnecessary features to make its products compete. Parasites become beautifully adapted to one method of transmission that works at the expense of the ability to use other methods. Sexually transmitted diseases gradually lose the ability to spread by aerosol and vice versa.

So the anxiety that AIDS would suddenly become a disease that could be carried by mosquitoes, or could be spread by aerosol, is largely misplaced. Diseases only very rarely change their modes of transmission. If an aerosol disease is to cause a plague it will not be AIDS, typhus or yellow fever; it will be one that is already spread by aerosol: influenza, for example.

Moreover, there is good reason to believe that aerosol and direct-contact diseases are getting milder in virulence, not stronger.

In large, crowded medieval cities with many people rubbing shoulders day and night, sharing beds or living five to a room, germs could afford to be as vicious as smallpox: ill people still touched lots of others. But in the modern suburb, where the average person has direct physical contact with almost nobody except his immediate family, a germ cannot afford to incapacitate its victims at all, because otherwise it will never get to spread by skin-to-skin contact. That is why cold viruses now thrive, using only the occasional contact between active people in playground or workplace to spread.

It is therefore no accident that many diseases did not just become rarer in the West during the nineteenth and early twentieth centuries as living standards rose, hygiene improved and crowding declined – they also became milder. The virulence of diphtheria, typhoid, tuberculosis, scarlet fever, whooping cough and many other diseases declined steadily after the middle of the nineteenth century. In these diseases more than three-quarters of the decline in deaths occurred before the appearance of drugs in the 1930s. About the only exception was polio, which for unknown reasons is more virulent in adults than children, leaving the gut and attacking the nervous system, so improved hygiene led to people catching it later in life and therefore more severely. By the early 1950s, 60,000 Americans caught polio each year and it was the most feared of all diseases.

It is also no accident that the sudden appearance of a highly virulent strain of flu coincided with a return to conditions of squalor, crowding and poor hygiene: the trenches, troopships and camps of the First World War. It is, I submit, no surprise that H1N1 flu was milder when it returned in 1977 and that no other really virulent flu strain has come out of China since 1918.

For this reason – that casual-contact diseases are mild and

getting milder – I rule out the plague of the third millennium being such a germ, and I even rashly assert that a return of virulent influenza is unlikely. Casual-contact diseases will continue to afflict us; indeed, they will thrive as never before in airliners, offices and above all schools. We place our children together in herds called nurseries, with much traffic between them, at the age at which they are unusually free with their saliva and unusually keen on body contact. But the bugs that enjoy these opportunities will not often kill us. We are more use to them soldiering on despite a 'nasty cold'.

So, if insect-borne germs are going to be virulent but local, water-borne diseases rare and casual-contact diseases mild but common, that leaves one method of transmission: sex. We need no reminder that we live in an age of sexually transmitted infection. AIDS is not alone. Scores of nasty infections have been on the increase because of our changing sexual habits: chlamydia, herpes, genital warts, yeast infections, hepatitis B, chancroid and others. Only gonorrhoea and syphilis have continued to decline. Never before, in the history of the world – not even in the heyday of syphilis – has sex been so risky. The reason for this is partly the greater promiscuity of the modern age: promiscuous heterosexual sex unleashed by the contraceptive pill in the 1960s and promiscuous gay sex unleashed by gay rights campaigns in the 1970s multiplied manyfold the opportunities for pathogens in the West. But there is another, larger reason. When a woman has sex with a man in the modern urban West, each of them could have just been travelling in a distant continent. As far as sexually transmitted pathogens are concerned, the world has become a village. The 'herd' available to an organism has become so much greater that diseases which do not even have means of persisting silently can now sustain epidemics. The vast ingenuity of syphilis, in concealing itself for years inside the body, is no longer a prerequisite of a sexually transmitted disease. Something as unsubtle as yeast can do as well. Nonetheless, for a virulent plague, the ability to make asymptomatic individuals infectious is very valuable. The remarkable thing about AIDS, which made it so resistant to preventive measures, was how little effect it had on its victims for the first few months and even years. This latent time, during which it survived inside T cells, was a form of weakness: the virus could not overcome the antibodies of the host. But, for a sexually transmitted disease, it was also an advantage. It enabled the virus to overcome the problem of spreading to entirely new sexual partners of the victim. By the time symptoms appeared, even quite monogamous individuals had often infected several people.

The one thing that sexually transmitted diseases find very hard to do is jump between species, for obvious reasons. It is possible that AIDS came into the human species by sex, but more likely that there was some kind of blood mixing in the first cases. For this reason, although new sexually transmitted plagues would make short work of such a tempting target as the modern human race, there is not a ready supply of them. Bats, for example, may be equipped with a variety of virulent sexually transmitted diseases, but we would be unlikely to acquire them that way. It is by this thread that our future hangs. We must hope that new sexually transmitted viruses never find the opportunity to pass from other mammals to us.

But mention of blood mixing brings me to needles. We have invented all sorts of entirely new ways of spreading disease: modes of transmission that were not available to diseases in the past. Open surgery, injections and air-conditioning systems are three obvious avenues for bugs worth their salt. We provide ourselves with services – water, air, food – from systems of great complexity in which a single location may serve a whole herd and in which much emphasis is placed on sterility. Sterility to bugs is another word for invitation. It means vacant niche. And when members of our species get sick or weak we pack them off to buildings full of other sick or weak people, called hospitals, all the better to share any germs among the most vulnerable.

Various germs have tried to exploit each of these vulnerabilities. Compulsory mass education has undoubtedly been of enormous benefit to rhinoviruses, which cause most colds, not to mention all sorts of other germs. An average schoolchild catches maybe eight such viruses each year, a number that would undoubtedly seem astonishing even to our great-grandparents, let alone to our Stone Age ancestors.

As for our mass-distribution systems, Legionella has gone for air conditioners, cryptosporidium for clean-water systems and E. coli 157 for huge modern abattoirs where it can jump in a flash from faeces to meat intended for a score of cities. Each of these deserves credit for ingenuity and skill, but none has yet managed to cause more than a local nuisance to the human race. Legionella killed thirty-four in its first recognized outbreak in Philadelphia in 1976 and continues to plague air-conditioning systems to this day; cryptosporidium laid 400,000 low in Milwaukee in 1993, and has shown a remarkable ability to invent chlorine-resistant strains. E. coli 157 killed nineteen people in Scotland in 1996–7 and seems to find abattoirs, however clean, the perfect environment to pass from faeces to meat.

We should not neglect the gallant effort of BSE, the most bizarre disease of all because it seems not to possess any genetic material, just a rogue form of protein that catalyses its own creation. BSE took splendid advantage of a closed cycle created when cattle offal was fed to cattle without being heated sufficiently to kill the protein. An epidemic resulted in cattle, but failed to spread to human beings in any numbers. By mid-1997 there had been fewer than twenty cases of 'new variant' Creutzfeldt-Jakob disease, the kind apparently caused by eating infected beef.

As for hospitals, the opportunities for ambitious pathogens are immense. True, since doctors were bludgeoned into hygiene during the nineteenth century, the days when scarlet fever and childbed fever could move from one patient to another on the apron of a doctor who had just done an autopsy are long gone. The danger of shared needles has been recognized, too, even in remote mission hospitals. But, even so, hospitals are the perfect environment for many strains of disease to turn virulent. There is a steady supply of new, vulnerable hosts and all sorts of mechanisms for germs to spread from one person to another. Immuno-suppressive drugs used during transplants make weak people still more vulnerable to infection, and open surgery makes it far easier for a bacterium to gain access to body cavities, bypassing the defences in the body's skin and mucus. The frequent prophylactic use of antibiotics selects for strains of germ that cannot be easily killed. Nearly one in twenty Americans who goes into hospital catches an infectious disease while there. In other parts of the world, the proportion is probably greater. These so-called 'noso-comial' infections include staphylococcus, streptococcus, hepatitis B, pseudomonas, clostridium and E. coli 157. However sterile we make our hospitals, however rigorous we make our procedures and however well we educate each other about dangers, hospitals represent, for virus diseases, an enormous opportunity – and evolution is adept at exploiting opportunities.

The Task of Sisyphus

Not all emerging diseases cause new symptoms. In recent years there has been a growing recognition that all sorts of diseases that were once thought to be nothing to do with infection may actually be caused by viruses or bacteria. The comfortable distinction between infectious disease, which people used to die of, and non-infectious disease, which people now die of, is breaking down.

The most dramatic case of this is ulcers. Pharmaceutical companies grew rich on ulcer drugs designed to fight the acid that supposedly caused them. It now turns out that this was treating the symptoms, not the cause, and that by far the most important cause of duodenal and to a lesser extent gastric ulcers is a simple bacterium called Helicobacter, easily killed by certain antibiotics.

Browse through the medical literature and you will find frequent hints that other diseases are about to be subject to the same revision. An obscure virus infecting nerve and brain cells called Borna disease has been killing horses and occasionally cats in the former East Germany. Now two studies have discovered that people subject to psychiatric illness may be infected with Borna virus. In the first study, in Germany, neuropsychiatric patients proved six times as likely as people at large to be carrying antibodies to the virus, and fully 30 per cent of those suffering acute depression had been infected with the virus. More convincing still, in people whose depression comes and goes the virus was active during their depressed phases and inactive during their normal phases. The same news comes from Japan, where schizophrenics as well as depressives are far more likely to have the Borna virus than the public at large. The Japanese scientists thought it might be something to do with eating horseflesh raw, but they found that virtually everybody in their sample regularly ate raw horse so they cannot tell if that is what makes them depressed.

The Borna virus is not going to be the whole answer and the suggestion that people might catch it from horses rather than from each other is premature. But for those who are struck, like a bolt from the blue, with a sudden and inexplicable burst of severe depression, the explanation that it was a germ they caught, rather than something they ate, remembered from their childhood or brought upon themselves by worrying too much, will perhaps be a crumb of comfort.

Other diseases that might prove to be caused largely by germs include rheumatoid arthritis, Crohn's disease, diabetes mellitus and several cancers including lymphoma, leukaemia and cervical cancer. Suspicion is growing that many cases of kidney failure, stroke and hypertension are actually caused by Hanta viruses and their relatives. We have only just begun to realize how important infectious proteins (prions) may be in causing neurological disease – not just Creutzfeldt-Jakob disease, but perhaps Parkinson's and Alzheimer's diseases as well. Even heart disease, that most occupational of hazards, may have a strong infectious component. Chlamydia, cytomegalovirus and herpes have been implicated in causing or worsening the atherosclerosis that leads to heart attacks. A study published in 1997 showed that antibiotics that kill chlamydia can reduce the risk of heart attacks by 30 per cent.

For all the emergence of new diseases, some are also disappearing. Like any other species, they are vulnerable to extinction. Smallpox is already extinct in the wild and polio will soon follow it, both driven there by vaccination. But the extinction of a disease merely opens an opportunity for another disease. The disappearance of smallpox means that more and more children are now growing up unvaccinated. Monkeypox, a closely related disease of monkeys, is therefore presented with a tempting target. Sure enough, in 1997, the first widespread epidemic of monkeypox was reported from Zaire: at least 160 people were infected.

Medicine has underestimated not only the prevalence of infectious disease but the resourcefulness of it as well. The enemy is not a static, fixed, finite force, but an infinitely inventive complex of genetic combinations engaged in a massive campaign of trial and error. That is what natural selection is. The whole point of being a parasite is to make a living inside a host. The stakes may seem high to us, the hosts, as we face the AIDS epidemic or remember the Black Death, but they are much higher for the two germs in question. Breeding within our bodies, passing through more generations in one epidemic than we have passed through since the beginning of recorded history, they evolve at a far more rapid rate. They need to, because the parasitic lifestyle is an immensely difficult one to achieve. Not only must the organism evade or overcome the host's defences, it must then change tactics altogether and find a way to move to a new host, and not just any new host but one that has not already acquired immunity.

Effective antibiotics merely put bacteria under evolutionary pressure to invent a way round them. The more widely the drug is used, the more likely it is that it will stop working well. This is a concept people have had great trouble understanding. It is an arms race. The enemy changes. Or, as the Red Queen put it in *Through the Looking Glass*, 'Here, you see, it takes all the running you can do, to keep in the same place.' Doctors have tended to act like engineers and treat germs as static enemies. Imagine if every time you invented a new way of pumping water, the water found a new way of not being pumped. That is the reality of medical treatment. Indeed, the analogy is surprisingly apt. Some of the drug-resistant strains of bacteria are equipped with special molecular pumps, which expel the drug from the bacterial cell as fast as it comes in. Others are more precise, disabling the drug by digesting it with special enzymes. Like the legendary Sisyphus in Hades, medicine is condemned to keep rolling a stone up to the top of a hill only to see it roll back down again.

Moreover, bacteria seem to engage in a sort of genetic free trade, whereby they ingest genes from each other, particularly in the form of 'plasmids' – closed loops of DNA. Many resistance genes are on such plasmids. Good plasmids, like good technological products in world trade, spread rapidly. Bacteria do not need to rely on their own inventiveness; they can copy it from others. Nor should it be forgotten that antibiotics are natural substances. Most are found in soil fungi, which use them to fight chemical warfare against bacteria in the soil. Resistance is therefore an ancient characteristic that many bacteria have possessed for a long time. Parasitic bacteria, not encountering fungi in our bodies, dropped their resistance to save energy for other things. This often meant just switching off the genes concerned. Switching them back on again was a simple evolutionary step once they were being put to the sword by drugs.

Strains of bacteria resistant to antibiotics are encouraged by the misuse of the drugs. Every time you take antibiotics for a cold, which is a virus and therefore unaffected, you give the billions of bacteria in your body a quick training session in how to resist. You are making it that much harder to treat a future outbreak of bacterial disease in yourself. Every time you fail to complete a course of anti-tuberculosis treatment, you leave alive only the tuberculosis germs that have a slight ability to resist the drug. Every time a farmer doses his cattle with antibiotics merely to make them grow faster, he risks creating an untreatable strain of bacteria that could spread to human beings (although the evidence linking such growth promoters to antibiotic resistance does not so far exist).

Antibiotic resistance has emerged in most bacterial diseases, notably typhoid, gonorrhoea, pneumococcus pneumonia and tuberculosis. Staphylococcus has lost its susceptibility to penicillin almost everywhere. In 15 per cent of cases it is resistant to methicillin as well. Drug-resistant pneumococcus has been found in up to 50 per cent of samples in Spain, South Africa and Hungary. Streptococcus has achieved resistance to all but the newest antibiotics such as vancomycin. And vancomycin resistance has appeared in enterococcus bacteria already. It cannot be long before it spreads to even more dangerous pathogens. Tuberculosis is increasingly resistant in some patients to all drugs thrown at it. Rifampin, the last drug to resist resistance, has been around since the 1960s.

The problem is similar among protozoa, which have had little difficulty evolving resistance to most of the drugs we invent. Falciparum malaria, the most dangerous kind, may soon be resistant to all drugs except artemisinin and its relatives. The case is not helped by legal problems. The drug company Hoffman-La Roche is being sued over side-effects caused by mefloquine. If Roche loses and the drug is withdrawn, where will the next drug come from?

The eventual ineffectiveness of most or even all antimicrobials is certain. We are on a treadmill and we cannot stop it. If we are to keep infectious disease at bay we must invent new chemicals for ever. Unfortunately, that looks increasingly difficult. The rate of invention of new antibiotics has slowed down measurably in recent years. There has been no new class of antibiotic since the carbapenemes, developed twenty years ago. The great age of antibiotics, during which 4,000 different chemicals were produced, ended in about 1975.

This is an alarming picture. Pessimists believe that we will look back with nostalgia to the age when antibiotics worked and that, as the next millennium unfolds, we will find ourselves back in a war of attrition with bacteria, afflicted for the first time in decades with dreadful premature mortality. But this is a counsel of despair. It ignores the fact that changing lifestyles had already lifted the threat of bacterial disease substantially long before the invention of antibiotics. Tuberculosis was declining in Britain by 1920. Antibiotics did not even accelerate the decline. Even if they are incurable, bacterial diseases will be much scarcer and less virulent than they were in the days of slums, open sewers and flea bites. Besides, there has been a tendency to exaggerate the trend towards antibiotic resistance. It is not always an inexorable advance, but a sporadic and reversible process. Resistance appears in a hospital, gets worse for a while and then sometimes dies away, especially if the hospital ceases to use the drug in question. Resistance can be an expensive process to maintain, from the bacterial point of view; when it is no longer needed, the creatures tend to switch it off again.

Moreover, there is no reason on earth why we need to lose our ingenuity, just because our enemies have kept theirs. We should take a leaf out of their book, and analyse every trick they use to disable our poisons, the better to undo that trick. If, for instance, an antibiotic is resisted by an enzyme that takes it apart, then invent a new antibiotic that the enzyme cannot fit, or a chemical that attacks the enzyme. For example, amoxicillin is resisted by a bacterial enzyme called beta lactamase, which in turn is inhibited by a drug called clavumalate. Round three to us. If the drug is resisted by a pump that excludes the drug from the bacterial cell, then find a way to attack the pump. So clever are we getting at visualizing the true shapes of molecules that we no longer perfect chemicals by trial and error – as bacteria do – but by design. The age of unchallenged antibiotics may soon be over, but the age of other drugs is only just beginning. Monoclonal antibodies, haemopoietins and magainins (from toads) are antibacterial chemicals that we have barely begun to develop. As long as we recognize that we can never declare victory, and that each advance against disease will be followed by a later reverse, there is no reason why today's exploding biological research in the human world cannot stay one step ahead of the natural-selection research undertaken in the bacterial world.

There is a class of drugs on the horizon that shows special promise not only against bacteria, but against viruses as well: the DNA vaccines. DNA vaccines consist of small stretches of DNA code which carry the instructions for how to build particular proteins belonging to a parasite. Many viruses have proteins that do not work well as antigens – that is, they do not elicit an antibody response – perhaps because they lurk in crevices on the virus's coat where antibodies cannot get at them. Others – flu being a good example – have proteins that work well as antigens but they change so fast that immunity does not last; and they have other proteins, inside, that do not change so fast but are not accessible to the antibodies. So a scientist takes that protein, writes out the DNA recipe for making that protein, constructs the appropriate DNA message and fires it into a mouse on a particle of gold. What happens next is mysteriously fortunate. The DNA is absorbed by some of the mouse's cells and inside the cell it is treated like a normal gene: it is transcribed into RNA and translated into the protein again. That protein is somehow recognized as foreign and the immune system is alerted to kill the cell that has produced it. But it is a different part of the immune system that comes into play: the so-called MHC Class I system. This generates an attack by whole white blood cells, not by antibodies. The reason for this is rather curious. During infancy, your body educates its immune system by teaching it which proteins are self and which are non-self. It does this by the simple, if ruthless, technique of destroying those T cells that recognize any home-made protein. This leaves only those T cells that recognize and attack non-self proteins. Make a human cell produce virus proteins and it is soon attacked by one of these T cells. Why this

Class I attack works better than Class II attack from the antibodies remains enigmatic. But the important fact is that just such an experiment has rendered a mouse resistant to all strains of flu for at least a year.

It will be many more years of research before we are sure that DNA vaccines are safe and effective. Nonetheless, I am prepared to predict that DNA vaccines represent the future. For a start, DNA vaccines are cheaper, easier to prepare, less fragile, more easily stored and easier to transport than normal vaccines. They are more stable and long-lasting, which means they can be carried to remote, unrefrigerated clinics. A decade or two into the new millennium they will be standard treatment (or prevention) for viral diseases that are presently incurable and for bacterial diseases that have developed resistance to antibiotics. They are also showing promise already against an auto-immune disease that resembles multiple sclerosis in mice. But they are only the start. Reading the library of DNA that lies inside every organism is going to transform medicine and lead to cures, treatments and vaccines we cannot even imagine. Far from looking back at the late twentieth century as a golden age of medicine, we will look back in contempt at the primitive, ineffective and costly tools that were then available.

Ah, cost. The last and best argument of the pessimist. What use is a therapy for a viral disease if it costs six months' wages for the typical inhabitant of an African country? Extraordinary advances have now been made with AIDS treatment. Protease inhibitors can halt and perhaps even reverse the progress of the virus in a patient's body. AIDS will soon no longer be an incurable disease. But protease inhibitors are immensely expensive: a course of treatment costs many thousands of dollars. What use is that to a truck driver in Zaire, or a prostitutue in Bombay? Drugs such as these, even if they prove to be miracle cures, will do nothing at all to stem the epidemic in poor countries. And who could justify spending anything on AIDS when a simple filter made from five thicknesses of cheap Bangladeshi sari can save lives by straining out the minute crustacea that carry cholera? The cost-effective solutions to disease are never the cures, they are always the preventions. The money spent on AIDS in the West could have done wonders if spent on preventing malaria, cholera and tuberculosis.

However, even from this I take some comfort. The great majority of deaths in the world are caused not by new, incurable diseases but by old, preventable ones like tuberculosis, dysentery and malaria. Preventing them, and driving down death rates, is a terribly challenging task. It will require money, political effort, economic reform and courage. But it is not impossible that things will get better. It is mere defeatism to reject the possibility. The promise of DNA vaccines, in particular, is remarkable. If they live up to expectations they will provide effective, safe vaccines for all sorts of diseases at a cost that even poor countries can afford and in a form that can be distributed by even the exiguous infrastructure of a poor, tropical country. The chances are high that the third millennium will not be punctuated, as the second was, by terrible plagues.

10 Media

PADDY BARWISE
AND KATHY HAMMOND

The digital revolution

In 1840, midday local time in Bristol was ten minutes later than in London, 105 miles to the east. The mail coach took twenty hours to do the journey, so the time difference was of little concern except to sailors (who needed accurate time measurement to know how far east or west they were of the Greenwich meridian). The normal way to send an urgent message was by horse – just as it had been for the ancient Romans (who had better roads but smaller horses) and would still be for the US Pony Express twenty years later.

By 1856, the Great Western Railway and the electric telegraph had reduced the journey time to three hours and the communication time to a few seconds, and put Bristol and the rest of Britain on the same time as London. These two technologies dramatically reduced the effects of time and distance in Europe, and even more in large countries like the United States. A third technology, the steamship, accelerated emigration by poor Europeans to America and elsewhere, and helped European states to maintain global empires.

Twentieth-century communication technologies – telephones, cars, planes, radio, television – have increasingly shaped everyday life, now even in the poorest countries. Where, how and with whom we live and work, what we buy and where, how we relax, what we know, think and feel, have been determined as much by these media as by any other technologies, and this process has been almost continuous for at least 150 years.

Yet suddenly, since the mid-1990s, communication technology and its potential impact on everyday life have become hot topics. It is widely argued that we face a period of change even more dramatic, wider ranging and faster than any we have previously experienced. On this view we are in the early stages of a revolution comparable in scale to the biggest changes ever experienced by humans – the development of language, the change from hunter-gathering to farming, or from farming to industrial production. But today's revolution is happening much faster. According to some, within a generation – that is, by the time our children reach the age that we are today – everyday life will have changed completely.

This revolution and the society it heralds have been variously described: the 'information age', 'cyber-society', the 'third wave'. Here we use the term *digital revolution* to draw attention to its defining characteristic: the conversion of every kind of information into digital data.

Going digital

Traditionally, messages were copied, stored and transmitted using *analogue* technology. For instance, a telephone converted the sound waves of the speaker's voice into an electrical signal with a waveform as close as possible to that of the original sound. This signal was transmitted down the line to the receiver, where it would be converted back to sound waves. During transmission, the signal would become distorted and attenuated and pick up other noise. Because of high cost and low capacity, long-distance calls were expensive as well as poor in quality. Recorded music also used analogue media – a variable groove on a disc or a magnetic signal on tape. Radio, TV and mobile phones used electromagnetic analogue signals over the air. Cable and satellite TV, VCRs and even – until 1991 – the proposed high-definition television (HDTV) were all analogue technologies.

All these and other media are now converting to *digital* technology. For instance, on a modern phone network the sound of the speaker's voice (essentially, its loudness at different frequency bands) is sampled many times per second and converted into electronic pulses or 'bits'. A bit (short for BInary digiT) is the smallest unit of digital information, corresponding to some part of a storage or transmission medium which can be in one of two states like a light being either off or on, usually represented by 0 and 1. Replacing analogue with digital media brings several advantages.

Reproduction quality

Unlike a phonograph, which reproduces every scratch and distortion in the analogue recording, a digital system like a CD player merely has to decide which bits are zeros and which bits are ones. Digital media also encode extra bits which help error checking and correction. The original recording can thus be exactly reproduced.

More efficient channel use

With analogue technology, if you make a three-minute call from London to New York you tie up one of the lines on that route for the whole three minutes – no one else can use it at the same time. With digital telephony, several calls can share the same line without even being aware of it.

A common language

Unlike analogue technologies, which represent information in ways that reflect specific physical media (electric waves on a wire for telephony, radio waves for broadcasting), digital technology uses the universal language of bits. Any channel which can transmit or store bits can do so regardless of the content. So, subject to capacity, the same channel can be used for transmitting any combination of video, still pictures, audio/voice, text and data. For example, using the same channel you could contact a theatre, view a video clip of the play, check performance times, seats and prices (including what the stage looks like from each seat), select the day, time and seats that you want, have your credit card details verified, and print your own theatre tickets – although printed tickets will gradually disappear as the world becomes more electronic. All these different types of information can be transmitted as packets of bits, with each packet having additional 'header' information to ensure that it reaches the right destination and that the receiving equipment knows what to do with it (for example, convert it back to audio or video).

The common language of bits also makes it possible to produce *multimedia* products: for instance, a CD-Rom or Internet website can have any combination of text, sound, still pictures and – again subject to capacity – video.

Data processing

Bits have always been the language of computers. Using computer programs, digital data from communication media can be manipulated, compressed, combined with other digital data such as customer records and processed in almost any way we like.

Because bits are a common language and can be manipulated, people often refer to *convergence*, meaning that, since different media are increasingly using the same digital technology, the past distinctions between them are disappearing. This has huge implications not only for how we can use media, but also for the media industries themselves. In particular, three large industries that were previously separate – telephones, television and computing – are becoming a huge industry which directly accounts for perhaps 10 per cent of world economic activity, and strongly impacts every other industry.

Why now?

People have been heralding the information revolution in various guises for at least thirty years. In the 1960s we already had talk of a post-industrial economy dominated by 'knowledge workers'. High hopes were held for the ability of computers to take over both routine tasks and strategic decisions, bringing in an age of unprecedented leisure for everyone. Some of these predictions were vividly illustrated in the 1968 film *2001: A Space Odyssey*, which introduced us to HAL, the highly intelligent talking computer which stole the show. The Japanese and US governments both studied the concept of 'wired cities' using cable TV to deliver entertainment, information and educational services similar to those discussed today in the context of the digital revolution. On the basis of these hopes, the US government allowed the cable companies to set up local monopolies. In the event, these never delivered anything other than television – with the understandable justification that user trials found minimal consumer interest in any of the other services, including interactive TV.

What, then, is different this time?

First, computers have become more powerful, cheaper, smaller, easier to use (although they still have a long way to go on this front) and more widely distributed, especially within businesses and especially in the US. Many of us now have personal computers (PCs) at home and also interact with computer technology in many other guises – games machines, automatic teller machines (ATMs) and the fifty microcomputers in a typical modern car.

Second, the Internet. The Internet is a loose network of networks which enables PCs in most large organizations and many homes and small businesses (using a standard connection to a telephone line) to communicate with each other around the world at low cost. The Internet belongs to no one (although it uses telecommunication links which do) and has no central authority; it is really a set of 'communication protocols', more like a language than a physical network, which means that any computer, whatever its internal language, can communicate with any other. The Internet has existed for many years as an academic network, but took off as a mass application only in the mid-1990s. This was partly because of the invention of new software (the World Wide Web and 'browsers') which made it easier to find useful information and move between different sites.

The Internet exhibits a characteristic crucial for all successful communication networks: that their value to each member increases with the number of other members. The same happened with telephones and, more recently, fax machines: neither would be useful – except as a status symbol – if no one else had one. Once enough other people were on the Web, it became worth while for yet more people. In reality, despite all the talk of Websites, 'surfing' and cyber-commerce, the main way most people (including the authors) use the Internet today is for electronic mail (email) – typed messages and documents sent from one PC to another. The email population reached 'critical mass' in about 1995.

The extent and speed of the digital revolution

Futurologists have not been very precise about how, and how much, digital media will change our lives. Most comment has focused on the expectation that consumers will soon be able to use their TV or PC to shop, bank and order movies from their armchair. Some commentators envisage more dramatic changes to everyday life. Nicholas Negroponte, director of MIT's Media

Lab, believes that a key development over the next five years will be the 'personalization' of the computer, with wearable devices such as a wrist-mounted TV, computer and telephone. Peter Cochrane, head of research at British Telecom, looks further ahead, asking us to 'Imagine a virtual-reality interface, with your visual cortex flooded by information from spectacle-mounted or contact lenses augmented by directional audio input, tactile gloves and prosthetic arms and fingers that will give you the sensation of touch, resistance and weight.'

Historically, enthusiasts for new technologies have usually been over-optimistic about the *speed* of change. Most new technologies take longer to be adopted by the general public than these enthusiasts expect, although there have been exceptions: once they had reached critical mass, VCRs and mobile phones took off faster than most experts predicted. Arguably, everyday life in the advanced economies changed more between the 1880s and the 1930s than in the last fifty years or, possibly, the next. Nevertheless, it is valid to talk about a digital 'revolution', since the extent of change is dramatic by any standards and digital technology is its biggest single driving force. Even if the enthusiasts overstate how quickly things will change, they may turn out to be right about the *scale* of that change.

At this stage, no one knows how the digital revolution will develop. Although the technology itself is now becoming somewhat more predictable, exactly how, and how fast, things change will depend not only on technical developments but also on the policies of key commercial and political players, especially in the US. Less predictable is how enthusiastically consumers will take to this technology on an everyday, mass-market scale – the focus of our own research at London Business School. Least predictable are the sociocultural and geopolitical responses: will the digital revolution lead to greater international understanding or bitter rivalry? Will it encourage materialism and erode religious belief, or lead to a religious backlash? Will it make people happier? Here we concentrate on the likely impact of digital technology on everyday life.

To illustrate this impact let us fast-forward to the year 2010 and see what a typical day looks like for the Jacksons – an upper-middle-class nuclear family in the US, who have enthusiastically adopted digital technology.

The Jacksons in 2010

Pete Jackson is a manager and his wife Marion Jackson is a lawyer. They have two children, Lisa (sixteen) and Tim (twelve). In 2010 the Jacksons have a fully cabled home with a network connection in every room. Interaction with the household communications system (H-COM, described in more detail on page 440) is via a personalized intelligent agent, which the family call 'Bob'. What sorts of things do the Jacksons do in their interactive digital home?

Watching any programme you want, when you want

Tim Jackson has finished his school work. Some friends come over and they decide to watch an old movie, *Lethal Weapon*. In the family room there is a large flat screen on one wall. Tim presses his palm against the bottom right corner of the screen. It displays a picture of the Mars space probe and a menu with 'Tim' written in the centre. Bob's voice says: 'Hello, Tim.'

> Tim: 'Hi, Bob. Movies, please: *Lethal Weapon*, to start now.'
> Bob: 'Tim, *Lethal Weapon* is R-rated. I'm afraid you do not have permission to watch this film.'
> Tim and his friends decide on another film.
> Tim: 'Bob, movies, please: *Space 2000* or something.'
> Bob: 'Tim, is your chosen film *2001: A Space Odyssey*?'
> Tim: 'Yes, that's it, Bob, yes.'
> Bob: 'Tim, this film has a parental guidance rating, it is a Classic Movie, cost 99 cents. Please confirm when you are ready to start.'

Tim is allowed to watch parental guidance films and he has more than 99 cents left to spend this month in his personal

H-COM account (Bob knows all this already). He confirms his choice: 'OK, Bob.' As the movie starts, a visitor from today would be struck by the wide, bright, sharp picture and – even more – the superb sound quality.

Ten minutes into the film another friend arrives. Tim says, 'Bob, pause the film, please. Restart from the beginning.'

The Jacksons can also ask Bob for more recent releases – at a price of up to $10 – or for any programme shown in the last twenty-four hours on any of 300 channels. Major live sporting events like the annual American Football 'Superbowl' cost up to $25. Most of their viewing, however, consists of watching programmes as they are transmitted on one of six main networks showing a mix of programmes, or one of the dozen bigger specialist channels showing news, sport or movies. Excluding 'video on demand' (for movies and classic TV shows) and 'pay per view' (for live special events, mostly sport), the H-COM service costs $50 per month (prices in 1998 dollars).

Homework, music and chat

Tim's sister Lisa is in her bedroom doing a school assignment on Stalin's purges. She uses paper and pencil to plan it and scribble notes, and a couple of textbooks as her main sources. She wants some background music, so she presses her palm against the teleputer screen in her room. It displays her menu and Bob says, 'Hi, Lisa.' She asks for her favourite radio station and then asks Bob to turn the volume down. She then asks for material on Stalin's purges and after a few minutes finds a good summary from *Encyclopaedia Britannica* which she downloads and prints out for easier reading and note-taking. She is also able to draw on material assembled by her teacher on the school's website, including film footage, maps and photos. Finally, she writes her assignment using a mixture of dictation and the keyboard, and incorporating – with attribution – pictures and text from several sources. When the assignment is complete, she submits it by email.

Bored, she decides to watch some music videos. She chooses 'new releases, UK', tries a couple of ten-second samples, and picks an album she has not heard before. She decides to buy it outright (that is, download it) for $10.99 rather than pay 99 cents for one play. As she has no more credit in her personal H-COM account, she checks her bank balance. Lisa's bank details are automatically encrypted and relayed to the music store. Authorization and download of the music video takes about thirty seconds. During the wait there is an ad for an online sportswear company.

Sitting down with a coffee to enjoy the music, Lisa decides to call her best friend Amy. She just says, 'Bob, I'd like to call Amy' (no hand-held receiver needed). An hour later, the music has gone back to the first track and the two friends are still chatting.

Grocery shopping

It's Pete's turn to cook this weekend. He turns on the kitchen H-COM teleputer. This is older than the family room screen or the bedroom teleputers and the built-in microphone no longer works well. Pete uses the menu system to select 'shopping', then 'weekly grocery list'. The Jacksons have a home-shopping account with their local supermarket, since they are not within the catchment area of any of the specialist online grocery warehouses. Pete calls up the weekly list and scans through it, deleting a few items with a screen pen.

The beer he usually buys is unavailable, so he checks the suggested alternative. Bob then lists some relevant special offers. The store brand of laundry detergent is being offered as three packs for the price of two. Pete checks 'yes'. He's asked whether he wishes to cancel his usual detergent order. He checks 'yes' again. Pete then selects 'browse' and then 'fruit and vegetables'. He chooses two ripe avocados and some multivitamin tablets from the healthcare section.

The home-shopping option adds $5 to the grocery bill and the boxed goods can be collected from the store or delivered to any address within ten miles. Pete decides on home delivery this week. It costs an additional $5 if the groceries are delivered Monday to Thursday (8.30 a.m.–5.00 p.m.), $8 for Friday to Sunday or between 5.00 p.m. and 11.00 p.m. any evening. Pete chooses Thursday morning, when the home help comes, so she will be around to receive the delivery and pack the food away. The total bill plus delivery will be charged to the Jacksons' H-COM account.

Apart from groceries and entertainment, the Jacksons also use the H-COM to buy books, holidays, insurance, electronic equipment and many other products and services. For large purchases like a house or a car, they use it as an information source and to compare prices, or even to make the deal after a visit or test-drive. Most of their home shopping is initiated by themselves, as in the grocery example, but some is in response to a commercial. Instead of calling a freephone number to ask for information or make a purchase, they can do so via any of their teleputers.

Daily news

It's Marion's day for going into the office. Unusually for a US lawyer, she goes by train. On the journey, she uses her notebook communicator, a lightweight, touch-sensitive screen which opens to A4 size. She uses it mostly for reading and note-taking (with a screen pen). Marion forgot to connect her notebook to the H-COM before she left home, so to get her latest messages and updated personal news service, she connects to Bob through the mobile network. She pays for the connection by authorising a credit card payment. She then selects 'news', and then 'daily personalized information'.

There are eight stories on trademarks, her area of work. She reads these first, writing screen notes on three articles. She then flicks through the general news, stopping to read an item on educational reforms in Japan: secondary-school education is one of her interests and she is a parent governor of Tim's school. She reads some more articles from her special-interest sections, selecting some for transfer to a personal information folder. She also has eleven email messages. Four are in her work folder – she'll look at those in the office. Two messages are thought by Bob to be 'junk mail' (she has asked him not to delete messages unless he is pretty sure); one from a company she previously bought some educational software from, the other from a financial services site she visited on the Net. Marion deletes these as soon as she reads the title. There is also a message from Tim's school about an open evening, two bills, an email from her mother, and one from the local council, with a questionnaire on a proposed car toll system. Marion just has time to read and answer her mail before the train reaches her station.

Chatting with 'virtual' friends

Lisa and Tim's grandmother, Dora, belongs to several chat groups and also contributes to a bulletin board and newsletter for skin-cancer sufferers. The skin-cancer awareness newsletter (SCAN) is emailed to her once a week. Dora does not have an H-COM but her cable TV has a set-top box with a card reader and an infrared keyboard, so she can shop online and (most important) send and receive email.

Dora logs on to the Net at least twice every day. First thing each morning she checks her email. She has many friends and relatives around the world and locally (but not near enough to visit very often). Much of the morning is taken up with reading email messages and checking bulletin boards. Today she has seven messages including a long one from her friend Lilien about a recent holiday in Italy, together with video stills of Lilien with her grandchildren. Another is from her neighbour saying he has lots of spare tomatoes from his garden and he'll be round with them at 3.00 p.m. – Dora will not open her front door unless she is expecting someone.

There is also a message from the local church about a special service for seniors next week; a reminder from the health centre to come along on Thursday for a skin-cancer check-up; and a note from her daughter Marion inviting her to come on a family picnic this Sunday. Dora's bills also come by email – an electricity bill and a bank statement today. Dora has difficulty seeing fine print, but with email she can have every message displayed in large type on her TV screen.

After reading and replying to her email she goes to the SCAN Website. Dora is going for a skin-cancer check soon; she will go to her local community health practice for this, but will be examined and questioned remotely by a specialist in Boston. Dora has not had this type of examination before, so she wants to see if SCAN has an information page on remote health consultations.

A working day for the manager

This morning Pete is working from home before he makes a trip to check out a potential new site for the company, two hours' drive away. One reason for working at home this morning is that Pete's medical check is due. He had a minor heart attack last year and now has regular checks. A watch monitor logs his pulse and blood pressure. Once a week he connects to his clinic to transmit this information. If there is any cause for concern a health worker can call him on his video phone and, if necessary, he can chat to his doctor or arrange a personal visit.

Pete's home office has a teleputer like those in the bedrooms and kitchen, but he also has a video phone. While waiting for the results from the medical monitor, Pete dictates three letters and the draft outline of a report. He looks at the completed letters on his screen and makes small changes to the layout and wording using screen pen and voice. Pete then asks Bob to send the letters to his work network, to mark them as business (they are then automatically reformatted in line with the company corporate identity) and to see that the firm's system sends them out (electronically) with Pete's official signature and this morning's date and time stamp. Pete also asks Bob to copy the draft report to the other members of a task force on which he is working, with a note saying 'Draft, comments please.' The medical monitor report comes back, 'Fine, no action needed.' Pete slots his wallet computer into his terminal and says, 'Bob, copy my work in-tray to the wallet computer please.' Pete puts the wallet computer back in his pocket and is ready to leave home.

Pete's car has a personalized locking and ignition system which as he touches the door recognizes the wallet PC; the car requires the presence of the wallet PC and Pete's hand on the door to open, making it very difficult for any unauthorized person to open or start the vehicle. The garage opens up for him, he drives out and the garage closes after him. He slots his wallet computer on to the dashboard and presses 'on'. Bob makes contact with the car's voice-activated onboard system.

Pete says: 'Hi Bob, directions please to a new destination, the old E-Zee-Rite paper factory at Rock Hill West, zip 22334.'

Bob: 'Pete, would you like those directions as a printout, screen display or ongoing voice direction?'

Pete: 'Bob, ongoing. Oh hell, I've forgotten to set the security.'

Bob: 'Pete, I'm sorry, I do not understand. Please repeat.'

Pete: 'Bob, ongoing voice direction, to start now. Also please set the house alarm and turn the heat to low.'

Bob: 'Pete, ongoing voice direction activated. Journey time estimated at one hour forty minutes. From La Forge make a left on to Main Street, then first right to join the Interstate towards Rock Hill.'

Bob continues: 'I have set the house alarm. Do you want the house heating set to low or the oven set to low or the car heating set to low?'

Pete: 'Bob, the house heating. Now please connect me to my work in-tray and read out my messages.'

Bob: 'Pete, Message 1 is a voicemail plus document from Jane Maynard in LA. Message follows: "Hi Pete, it looks as though that European deal may be trickier than we'd assumed. I've got the figures here. Have a look at them and let me know what you think." Pete, a three-page document is included – do you want me to read it out?'

Pete: 'Bob, no, just give me a 10 per cent summary.'

Having listened to the summary, Pete says, 'Bob, call up Jane Maynard, please – her work number.'

Pete talks to Jane, then goes back to his mail, answering some, filing or deleting others. Bob tells him when to turn off the Interstate and directs him to the factory. From there Pete makes several phone calls on his wallet computer. On the way home he dictates his report. The following morning he is back in the office. The first meeting of the day is a video conference with other regional managers, builders and planners, to discuss the purchase of the site. Everyone has the plans, financial statements and draft reports available in the lower half of their screens. One accountant joins in the conference from home (though nobody notices as his video image is backed by his virtual office logo).

What have we assumed in these scenarios?

All the technology in these scenarios already exists, at least in a basic form, and is likely to be fully commercialized by 2010.

The Jacksons have access to a global communication system which is brought into their home and runs through it using cables, with one or more connection points in each room just like the electricity or telephone system today. Most of the intelligence is on a powerful home computer which is boxed away somewhere, like an electricity meter. Around the house the various digital appliances are plugged into this H-COM network. There is a large, flat, wall-mounted screen in the family room – probably still called the 'TV'. There are smaller teleputers in bedrooms, studies and the kitchen. These are like a present-day PC, but the screen is flat, thin and touch-sensitive and the keyboard is optional and not linked by wires to the screen. The teleputers also have speakers and a microphone, and some have a scanner, smart card or pocket communicator slot, camera or printer.

The Jacksons will probably have no telephones as we know them; all the terminals support voice calls, while some support two-way video. There are also pocket communicators with touch-sensitive screens, which combine a mobile phone, hand-held computer, smart card and so on. Some of these pocket communicators are fairly large (that is, book size), while others may be wallet, earphone or watch versions. They are mostly used when the Jacksons are on the move – in the car or train, or just in the garden. Using the network while on the move is possible with satellite/wireless technology.

Talking to Bob

One striking development is that the main way the Jacksons communicate with the H-COM is by voice rather than keyboard and mouse. All screens are also touch-sensitive and can be written on with screen pens. Some of the appliances still have keyboards. These are partly for backup (the way some cars still had a starter handle in 1960) but their main use is for error correction in complex documents which are mainly produced by dictation. A few very techno-enthusiastic friends of the Jacksons use gaze direction instead of touching the screen: some camera-equipped computers can tell where you are looking on the screen – even quicker and easier than pointing.

The other striking feature of the way the Jacksons communicate with the H-COM is the extent to which they rely on Bob, their software agent. Bob is usually represented by a disembodied male voice talking standard American-English. But he can be given a face and can talk in a number of different voices. Some households – or individuals within households – might choose a female persona and say 'she'. Hardly anyone refers to their software agent as 'it'. (Research by Byron Reeves and Clifford Nass at Stanford University shows that people naturally treat computers in many ways as if they were other people.) In 2010, Bob still sounds somewhat artificial but is improving all the time, both because of advances in technology (new software releases distributed automatically online) and also because 'he' is able to learn from experience.

An important part of the technology is Bob's ability to perform automatic speech recognition. Most communication with computers will be by people whose voices they already know, the main exception being organizational systems dealing with the general public. It should be possible to talk to a computer which knows your voice at normal conversational speed using natural language with its normal slurring ('how to wreck a nice beach' = 'how to recognize speech') with few errors. As with email today, for many purposes we will not be too fussy about errors, provided that they cause no misunderstanding. If a particular message or document needs to be 100 per cent correct, the system will be able to tell us about any words it was unsure of or, if necessary, we can go through the document on-screen or on paper and use voice/screen pen/keyboard to make corrections.

Technically, Bob is primarily an interface. Most of the intelligence he uses is distributed across different applications and other people's and organizations' systems. With both speech recognition and production, the system will need to have some understanding relevant to the particular context. The software is likely to be 'modular' with one module for each main application. One of the modules will be in effect a menu and will need enough vocabulary and knowledge to be able to route you into the appropriate application module. For instance, you should be able to say 'I'd like to read my email' or just 'email' or 'messages'. Similarly 'TV' or 'television' or 'what's on TV?' would trigger the television module, and so on for making a telephone call, dictating a message, shopping, watching a movie or conducting an information search (for example, 'I'd like to find out about . . .' or 'I want to look up flights to Chicago').

The reason for this approach – application-specific modules – is that, after more than thirty years of research, the goal of *general* artificial intelligence is still a long way away. Computers lack common sense, meaning the widely shared knowledge that people take for granted. For instance, if I enter a building on the ground floor and go up two floors I do not expect still to be at ground level. It is not hard to program a computer to know this too, but it will not know unless you have programmed it to do so. Similarly it is obvious to a person that it is usually inappropriate in the office to jump up, punch the air and scream with delight when something goes well; at a football match it might be inappropriate not to do so. Again, it would be anomalous for a cat to talk in real life but quite normal in a fairy story. To interpret speech enough to turn it into text requires some understanding of the immediate context in terms of other words and perhaps some specialized knowledge (for example, for a medical or legal context), but not this kind of broader common sense.

The only practical way to achieve anything like this apparent intelligence – essential, for instance, to produce more human-sounding speech from the computer – is to develop a series of specialized modules with detailed local understanding. If you ask Bob a question or ask him to do something that does not map on to one of these areas he will probably not understand – but should, at least, tell you so. In other words, the system in 2010 will be a collection of specialist parts tailored for particular applications, but sharing a common interface (unless you choose to have different interfaces for different applications). Increasingly, the different subsystems will also communicate with one another, so that if you are using Bob to keep your diary he might automatically remind you to buy a plane ticket or ask if you would like him to find out about flight times and prices. The nearest equivalent today is a good personal assistant with full access to most of your personal information and who also knows a lot about your habits and preferences.

By 2010 computers should also have some rudimentary emotional intelligence – something they totally lack at present. Bob's voice and talking head should be able to communicate some feeling through facial expression and intonation but are unlikely to look and sound natural. Similarly, Bob may be able to pick up some emotional signals, probably from the speaker's tone of voice. (Other possible cues include facial expression, body language, pulse and so on.) By 2010, manufacturers with more powerful computers may be able to use this facility to improve the design of products and services by detecting users' emotions during trials – such as irritation or pleasure. Examples might be the human interface with a banking system or a multichannel TV system, or the design of a new car.

For some applications, you will experience 'virtual reality' (VR). VR refers to technology which can be used to convince your senses that you are somewhere else, for example walking through an imaginary castle or a molecule, or flying a jet fighter; VR was initially developed for military training, where it is still widely used. The key component of VR is a helmet which immediately and accurately detects head movement and displays the resulting change in your field of vision. The Jacksons have a basic VR system for games. There are more advanced ones in Lisa's and Tim's schools, which are used for teaching history, geography and science.

The Jacksons can use Bob to access a wide range of services – live TV (which still exists), movies and other archival video and records, games and gambling, home shopping and banking, electronic 'newspapers', radio stations (which also still exist), educational services, email, voice and video phone, links to school and work networks, companies and information on the Web, and so on. Long-distance connections are so cheap as to be almost costless. Voice telephony and most data transfer (including audio and some video) are also virtually free: you will pay mainly for access to a specific level of capacity on the network, with little or no charge for usage. Payment for other services (Tim's movie, the grocery bill, Marion's mobile network connection) can be added to the monthly H-COM account with the Jacksons' communication services provider (for example, a phone company) or paid with a smart card or bank account details, with verification through a password or thumb print, for instance. Such systems can also deal with small amounts of 'cash'. Communications are scrambled ('encrypted') for security and electronic money exchange is at least as secure as with a credit card today.

There is a personalized menu for each member of the household. The menu offered to Tim and Lisa excludes 'adults only' channels: gambling, pornographic videos and virtual-reality shows, and adult-only chat lines. These can be accessed only by an identified adult. The communication link is two-way and interactive – that is, Tim can choose a movie (from a predetermined set) and when to see it, with rewind, fast-forward and search facilities, while the system knows which household to bill.

The H-COM does not have to be turned on. It is on all the time – monitoring lighting, heating and home security, receiving email, and so on. Meter reading is also done electronically. However, some applications do need to be activated by a switch or just a voice command. The identity of each user is usually verified by their voice, hand or thumb print, or iris pattern.

Many digital goods are delivered 'down the line'. Much of the information that exists on paper today will be available online, such as newspapers, telephone directories, travel timetables, price lists, personal records. Most video and audio has become pay-per-view or available for purchase online. Groceries and other physical goods can be ordered online – but still have to be collected or delivered to the home.

For some sections of society, many more things are delivered to the home than at present, partly because of increased home working, partly because of the growth in domestic help. Society has become more polarized, with more work and rewards for successful knowledge workers, fewer and less skilled service jobs for the rest.

Will it happen? Technology and the market

Whether and how the digital revolution happens depends mainly on two factors: the continuing development of digital technology and the response of the mass market to the new products and services this technology makes possible. Also important is regulation. In the US, which will continue to dominate, the general trend will be for the role of government to be limited mainly to ensuring or encouraging competition. Other, more interventionist governments may slow down the pace of development but seem unlikely to change things fundamentally. Similarly, the way in which both technologies and markets are developed – and how quickly – will depend on the strategies of particular firms, especially those with a strong share of one of the important markets such as, currently, Microsoft in software and Intel in microprocessors, or an alliance between several such strong players. However, provided that the regulators ensure fair competition, the pace of technology and market development should be sustained.

In terms of infrastructure, we do not expect a switched broadband cable 'superhighway' reaching into almost every home like today's electricity grid. More likely is a continually evolving mixture of satellite, optical fibre, coaxial cable, various local wireless technologies – and many of the existing, ordinary telephone lines, especially if data compression techniques continue to improve. There may also be competition from electricity suppliers and other utility companies to carry data into and out of the home.

The terminal devices in the scenarios – screens, teleputers, Marion's electronic notebook – are simply later generations of existing technologies. One change over the next ten years will be the replacement of bulky cathode-ray tubes (in televisions and desktop PCs) with lighter flat-screen displays of equal or better brightness and sharpness.

Overall, the evidence is that the technologies assumed in our scenarios will be available as consumer products affordable by people like the Jacksons by 2010, and in some cases much sooner. The big question – more important and, at this stage, more difficult – is whether people will adopt and use these technologies on a large scale. No one knows, but by focusing on the consumer needs that the technologies are supposed to meet and the benefits that they are supposed to provide, we can make some informed judgements about the way the market is likely to develop.

In the next two sections we look at the impact of digital technologies on how media are used in the home for relaxing (such as watching TV) and keeping in touch (mostly by phone). We then look at some activities which presently take place largely outside the home – shopping, work, education and healthcare – and consider if, and how much, the digital revolution will change these activities, especially by bringing them into the home.

Relaxing

People watch television, listen to the radio and read newspapers, books and magazines mainly to relax. Of course, this is not clearcut. The BBC's mission is to 'entertain, educate and inform', and a good documentary or wildlife programme can do all three at once, as can a feature article in a newspaper. People also use media for other purposes: to energize them in the morning, to provide a shared viewing experience with their family, to give them something to talk about at work, and to reinforce their self-image.

The 'digerati' foresee massive change, with new interactive media largely replacing traditional forms, leading to quite different patterns of consumption and a blurring of the distinctions between media. Specifically, they foresee an end to the passive mass audience in which large numbers of people are simultaneously consuming the same content, chosen, packaged and scheduled by a small number of producers and editors. Instead, we are told, media audiences will become individualized and active. You will watch, read and listen to whatever you want, whenever you want, so that your morning paper and your evening TV viewing – and any advertisements you allow them to include – will be tailored to your individual preferences. Mass media as we know them will disappear.

This is largely hype. It is true that by 2010 most of the necessary technology will both exist and be affordable by people like the Jacksons. Media content will be produced in digital form and much of it will include extra index or keyword information – to allow easy storage, retrieval, sorting and other processing – such as which countries, people and topics are covered by a news item. However, the fact that technology exists does not in itself mean that it will be widely adopted and used. Changes will be both slower and less dramatic than the digerati predict, for two reasons.

First, economics. Despite the use of new technology to cut production costs, high-quality content will always be expensive and may become even more so as global media companies compete for the top events and talent. Interactive content will be even more expensive. The scope for general extra revenue from subscriptions and advertising is limited, although transactions like Pete Jackson's grocery shopping will bring some new money into the system (diverted from traditional channels like shops and bank branches and the cost of driving to them).

Second, and even more important, is human psychology. At least in its more extreme forms, the revolutionary vision ignores the fact that most people, most of the time, relax by being passive. This is typified by television, which people around the world watch passively for an average of about three hours a day.

Historically, old media have tended to adapt and find new roles in response to the launch of successful new media. Thus, both radio and magazines are thriving in new roles which complement television. Newspapers are still very much alive and so is the cinema, albeit on a much smaller scale than before TV. We expect all the existing mass media to survive, although there will be some minor exceptions. (For instance, we expect chemical photography to disappear as a mass market, continuing mainly as a medium for artists and hobbyists, like calligraphy today.)

Television: from broadcasting to narrowcasting?

Digital television (by satellite or cable) allows literally hundreds of channels. Many people expect this to change fundamentally the nature of television programming and viewing, from a 'broadcast' medium (dominated by big networks like Britain's BBC and ITV and the big US networks, showing a mixture of programme types with something for everyone) to a 'narrowcast' medium more like today's magazines and radio. On this narrowcast model, each channel would specialize in a particular niche: one programme type aimed at one specific target market.

One widely assumed benefit of this approach is that, as with magazines, the audiences of these niche channels would be strongly segmented, so that, for instance, the gardening channel would be mostly watched by home owners with gardens, many of whom would be relatively affluent retired people. The argument is that, as with gardening magazines today, such a channel could generate revenue both from subscriptions (since it would be tailored to that target audience) and from advertising (not just for gardening products, but also for other products and services such as cruise holidays and financial services aimed at the same target market).

Some of this is happening already, especially in countries with high cable penetration, notably the USA where the average family already has fifty channels. However, even in homes with fifty channels, half the viewing is still of the four national terrestrial networks or of local, public or cable channels showing general mixed programming.

More important, even for the niche channels the degree of audience segmentation and involvement is surprisingly low. For instance, whereas US radio stations are typically listened to by relatively few people but for many hours per week, the niche TV channels are watched only occasionally by those who watch them at all. This reflects a fundamental difference between radio, which people mostly listen to as a secondary activity while working or driving, and television which – although watched fairly passively and often combined with desultory eating or conversation – is a primary activity. People listen to radio to take their minds off what they are doing. They watch television to take their minds off what they are not doing.

Of course, the audience for sport channels – especially some sport – does tend to be male and that for music videos tends to be young. These differences are reflected in the products and services advertised. But these audiences are not distinctive enough to persuade advertisers to pay more per viewer on these niche channels than on the big general programming networks. This is quite different from, say, national newspapers in Britain, where the advertising cost per 1,000 readers of the *Financial Times* is twelve times as much as for the mass-market *Sun* or *Mirror*.

What, then, will happen if we have 500 channels rather than 50? First, many of those channels will be used for 'near video on-demand' (NVoD), where a two-hour movie is shown continuously on, say, six channels with start times at twenty-minute intervals. On this basis, a choice of twenty movies would require 120 channels. This would reduce the market for video rentals and perhaps, at the margin, outright sales of video cassettes.

Second, channels with spare content will repackage it into several narrower offerings, such as a channel owned by a Hollywood studio showing only classic horror movies or westerns. This approach will give content owners and producers more options to generate viewers and a way to try and develop a distinctive positioning in an increasingly crowded market.

The main constraint is the scarcity of high-quality programming. Increasing the number of channels in itself has no more effect on the supply of programming than increasing the number of estate agents would have on the supply of houses. For the same reason, the scope for locally originated television (for example, from the local community) is quite limited: the local audience is too small to support high-quality programming. The best that can be realistically achieved is some viewing of local news and sport.

Putting the consumer in control

Simply increasing the number of TV channels, then, seems unlikely to change radically what and how people watch. Potentially more important is the ability of digital technology to shift control from media producers to consumers. Increasingly, technology will allow us to ask for the information we want, whenever we want it. Initially this may be mainly through explicit selection by browsing a menu or conducting a search using keywords. Over time, you will be able to delegate more to a personal assistant like Bob.

This potential shift from a model where producers 'push' information out to the public to one where consumers 'pull' only what they want, when they want it, applies to all media including television. The networks will still, as now, broadcast a continuous schedule of programmes, with the most current (especially sport) and appealing shown at prime time to maximize the number of people who watch them as they are shown. But, well before 2010, you will be able, with little effort (and without having to remember to ask a teenager to set the VCR), to watch any programme from any channel, shown any time in the last week, or year, whenever you like and in any order. *You* will be in control.

It is hard to say how much this will actually happen. Our hunch is that, most of the time, people in 2010 will still switch between a few main networks and a few more specialized ones, watching the best (or the 'least worst') programmes on air at the time. As now, they will use habit, memory and familiar brands – particular channels, shows and artists – to simplify programme choice. Nevertheless, we expect the amount of time-shifted viewing to increase and at least some people to use their personal assistants to search out and filter much of what they watch. In Nicholas Negroponte's words, 'Today's TV set lets you control brightness, volume and channels. Tomorrow's will allow you to vary sex, violence and political leaning.' One result may be that you are less likely to see anything that questions your beliefs or values.

Interactive TV

Digital technology can also make the experience of watching a particular programme more interactive than now. So far, the most successful application of interactive TV has been to game shows. You, the viewer at home, can also have your finger on the buzzer and compete against the studio contestants – or against others in your own and other homes. With an online connection, this can be for prizes or for the chance to be a studio contestant next week. It costs little to add the required data to an existing game show and increases the audience's involvement and enjoyment. Once enough homes are online, new game shows will be designed specifically to exploit this technology.

Another application is to overlay a programme with further background information. Examples include detailed team news and statistics for sports enthusiasts (especially suitable for sports like American football where the action is discontinuous), recipes on food shows and booking information on holiday programmes. The ability to 'find out more' is one of the hallmarks of digital technology.

With sports, the technology can also let you select camera angles, look at action replays, pit your wits against the coach by calling the next play, join in fantasy football, or (subject to regulation) place a real bet on who will win. Sport generates high viewer involvement, so several of these applications may be viable, although some – such as choosing camera angles – may increase production costs too much.

There have also been many experiments with interactive fiction or drama in which your own actions affect the plot – deliberately or otherwise. This is true of fantasy games, although these happen in real time using the present tense ('you are in a room with three doors . . .') rather than telling a story about something which has supposedly happened in the past ('it was a dark and stormy night . . .'). Generally, narrative fiction – novels and movies – will stay linear and always aim for involving characters and a strong plot with a beginning, a middle and an end. And, on the whole, consumers will prefer to continue delegating the storyline to Shakespeare or Jackie Collins.

Interactive TV will enhance many viewers' enjoyment of game shows, sport and magazine-type programmes. However, it will not turn television into something quite different, partly because some of the more radical options would be too expensive to programme routinely, partly because even in 2010 people will not want to read large amounts of text on a TV screen, and partly because interaction usually requires more effort than most viewers want to make most of the time.

The evidence, then, is that TV viewing will not be so very different in 2010 compared with now. The total amount of viewing may decline, especially for younger people, as the number of competing activities increases. We will also have to pay directly for more services – that is, there will be relatively more pay-per-view and subscriptions and perhaps less advertising-funded TV. There will be somewhat more timeshift viewing, more fragmentation of the audience because of the increasing number of channels, probably even more channel switching and 'grazing' than today, and rather more lone viewing, partly because of the increasing number of screens per home, but also because the number of one-person households will increase.

None of these trends is new. Remote switches, multiset homes, video games and VCRs have been with us for many years – and yet what and how people watch is not different in kind from thirty years ago. Major live events – the Olympic Games, the arrest and trial of O. J. Simpson or the funeral of Diana, Princess of Wales – provide a widely shared experience. Live events and top-rated movies and TV shows will continue to do so. In fact, with a global audience and multiple screening opportunities, the most popular aspects of mass culture will be even more widely shared than today. We also expect much TV viewing – more than half of evening viewing, except in single-person households – still to be done in company. People will still want to flop down in front of the television in 2010 much as they do today. In an increasingly complex and stressful world, the need for relaxing, passive entertainment – epitomized by TV – will be greater than ever.

Turning to other entertainment media, high-definition TV and video on-demand will not kill off the cinema. We like to go out in company and there will always be technologies which are too expensive to bring into the home. Some cinemas in 2010 may allow us to experience state-of-the-art virtual reality or holographic imagery. Computer games – mainly played by boys and young men – have boosted the acquisition of powerful home PCs. Multiplayer games can also lead to experimentation with other online relationships (for example, electronic 'bulletin boards' to exchange ideas or products). Games are now poised to become one of the main uses of virtual-reality technology, although this is likely to occupy only a small corner of the overall interactive media market.

Gambling will probably be a larger industry than games. It is already larger, in terms of annual revenues. In many countries gambling is state regulated and taxed, and offshore online gambling can evade these controls. The opportunity for gambling on live broadcast events, and the immediacy of the (possible) rewards, also make online gambling an exciting prospect. We are more sanguine about the possible increase in pornography. Concerns over pornography have dominated the early years of the Internet, as with most media when new, from books to videos. Sites with an overtly sexual nature will continue to grow on the Internet, but they will make up a small and ever-decreasing percentage of total content and usage. As Internet guru Esther Dyson suggests, a combination of rating and filtering services will emerge which will make it easier for families to control which information comes into the home.

Print media

The main current barrier to the general adoption of online newspapers is the lack of a small, light, cheap, robust storage device with a bright, sharp, page-sized viewing screen. As batteries get smaller and longer-lasting, and screens become easier on the eye and touch-sensitive (so keyboards are no longer needed), we will see more computers being read on the move. Even so, it is unlikely that many people will switch to simple electronic versions of today's newspapers. This is partly because printed newspapers cost so little and partly because, even in 2010, electronic newspapers will still be expensive to provide to people on the move.

The main attraction of an online newspaper is that it can be customized and is interactive. Customization means that you can choose what sorts of stories to see. You might select all the major news items, plus anything on New Zealand, all items on children's education, no fashion stories, no sports, and the weather/traffic and news for your local area. Again you may wish to see no advertising, or only specific types of ads, or you may subscribe (free) to various advertising-only services. You could also choose from a variety of editorial styles – perhaps a different style and content for Saturday and Sunday compared with the weekday/workday format. It would be hard to get the mix right first time, so you would continue to adapt and personalize it over time.

Digital newspapers have another advantage over print-on-paper: they can contain audio and video clips as well as print. Also, the advantage of interactivity means that you can point (or click or touch with a light pen) and request more information on a topic, or send an electronic message to the author or editor, or respond to ads, or race to be the first to finish the crossword. As described in the Marion Jackson scenario, portable notebooks or 'tablets' can also be used for sending and receiving both real-time (phone) and delayed (email, voicemail) messages. Turning to books, non-fiction and – especially – reference books will adapt well to going online, but books, particularly fiction, will not disappear.

Staying in touch with friends and family

Apart from relaxing, the other main use of media in the home is to keep in contact with people we like or love. Most residential telephone use today is social and local. We expect this to continue in the future. In 2010, there will be three interpersonal digital media – email, voice phone and video phone – although the distinctions between these will blur.

Email

Email is the great recent success story of digital technology. It is simple, cheap and meets real needs. Although all the hype about the Internet focuses on sophisticated applications like complex information searches or home shopping, most of the actual use of it is for email. Much current growth is among the retired: email is a wonderful medium for keeping in touch with people around the world at low cost, with little effort and with minimal delay from the time a message is sent to the time the recipient can read it. Unlike the phone (unless you have switched to voicemail), email is non-intrusive: you look at your messages when it suits you. This makes it especially well suited for communication between very different time zones.

Email is also flexible. For people who know each other well, most email messages are short and informal, without much fuss about usage or spelling – more like a casual spoken conversation than a written document. At the same time, email can also be used more formally – an email contract can be legally binding – or to transmit a large document. Again, an email can easily – perhaps too easily – be copied to large numbers of people with minimal extra effort. It can be as complex and elaborate as any other document: Bill Gates, Chairman of Microsoft, likes to handcraft birthday cards for his close family using recent digital snapshots.

As with the telephone today, not everyone will have email at home in 2010, even in the most advanced economies. This problem can be reduced by recycling terminals, by the market supplying some very cheap and simple ones (probably combined with a voice phone) and by providing access in community centres and other public spaces. In addition, governments may allocate a 'default' email address to every citizen.

One development of email is the growth of 'virtual communities' sharing a common interest such as Corgi toy cars or the genealogy of Clan Maclean. Electronic media are ideal both for identifying people with similar interests and for servicing the shared needs and tastes which come about from hobbies, lifestyle or illness. For some people, such virtual communities will be the 'killer application' that grabs and keeps their interest in the information network.

Voice phone

We also expect continuing growth in voice telephony, especially long-distance and mobile telephony. By 2010, when the normal input device will be a hidden microphone rather than a keyboard, the distinction between email and voice phone will be less clear-cut than today – a question of which form of output the receiver chooses (assuming their system has up-to-date voice processing). For simultaneous dialogue, people will usually choose voice, as now. This will normally be the unprocessed voice of the speaker, with perfect clarity and no perceptible time lag even for a conversation halfway round the world. By 2010, the H-COM should also be able to translate between languages in real time, although both the translation and the synthesized voice will be less than perfect, especially if the system does not know both speakers.

Increasingly, however, we will be leaving each other messages. For a short message, you will just leave a recording of your voice, like voicemail today. For any longer or more complex message, you will tell the system to leave an email and it will automatically convert what you say into digital text. In 2010, the coding will still be less than perfect, but the sender will be able to make corrections on her own screen if the detail of the message is important.

The main difference in 2010 is that telephony will be mostly 'hands off' – as in Lisa's conversation with her friend Amy. Calling someone should be easier than now. For close family and friends, you will be able to say just 'Call Janet' or 'Get me Janet'. (If that sounds too abrupt, the personal assistant can easily be instructed not to respond unless you also say 'please'.) Most phones are likely to be portable and pocket-sized. Telephones today are actually harder to use than in the past, because they have so many features. By 2010, they should have become simple again, since all the features will be managed by software with little effort by the user.

Video phone

What is less clear is the extent to which we will have two-way video capability. Leaving aside the technology and the costs – these will already be less of a barrier by 2010 – the main objection to video telephony is that few of us want to be seen at home by strangers, even if we ourselves can see the other person on our screen. In one of the early Japanese trials of interactive TV with two-way video, families put on their best clothes and specially cleaned their – doubtless already spotless – homes before each evening's transmission.

This problem is easily solved. If you do not want callers to see you, you can simply turn off the two-way video link, or substitute a picture of yourself, your family or anything else. We believe close friends and family may over time prefer to see each other as they speak. The growing use of video conferencing at home by professionals, like Pete Jackson, will make people increasingly comfortable with this technology. The trick will be to make it more like a face-to-face conversation, for instance by ensuring that the image of the other person is at a comfortable distance and that the speakers maintain sufficient eye contact without staring at each other in an unnatural way. Assuming this happens, we expect most domestic video telephony to be among people who know each other well and talk often, mostly women and teenagers. We also expect most of the use to be local, as with the telephone today. This assumes that by 2010 families like the Jacksons are paying for a link to the network with enough capacity to support two-way video telephony and that most of the cost is for access rather than usage.

One consequence of what the *Economist*'s Frances Cairncross calls 'the death of distance' is that by 2010 it should cost little more to conduct a video conversation over any distance than it does to conduct a voice conversation today. The only exceptions will be where the person at the other end is somewhere very isolated or with underdeveloped infrastructure.

Firms may take a lead by adopting a video telephone number for their customer service department. This is likely to happen first in a business-to-business context and then in organizations dealing directly with the public. Our hunch is that most firms will prefer to show the service representative in person (rather than a computerised talking head), which will seem more human, natural and sincere. A possible scenario is a customer service representative who can be seen by, but cannot see, the consumer (this will, however, be quite stressful and difficult for the service representative, who will require training and support). The consumer may then choose to reveal her real face too, although this will mean sitting down in front of a camera-equipped terminal – something that one-way video telephony would not require.

However, people may still prefer voice-only telephony in 2010, even with their closest friends. Research suggests that people talk more freely, deeply and intimately on the phone than face to face. Even if video telephony does take off, most telephone conversations are likely to be voice-only in 2010, especially those conducted on the move.

One issue in the information society will be for people to keep control of the mass of incoming communications including unwanted phone calls and junk email. By 2010, a personal assistant like Bob will be able to put you largely back in control. Bob will know who you are happy to receive messages from at all, and with what priority (for example, live phone, voicemail, email), and will be able to sort and categorize recorded messages and, increasingly, summarize them too: just like a good personal assistant, and improving all the time with experience and feedback.

'A shopper's heaven'?

Bill Gates's view is that:

> All the goods for sale in the world will be available for you to examine, compare and, often, customize. When you want to buy something you'll be able to tell the computer to find it for you at the best price offered by any acceptable source. Servers distributed world-wide will accept bids, resolve offers into completed transactions, control authentication and security, and handle all other aspects of the marketplace, including the transfer of funds . . . It will be a shopper's heaven.

Gates also suggests that we will examine product reviews online, check out relevant regulatory data and email people we know for recommendations.

Well, maybe, for some people and for some types of product. While online shopping will grow, there are several problems. Buying computer software online is straightforward and reliable. Buying peaches, crockery or a dress is not, because of the problem of physical delivery and the difficulty of judging colour, texture and quality from the screen.

Information will probably eventually be digitized for almost all products and services. But because it has to be made available to home online systems, different H-COMs must be on networks which are linked and can communicate with each other. Even more problematic, your intelligent agent ('Bob') must have access to all relevant information. For instance the system of which your H-COM is part might have exclusive rights to display Armani clothes or Sainsbury groceries, while another system might have exclusive rights to show Nike sportswear or Paramount movies.

Most fundamental of all, most people enjoy real-life shopping and browsing, at least for some products and services, some of the time. Bob will not have opinions on what suits you, nor will he be able to make small talk about last night's football match or the proposed city centre by-pass. Much shopping has a social side, especially for those who telework: home-based teleworkers are among the least enthusiastic groups when it comes to using their PCs for shopping and other non-work activities.

Electronic payment and banking

Telephone banking has been one of the success stories of the 1990s. This trend to remote banking will continue with screen-based services taking over from purely telephone-based services as more consumers go online. Successful online banks will be those who back up their system with helpful service staff. If you are reading your monthly statement on the screen and have a query, you will simply press or click an on-screen button which connects you by voice to a bank employee (perhaps working from their home) whose screen displays the same information as yours.

We will also see fewer cash transactions. Electronic cash or credit will become more widely used. One bonus is that this will simplify shopping abroad. Most of us are not too worried about giving our name, address and credit card number to a mail-order company or ticket agent over the telephone. Increasingly we will give this information via a screen-based display rather than by phone. Initially, screen-based transactions will involve menus and a little typing. Soon you will be able to speak your instructions (within a fixed format) and see them appear on the screen. Other forms of electronic payment, such as subscription accounts and digital money (held in the form of an electronic smart card) will also become widespread.

Professional services

For some kinds of people and for some sorts of advice, video consulting will provide many benefits. Video-consultations will probably involve the client and the professional each sitting in front of a screen, perhaps the same screen used for entertainment or work in the home. So if your time is valuable (and your income high) you may choose video consultation with your doctor, lawyer or interior designer.

It has been suggested that for the time-poor, especially those whose diaries are managed by others, software will be available to schedule meetings electronically. This may work for business colleagues who know each other well, or if you wish to meet with a lawyer, dentist or government official, where there are fixed booking rules. It will work less well for other professionals or for social appointments, which usually involve some polite negotiation.

Electronic information and advertising

If a TV commercial catches your attention, one or two clicks on your remote will get you more information straight away. You can view this information then or later and even order the product online. But often consumers want information about more than one manufacturer. An online information system may make it easier to obtain independent advice – for example, from consumer organizations or regulatory bodies. This online advice will especially appeal to the sorts of people who currently subscribe to *Which?* or *Consumer Reports*. The traditional bundling together of advice and sales may become less prevalent. More likely, markets will segment, as we are starting to see with people buying PCs: experienced PC users buy online while first-time buyers who need advice go to specialist retailers and pay a bit more for an equivalent machine.

As more of our TV viewing is elective (pay-per-view, video-on-demand), we may choose not to see as much general advertising as now. The trend towards more subtle advertising may continue – commercials that entertain, games and competitions, sponsorship. Classified ads will also naturally migrate to new searchable media. Elective viewing of advertising will help keep down channel subscription costs. You might also charge the company for this information – although how much you can charge will depend on how desirable you are as a potential customer.

The trend towards targeting and 'one-to-one' (that is, individual) marketing will continue, increasingly based on companies' records of people's individual characteristics and especially their previous transactions. For instance, you and your neighbour may both watch the same programme but see different commercials because one of you owns a cat (and buys cat food) and the other is a frequent business-class flyer. This raises privacy issues as well as other practical problems.

Work, education and healthcare

Apart from shopping, the new media will also allow you to do other things at home which now (since the industrial revolution) happen elsewhere.

Home versus office

As more people work from home, at least for some of the time, the line between work-time and home-time is becoming less clearcut. As industries become automated, more of the workforce is engaged in storing, processing and disseminating information, often using a telephone and a networked computer. Also, it is now easy and cheap (and becoming cheaper) to route information to and from any location. Virtual networks have developed where bank enquiries can be answered from operators sited anywhere, even abroad. A bank might have groups of remote enquiry handlers in a number of third-world countries, to benefit from both cheaper wages and time-zone differences.

Those who choose to 'telework' have tended to be the most autonomous workers: lawyers, accountants, academics or sales-people, who spend a growing – although still small – proportion of their work time at home in a room equipped with a networked PC/fax/printer and phone. These are not people who 'clock on' and work a set number of hours a week. Rather they are judged by results, and their jobs have always involved taking some work home. For such workers, offices might eventually become places you visit one or two days a week to share experiences with colleagues and have meetings. Digital technology will not greatly reduce travel by professionals: it can substitute for some journeys but also makes travel time more productive. Wherever you go, your virtual office can go with you.

The other group of people for whom telework is increasing may not welcome the change. These are workers whose job entails sitting in front of a PC wearing a phone headset: for example customer support staff can have access at home to both customer and company records. Such changes in workplace practices are primarily being driven by large corporations looking for savings in wages, office space and overheads. While the chance to work for a large bank from your cottage in the country may seem attractive, there are costs as well.

It has been suggested that telework is ideal for those with small children: the parent works in one room while children play in the next. If the baby wakes up and needs feeding, the mother can signal that she is unavailable for work until all is quiet again. This could approach the grim type of life experienced by out-workers in the clothing trade (the PC taking on the role of sewing machine, with payment based on the number of enquiries handled). It could represent a backward shift in employee conditions: no office or canteen socialization, less chance of training, promotion or even 'sick-pay'.

Both these types of telework will increase over the next twenty years, although much less than most of the digerati suggest: even in California, the actual incidence of telework from home using networked PCs is less than 1 per cent of total working days.

Education

Successfully exploiting computers in schools has proved to be a desperately slow process over the last twenty years, but the pace of change will accelerate over the next ten. Many changes will be incremental. As schools join the information network they will probably have access to a special school network and database where information has already been coded, vetted and sorted, and where children can chat online to other children around the world. Encyclopaedias are better online and computers are good at taking children in a measured and non-judgemental way through any learning which is based on facts and rules. However, establishing and maintaining such a project will require substantial government investment, especially if it is to help those most in need, children who are not linked to the network at home.

Without strong government intervention, electronic media will do little to equalize children's education. Some schools will have a state-of-the-art personal notebook computer for every child, others will have one older PC for every class.

Even with appropriate investment and teacher training, electronic media will play only a small part in school life in 2010. School is still about socialization and about learning things which cannot be digitized: the making and breaking of friendships, the meeting and melding – often more than at any other time in a person's life – of people from different backgrounds, cultures and physical and mental abilities.

Healthcare

Medicine is also benefiting from innovations brought about by the adoption of digital media. Patient records – doctors' notes, X-ray images, pathology slides, videos of speech impairment or behavioural problems – are starting to be routinely stored electronically and accessed remotely by different healthcare agencies. In the last few years we have also seen time-savings in the treatment of patients at small rural hospitals, where high-speed data links have connected local sensors, ultrasound scans or X-ray equipment to specialist doctors and diagnostic centres.

The most dramatic change (especially for the patient) is the ability for blood pressure, heart beat, body temperature and so on to be monitored remotely. This telemedicine saves time and money for healthcare providers and reduces travel and stress for patients in remote communities. With networked health centres and then individual networked homes, many more basic medical practices will take place remotely. Eventually, face-to-face contact with your doctor may be the province of the rich, the poor and the really sick.

Another trend in medicine is that people are increasingly seeking to become more knowledgeable about the workings of their own bodies. This is seen in self-diagnosis and patient (especially patient-to-patient) support. Computer-based patient support systems give users medical information – but at the user's own pace and preserving the user's anonymity. Patient-to-patient support is ideally suited to digital media. Some medical problems are like obsessive hobbies which can consume your every waking moment. What you need is fellow sufferers, who may not live near by. A global network such as the Internet is ideally suited for sharing and disseminating specialist medical information and experience – a good example of a virtual community.

A better life?

Some commentators predict a digital utopia: greater equality in education; more control over our lives; less pressure on natural resources (because more products will be in the form of bits rather than manufactured goods); politicians becoming more sensitive to public opinion; increased understanding, tolerance and global peace (due to increasing economic interdependence and more open communication); even improved writing and reading skills (as young people use email).

The most optimistic envisage a global communication network potentially linking every home with every other home and with all stored digital information. This will give us the ability to receive/send words, pictures and sounds from/to any other person or institution connected to the network. We will even be able to do all of these things while we are on the move. However, the ability to send and receive information, even if we can do it faster and more easily than ever before, does not necessarily mean that there will be more *communication* – or understanding. Below we consider other potential advantages and disadvantages for society in general.

The digital revolution will probably displace more jobs and create fewer new ones than earlier social revolutions. The fear of unemployment, automation or smart systems making your job redundant means that those who have work will work harder. As Frances Cairncross of the *Economist* writes,

> The fragmentation of the large employer has made many work-ers feel less secure. More and more people employed on short term contracts, or as freelancers, will be only as good as their last job and under constant pressure to find the next assignment before the current one finishes. The blending of leisure and

work may well mean in practice that work increasingly intrudes into leisure: it makes for more forceful demands.

A knock-on effect of less commuting (plus improved traffic management) would be fewer traffic jams, especially during rush hours. In reality, there is unlikely to be less traffic, but traffic will become more managed. Road pricing (electronic tolls), automatic speed traps (remote sensing of car registration) and smarter cars (that talk to you and, eventually, drive themselves, at least on main roads) will become widespread. Using low orbit satellites and radio sensors, vehicles can be tracked as they travel, enabling companies to fine-tune delivery schedules, or monitor expensive or dangerous equipment.

Digital video cameras, online networks and global positioning systems will be used to monitor employees, company equipment including vehicles, personal equipment (homes, cars or boats) and even family members (the young and the old or ill). Employees who might find themselves monitored by video include teleworkers and public employees potentially subject to abuse or claims of abusive behaviour (social workers, doctors, nurses, police).

Remote tracking is an example of a 'new' application rather than just a faster or cheaper way of doing an existing task and will find many more applications. For example, prisoners can be electronically tagged, or people with certain medical complaints can live at home on their own with a discreet monitor which sends a message to their doctor or hospital if they are in danger.

One widespread fear is that digital technology will lead to reduced human contact. This seems unlikely. As illustrated by the Jacksons, people with the technology, including the elderly living alone, will actually use it to increase their contact with others outside the home. Within multiperson households, however, communication between family members will continue to be reduced.

Inequality

All technologies tend to disadvantage those who do not have access to them. If you do not have a car, large out-of-town supermarkets are largely inaccessible, you miss out on lower prices and your local shop may close down through lack of business. On balance, the digital revolution will widen inequality in society. Once homes have paid to be linked to the information network, much of the information available to them will be free or cheap. Transmission charges will also be low.

Those not connected to the network may have to pay more than at present to receive information in paper form (for example, telephone directories, encyclopaedias, local newspapers). As electronic mail becomes widespread, postal charges may rise. With the increase in the take-up of satellite and cable television, the service available on UK broadcast TV is already narrowing: many sports events, previously broadcast free, can now be seen only on pay-TV. This trend will accelerate unless the BBC licence fee is allowed to increase more in line with the costs of world class programming.

Crime and security

City centres, car parks, playgrounds, homes, offices, factories and roads will all become equipped with video cameras. But although crimes will be more easily monitored, criminals will not necessarily be more easily identified. It is true that you can search digital video looking for a particular face – but that face then needs to be matched to a known existing one. Even if we all have compulsory identity cards with our picture and a full record of our visual characteristics, and this information is stored on a police network, it will be hard to match this information with video footage. For the foreseeable future humans will remain better equipped than computers to remember and recognize faces, especially at unusual angles and displaying unusual expressions. People in third-world economies may be employed to watch the security monitors.

Monitoring children in the playground or at the nursery may safeguard against kidnappers and abusers. But how many parents would be happy accompanying their child to the playground knowing that their every word and movement was being captured on video? The video camera can protect, but also frighten. Video images can easily be altered – the face of your child playing on the swing superimposed upon less innocent images. The power can also be switched off, the video camera covered or tricked into recording a picture which is not current. So video cameras are not a foolproof way of making the environment safer.

Data protection is more difficult with an electronic and interactive medium. Even the most secure encryption system is vulnerable to illicit access to the password. Those who have committed crimes on the Internet have tended to come from the same community as the developers; crime innovates at the same rate as anything else. So we will have theft and espionage and infringement of copyright and libel and child pornography in this new medium. Apart from the privacy issues, there will probably be few new crimes: just familiar crimes in new guises.

How will we prove that a crime has taken place? Paper records, audio and video tapes and photographs used to be taken as hard evidence, as facts. In the future, if we do not agree with the evidence, we will assume that it has been digitally altered. Criminals will exploit this. One solution is for digital images to be 'stamped' with a time, date and electronic 'watermark', but this may be insufficient to provide the certainty we are accustomed to from physical evidence.

There are other dangers. Because of competitive pressure, companies are launching services based on cutting-edge, rather than tried and tested, technology. Software and networks are increasingly complex and interconnected. The whole system may have unpredicted weaknesses and vulnerabilities, exemplified by the 'millennium bug'. When information is available *only* online, what happens if the central server on which information is held breaks down or becomes corrupted by cyber-terrorists? What happens if an electronic 'Pearl Harbor' is launched by a hostile state? These are real risks, ignored by most techno-enthusiasts.

Privacy

Traditionally, your bank was the only commercial service that knew what you earned, how you earned it and (to some extent) what you spent it on. Various government agencies also recorded demographic details and noted which cars you had owned, where you had lived and if you had a criminal record. Now, an increasing number of private companies and agencies gather and store information about you, much of which you cannot easily check. This is held on networked computers and used for purposes that you might not like (if you knew). By 2010, Bob and other agents and systems on the network will hold all manner of information on the Jacksons' likes, dislikes and private habits.

Much of this information will be on your home information system, which is connected to the global information system. The advantage of this is that whenever you need to give out any information about yourself it will be so much *easier* than at present – no completing forms, just transfer across the relevant bits. Or companies can access your system and pull off the relevant data, subject to your permission.

Are people becoming more willing to let their personal details be stored on network devices? What are the potential pitfalls here? The police should normally have access only to your criminal record, the doctor only to your medical notes, your various banks only to their own account details. Who will guarantee this restricted access? How will you be able to check that it is not being violated?

Government and censorship

Government, so far, has had little influence on the shape of interactive media. It had a hand at the birth of the Internet (which grew out of the older ARPANET system, funded by the US military to link scientists at different institutions), but has since been conspicuously absent. Many Internet enthusiasts would like to keep government in all its guises – regulation, standard-setting, censorship and taxes – well away.

Networks and cheap telephone tariffs mean that more information-processing companies (and even individuals) may start to operate from countries with low direct taxes. Electronic commerce can also make it easier for shoppers to evade sales taxes, for example, by purchasing through offshore suppliers.

Censorship by government will be an issue, especially for those countries out of tune with the American way of life. What can a state do if it does not want its citizens reading material which its rulers deem profane or seditious? How will dictatorial governments react to information sites which criticize the ruling party?

Even the US is not exempt from censorship: countries such as Holland and Sweden have more liberal laws on pornography.

Most crime on the Internet is covered by present laws, but these are invoked only when a company is caught. Checking the Web (globally) for any sites which contain illegal material is increasingly difficult. It is almost impossible if you are a small country, English is not the national language, and you have many laws which will be broken by US sites. Realistically for the foreseeable future, US rules will become world rules. The only practical way for a government or religious community to restrict what its citizens/members can access is by excluding everything that has not been specifically allowed.

In terms of which countries will be winners and losers in the digital revolution, the evidence suggests that the US and Scandinavia (which are already ahead) and South-East Asia (with its young population and dynamic economies) will all benefit, while most of Western Europe will generally suffer.

Voting and community involvement

The local information network may over time supersede the local newspaper, although a likely outcome is that the same publisher will run both. The local newspaper is often free because it is supported by classified ads. As advertising migrates to a searchable medium, so local news and information will follow. Many people care more about their local community than about bigger and more remote issues (foreign policy, a unified monetary system), and so will take the effort to make their views known online if it is their local school which is being discussed in the council chamber. So the information network will not only provide the means whereby virtual communities seed and flourish, it may also help to cement the local physical community.

There is a view that the information network will involve us more in the democratic process. Yes and no. It may achieve little to ask the (online) public to vote electronically on policy matters, if only because the voting sample would be unbalanced by special interest groups. Also, it could encourage governments to opt out of difficult decisions by increasingly holding referenda on divisive issues. Even if online technology were universally available, the evidence is that the ability to vote electronically would not increase participation in national elections or referenda.

Looking further ahead

By some time in the second half of the twenty-first century, two developments are possible that raise serious philosophical, ethical and political questions. First, we may have technology that can 'read' or 'write' thoughts and feelings directly out of and into our brains. We accept that some of the processes of thinking and feeling can be 'read' – at least in crude terms – using modern brain scanners. But the idea of technology that can read or induce mental states accurately and reliably is not a comfortable one, raising serious issues of control.

Second, at some stage there will be computers more intelligent than people. The timing is hard to predict: the main result of artificial intelligence research to date has been to show that many of the skills we take for granted – like walking and talking – are much more complex than they seem. Even something as well structured as playing chess turned out to involve holistic processes like pattern recognition and feelings. Forty years ago, most experts thought it would take perhaps ten years for a computer to beat the best human chess player in the world. Although it took forty years, not ten, this has now happened. What will happen if, in another forty years, machines are finally more intelligent than people? Will they treat us as badly as we treat other animals?

And finally

Much discussion of future media is dominated by a kind of breathless enthusiasm. In this brief review, we have tried to be more balanced. Both the speed and many of the benefits of the digital revolution have been overhyped, and some of its dangers and disadvantages underplayed. Like genetic engineering, it will quite soon confront us with deep philosophical and ethical questions about the nature of humanity. The ultimate risk is that we, or our grandchildren, end up in a nightmare world dominated by machines.

The best protection against these dangers is a citizenry that is informed, involved, alert and questioning. We hope that *The Future of Media* will contribute to the development of such a citizenry. Of course, there are many other personal and professional reasons for finding out about, and experimenting with, digital media. Perhaps the most important is this: for most people in today's advanced economies, the digital revolution is likely to be the most interesting and wide-ranging social development of their lifetimes.

Some of you will find the scenarios we have described in this essay fanciful, others will feel that they are too cautious. We have aimed to predict realistically how media will influence home life in the next decade or so. Most, if not all, that we have described is happening now, somewhere.

Further Reading

Cosmology

George Gamow, *The Creation of the Universe* (Viking, 1952)
John Gribbin, *In the Beginning* (Viking, 1993)
John Gribbin, *Companion to the Cosmos* (Weidenfeld & Nicolson, 1996)
Laurie John (ed.), *Cosmology Now* (BBC Publications, 1973)
Martin Rees, *Before the Beginning* (Simon & Schuster, 1997)
Lee Smolin, *The Life of the Cosmos* (Weidenfeld & Nicolson, 1997)
Steven Weinberg, *The First Three Minutes* (Deutsch, 1977)

Religion

K. Armstrong, *A History of God* (1993)
M. Banton, ed., *Anthropological Approaches to the Study of Religion* (1966)
J. Bowker, ed., *The Oxford Dictionary of World Religions* (1997)
F. Coplestone, *Religion and the One* (1982)
J. L. Esposito, *The Islamic Threat: Myth or Reality?* (1995)
C. Flood, *An Introduction to Hinduism* (1996)
E. Gellner, *Postmodernism, Reason and Religion* (1992)
P. Harvey, *An Introduction to Buddhism* (1990)
H. Küng, *The Religious Situation of Our Time: Judaism* (1992)
N. de Lange, *Judaism* (1986)
C. McDonnell, *Material Christianity: Religion and Popular Culture in America* (1995)
D. Z. Phillips, *Can Religion be Explained Away?* (1996)
P. L. Quinn and C. Tagliaferro, *A Companion to the Philosophy of Religion* (1997)
M. Ruthven, *Islam in the World* (1991)
W. Sims Bainbridge, *The Sociology of Religious Movements* (1997)
R. Stark and W. Sims Bainbridge, *The Future of Religion: Secularisation, Revival and Cult Formation* (1983)

Warfare

The great classics remain indispensable, first and foremost Sun Tzu's *The Art of War*, of which there exist several translations into English (notably Oxford

University Press, 1963; available in paperback), and Carl von Clausewitz's *On War* (Penguin Classics, 1982). Of more recent vintage, Thomas Schelling's *The Strategy of Conflict* (Harvard University Press, 1960); Général André Beaufre's *Introduction to Strategy* (Faber & Faber, 1965); and Lawrence Freedman's *The Evolution of Nuclear Strategy* (Macmillan, 1981) are all first class.

For a long-term view on the history of war and strategy, Sir Michael Howard's *The Lessons of History* (Oxford University Press, 1991) and Paul Kennedy's *Grand Strategies in War and Peace* (Yale University Press, 1991) are strongly recommended recent works.

For an understanding of contemporary warfare, one author's contribution stands out most strongly, that of Martin Van Creveld, who teaches at the Hebrew University in Jerusalem. Some of his more prominent books include *Supplying War: Logistics from Wallenstein to Patton* (Cambridge University Press, 1977); *Command in War* (Harvard University Press, 1985); *On Future War* (Brassey's, 1991); and *Technology and War* (Brassey's, 1991).

The Penguin Encyclopaedia of Modern Warfare (1991) is a handy compendium of facts and concepts.

The Middle East

Ajami, Fouad, *The Arab Predicament: Arab Thought and Practice since 1967* (Cambridge, 1992).

Arjomand, Said Amir, *The Turban for the Crown: the Islamic Revolution in Iran* (New York/Oxford, 1988).

Gilbert, Martin, *Exile and Return: the Struggle for a Jewish Homeland* (New York, 1978).

Issawi, Charles, *The Middle East Economy: Decline and Recovery* (Princeton, 1995).

Jansen, Johannes J. G., *The Dual Nature of Islamic Fundamentalism* (London, 1997).

Laqueur, Walter & Rubin, Barry (eds.), *The Israel–Arab Reader* (5th edition; London, 1995).

Lewis, Bernard, *The Shaping of the Modern Middle East* (New York/Oxford, 1994).

The World Bank, *Claiming the Future: Choosing Prosperity in the Middle East and North Africa* (Washington DC, 1995).

Yapp, M. E., *The Near East Since the First World War* (London, 1991).

Zürcher, Erik J., *Turkey, a Modern History* (London, 1993).

Terrorism

It will come as no surprise to readers who have got this far that few of the specialist academic works on terrorism, of which there are hundreds, share the perspective that has been developed in this essay. Typical of the mainstream genre from whose title one of our central themes is drawn is Walter Laqueur's influential *The Age of Terrorism* (Boston and London, 1987). A good academic treatment of the subject is Grant Wardlaw, *Political Terrorism: Theory, Tactics, and Counter-Measures* (Cambridge, 2nd edn, 1989). The careful scholar alluded to on p. 206 is A. P. Schmid, whose book (with A. J. Longman), *Political Terrorism: A New Guide to Actors, Authors, Concepts, Data Bases, Theories and Literature* (Amsterdam, 1988) is a significant contribution to the literature. By far the best recent study of the subject of terrorism as a whole is Adrian Guelke, *The Age of Terrorism and the International Political System* (London and New York, 1995), whose influence I am delighted to aknowledge. Another major influence has been Noam Chomsky, whose political writings as a whole resound with a sceptical integrity which I have tried here to imitate if not emulate. On terrorism in particular see his *The Culture of Terrorism* (Boston, 1988). Some of the best work on terrorism does not describe itself as such, preferring to deal with the real issue of the morality of engaging in subversive violence. See in particular David Miller, 'The Use and Abuse of Political Violence', *Political Studies*, 32 (1984), pp. 401–19, and Tony Honoré, 'The Right to Rebel', *Oxford Journal of Legal Studies*, 8 (1988), pp. 34–54. Both essays are reprinted in C. A. Gearty (ed.), *Terrorism* (Aldershot, 1996), in the introduction to which volume I develop some of the themes discussed here. For an earlier version of the central argument in this essay, developed at somewhat greater length but (I think now) less completely, see my *Terror* (London, 1991).

The books mentioned in the text are, in alphabetical order, S. T. Francis, *The Soviet Strategy of Terror* (Washington DC, 1981); Adrian Guelke, *The Age of Terrorism and the International Political System* (London and New York, 1995); Josephus, *The Jewish War* (Harmondsworth, 1970); N. C. Livingstone, *The War against Terrorism* (Lexington, 1982); Dick Morris, *Behind the Oval Office* (New York, 1996); Benjamin Netanyahu, *Fighting Terrorism* (London, 1996); Benjamin Netanyahu (ed.), *International Terrorism: Challenge and Response* (New Brunswick, N. J., 1989); Benjamin Netanyahu (ed.), *Terrorism: How the West Can Win* (London, 1986); and U. Ra'anan, R. L. Pfaltzgraff, R. H. Shultz, E. Halperin and I. Lukes, *Hydra of Carnage* (Lexington, 1986).

Moral Values

Aristotle, *Nichomachean Ethics*
Berlin, Isaiah, *The Crooked Timber of Humanity*, John Murray, 1990
Dworkin, Ronald, *Life's Dominion*, HarperCollins, 1993
Hart, H. L. A., *Law, Liberty and Morality*, Knopf, 1966
Hume, David, *An Enquiry Concerning the Principles of Morals*
MacIntyre, Alisdair, *After Virtue*, Duckworth, 1984
Mackie, J. L., *Ethics: Inventing Right and Wrong*, Penguin, 1977
Mill, J. S., *On Liberty*
Nietzsche, Friedrich, *Beyond Good and Evil*

Russell, Bertrand, *Marriage and Morals*, Routledge
Williams, Bernard, *Morality*, Cambridge University Press, 1972

Disease

Bray, R. S., *Armies of Pestilence* (Lutterworth, Cambridge, 1997).

Ewald, Paul, *Evolution of Infectious Disease* (Oxford University Press, New York, 1994).

Garrett, Laurie, *The Coming Plague: Newly Emerging Diseases in a World Out of Balance* (Penguin, Harmondsworth, 1994).

Institute of Medicine, *Emerging Infections* (National Academy Press, Washington, DC, 1992).

Karlen, Arno, *Plague's Progress* (Victor Gollancz, London, 1997).

McCormick, Joseph B. and Fisher-Hoch, Susan, *The Virus Hunters* (Bloomsbury, London, 1996).

McNeill, William, *Plagues and Peoples* (Doubleday, New York, 1976).

Nesse, Randolph and Williams, George, *Evolution and Healing* (Phoenix, London, 1996).

Preston, Richard, *The Hot Zone* (Random House, New York, 1994).

Ryan, Frank, *Virus X: Understanding the Real Threat of the New Pandemic Plagues* (HarperCollins, London, 1996).

Wills, Christopher, *Plagues: Their Origin, History and Future* (HarperCollins, London, 1996).

Zinsser, Hans, *Rats, Lice and History* (Little Brown, New York, 1934).

Media

To explore the issues in this book more fully, a good starting-point is *Being Digital* by Nicholas Negroponte (Knopf, 1995). Negroponte, Director of the Media Lab at MIT, saw the importance of media becoming digital long before most experts. He believes that the digital revolution will be radical, fast and mostly beneficial. The Media Lab focuses on making technology easy for people to communicate with.

The Road Ahead by Bill Gates, Chairman of software giant Microsoft (Viking, 1995), is part autobiography, partly a history of the computer industry, but mostly Gates's view of the likely impact of digital technology on entertainment, commerce, education and society.

Frances Cairncross is a senior editor at *The Economist*. Her wide-ranging *The Death of Distance* (Orion, 1997) reviews the convergence of the telephone, television and computer, and the implications of the collapsing cost of electronic communication, especially over long distances. Topics include the further globalization of business operations, the glut of information but scarcity of key content, the growing importance of both price competition and brands and the increasing difficulty of nation-state government.

Governance is further explored in *Release 2.0: A Design for Living in the Digital Age* by Esther Dyson (Broadway Books, 1997). Dyson's Release 1.0 newsletter and annual PC Forum are highly influential among the top US digerati. *Release 2.0* is about ensuring that the digital revolution makes the World more, not less, civilized, by intelligently addressing governance, content ownership and control, privacy, anonymity and security.

The One-to-One Future by Don Peppers and Martha Rogers (Piatkus, 1993) is about the impact of digital technology on marketing. Peppers and Rogers argue that mass media and marketing will be replaced by interactive, individually customized media and marketing, 'building business relationships one customer at a time'. They also discuss privacy and other societal impacts.

Television and its Audience by Patrick Barwise, Andrew Ehrenberg, and Douglas Carrie (Sage, 2nd edition forthcoming) gives the background to the section on television in this book. It focuses mainly on the patterns of multichannel viewing behaviour, but also covers related issues such as TV advertising.

HAL's Legacy, edited by David G. Stork (MIT Press, 1997), is partly a tribute to Arthur C. Clarke's late-60s novel and Stanley Kubrick's movie *2001: A Space Odyssey*, and partly a review of the state-of-the-art and future prospects in artificial intelligence. The contributors include many of the top US researchers on computer science, voice processing, artificial intelligence, etc., but the writing is readable and mostly non-technical.

The Media Equation by Byron Reeves and Clifford Nass (Cambridge University Press, 1996) is about 'how people treat computers, television and new media like real people and places'. For instance, Reeves and Nass's research at Stanford University shows that people are polite to computers, respond differently to male and female computer voices and feel threatened by a large face on a PC screen.

Kevin Warwick is Professor of Cybernetics at Reading University. His *March of the Machines: Why the New Race of Robots Will Rule the World* (Century, 1997) explores the frightening long-term implications of the continuing growth of machine intelligence. Today's robots can learn, communicate, teach each other and treat human beings as objects or resources in their environment. Tomorrow's will also be smarter than people.

Tips for Time Travellers by Peter Cochrane, Head of Research at BT (Orion, 1997) also discusses the radical implications of digital technology, but more optimistically than Kevin Warwick. It consists of sixty 600-word chapters, ranging from purely practical issues like network reliability and voice processing, to philosophical questions such as whether our minds could outlive us within a computer. Full of ideas about the manifold knock-on effects of new technology in the twenty-first century.

Index

abortion 319–20
abuse, drugs 312–16
Adventism 68
advertising, electronic 460–1
aerosol diseases 407–8, 412
affluence, religion 78–80
Africa, viruses 386, 394–5, 398
African National Congress (ANC), terrorism 217, 218
age of terrorism 194–6, 199, 202–3, 204
  Middle East 214
  rise of 207
Agenda 2000 Europe 245, 256, 257, 259–60
aggression, male 358
agriculture 174, 266, 270
AIDS 386, 387, 392, 394–5
  initial symptoms 413–14
  misunderstanding 411–12
  treatment 423
air transport 140
air-conditioning systems 415
aircraft carriers 119–20
alcohol prohibition 313, 314
America *see* United States of America
American imperialism 148
amino acids, IVF 352, 354
analogue technology 428, 429

ANC *see* African National Congress
Ancient Egypt 334, 356, 388
animals
  cloning 367
  husbandry 334
  transgenic 359–62, 370
anthropology 47, 63
antibacterial chemicals 422
antibiotics 415, 419–22
antibodies, sperm 375
antimicrobials, effectiveness 420–1
Apes of Faith 46–51
Arab population 176
Arab-Israel relations 161–2, 182–3
Arafat, Yasser 224–5
arboviruses 404–5
arms race 141
arthritis, rheumatoid 418
artificial intelligence 472
Asia
  warfare 121–4, 138–41
  see also Central Asia; Transcaucasia
Assassins group (terrorists) 196
assisted suicide *see* euthanasia
Atlanticism, British 268
atoms 12–13, 19, 101
Augustine, Norman 105
authoritarianism, religion 70–7

Baader-Meinhof group (Red Army Faction) 213
bacteria 401, 419–20

baptism, Catholicism 93–4
Barwise, Paddy 425–61
baryonic matter 30–1, 33, 34
Basque Nationalist Party (PNV) 212
bats 402
battlefields, future 128–9
belief 44
  see also religion
Big Bang model 3–15, 24–5, 27, 28, 30–1
biological weapons 102–3, 138
biotechnology 102–3
black holes 23–4
Blair, Tony 239, 240, 241, 246–7
Blake, William 84–5
blasphemy 321–2
Bonaparte, Napoleon 125, 145, 150
Borna virus 417–18
Brown, Louise 337
BSE disease 415
bubonic plague 386, 389–90
Buddhism 54–5, 60
business success, religion 62–3
Butler, Sir Michael 252, 255–6, 257, 269, 279

cancer 347–8, 418
  awareness letter 437
Cao-Dai cult 74–5
casual-contact diseases 412–13
casualties, terrorism 204–5

Catholicism 62, 75, 250
baptism 93–4
ecumenism 88
visionaries 69
CDM *see* cold dark matter
censorship 470–1
Central America,
terrorism 204
Central Asia 172
Cepheids (stars) 9
de Charette, Hervé 255,
259, 260–1, 264
chatting, future of 434–5,
437
chemicals
perfected by design 422
as weapons 138
Children of God
movement 73–4
China
influenza 390–1, 407
Middle East interest
186–9
plagues 388–9, 390
warfare 119–21
cholera 386, 392
Christianity 52–3, 56–60,
75, 84
Crusades 152
ecumenism 88
fundamentalism 72
Middle East 184–5
transcendence 58
chromosomes
defects 340
sex selection 356
staining 346–7
Church
Europe 248
see also religion
Churchill, Sir Winston
252–3, 266–7, 278
citizens of Europe 247
civil society 324–5
civilians, warfare 133–4
Clarke, Arthur C. 43
classical wars 121–4
Clausewitz wars 121–4
clean wars 133–4
cloning
animals 367
ethics 368
humans 367–71
tissue creation 369
co-operation

oil states 173
religion 87–8
co-ordination, warfare
130
COBE satellite 15, 25, 36
cocaine 314
cold dark matter (CDM)
32, 34–5
Cold War 105–6, 110–11,
137
Colombian vaccine 400
colonial rule 201–2, 209
combat, footsoldiers
128–9
community involvement
57, 471–2
complicity, science 81–3
computers 101
foot soldiers 113
future 472
galaxies simulation
31–2, 34
warfare 105
see also personal
computers
confederations, Europe
269–70, 280
consent and reform,
family values 311–12
Conservative Party
Europe 239, 240, 241,
256
Social Chapter 246
constitutions, Europe 276
consumer control, media
449–50
consumer-terrorism 224
contagion of the future
404–9
contentment 86
contraception 334,
373–6
Copernicus, Nicolaus 81
Copts, Egypt 185
corruption, religion 62–6
cosmology 1–40
achievements 38–40
Big Bang 3–15
further reading 475
future 23–37
grand unified theory 20,
21, 35
now 16–22
cosmos, God 81

counter-terrorism 137,
213, 216–17, 220
crazies, warfare 130–2
creation 38, 82
see also Big Bang
crime 468–9
criminalization, drugs
314
Crone's disease 418
Crusades 152, 196
cults, religious 48, 72–5
cultural relativism 70
cyberspace wars 111,
117–18
cystic fibrosis 344, 362

daily news, in future
436–7
damming rivers, Middle
East 174–5
dark matter 29–30, 31,
32
Darwin, Charles 36, 48
data processing 430
death
diseases 424
moral values 317–22
religion 56
squads 213
decolonization 201–2,
207
decriminalization, drugs
314
deep ecology 76
defence budgets 139
Delors, Jacques 251,
263–4, 265
democracy
Middle East 150–1, 156,
180
Turkey 154, 159
the West 235
demography, traditional
religion 92–3
dengue fever 406
designer babies 362, 364
destruction, orchestration
129–30
Devil 59, 85, 110–24
diabetes 365, 418
differences, putting aside
87
digital media 428–30
digital revolution
427–32, 444–5

extent 431–2
speed 431–2
today 430–1
diseases 383–432
  aerosol 407–8, 412
  blood mixing 414
  casual contact 412–13
  cost of treatment 423
  deaths 424
  epidemics 397–8
  further reading 478
  future risk 402
  germ's point of view
    346–7
  haemorrhagic fevers
    397–9
  hygiene 412
  infectious 386, 391
  insects 404
  plagues 388–93
  sex as transmitter
    413–14
  virulence enigma
    410–16
  viruses 385–7
  water-borne 407
divinity 59
divorce 300–1
DNA
  cloning 368
  closed loops 419
  new genes 360
  occurrence 380, 381
  vaccines 387, 422–4
dogmas 52, 92, 317–22
Dolly the sheep 367
donations, to middle East
  177–8
Doppler effect 5, 7
drugs
  against viruses 422
  criminalization 314
  family values 312–16
Durham, Lord 276, 281

East Asia see Asia
Ebola virus 385–6, 388,
  397, 398–9
eco-terrorism 224
ectogenesis 372
ecumenism 88
education 326–7, 463–4
eggs see ova
egotism 86
Egypt 165, 169, 185

see also Ancient Egypt
Einstein, Albert 5–6, 7,
  17, 19, 37, 38
electromagnetic spectrum
  4
electronics
  advertising 460–1
  payment systems 459
  warfare 101, 106
Email 454–5
embryos
  abnormalities 347
  different species 353
  genetic manipulation
    365
  growth knowledge
    352–3
  manipulation 361
  measurements 351–2
  new genes 362
  screening 344–5, 347
  selection 350–3
empowerment, women
  373
encephalitis viruses 404
energy
  equations 17, 19, 38
  immortals 43
engrenage of institutions
  281
environment 76
  epidemics 397–8
ETA terrorists (Spain)
  207–12
eternity 44, 51, 92
ethics 291–2, 327, 368
Euro currency 259, 262
Europe 237–81
  agriculture 266, 270
  confederation 269–70
  Conservative Party view
    256
  constitutions 276
  currency 259
  enlargement 262–4
  federal system 250, 256,
    264, 269, 271–6, 280
  flexibility 265
  force between USA and
    USSR 258–9
  harmonization 277, 281
  hopes 280–1
  leadership 241
  monetary union 261–6,
    280

the nation state 247–55
policy making 243–4
single currency 262
union 261–6, 277–8
USA special
  relationship 253
warfare 138–41
European Commission
  255–7
European Community
  276
European Council 241,
  277
European Defence
  Community 261,
  266–8, 280
European Parliament 263
European Union 254,
  275, 281
  future 242, 268–9
  purposes 258–61
Eurosceptics 240–1, 251,
  253
euthanasia 317–19
evangelization 69
evil 84, 118

faith
  age of 93
  Middle East 150–7
  survival 80
faiths 46–51, 62
  ancient 43
  healing 76
  suprarational 91
  see also religion
fallibility, God's
  representative 58
families, in year 2010
  433–45
family values 297–316
  consent and reform
    311–12
  divorce 300–1
  drugs 312–16
  homosexuality 307–9
  marriage 300–1
  nuclear family 297,
    298–300
  one-parent families
    301–2
  pornography 309–11
  prostitution 307–9
  relationships 305–7
  sex and morals 302–3

sex and society 303–5
fascism 71–2, 252
federal systems
  Europe 250, 256, 264,
    269, 271–6, 280
  Switzerland 269
  USA 274
  see also confederations
females *see* women
feminism, pornography
  310–11
fertility, manipulating
  336–55
fevers, haemorrhagic
  397–9
fireballs (Big Bang) 13–14
flexibility, Europe 265
folk religion 75, 76–7
footsoldiers 113, 127–9
forebodings, apocalyptic
  92
France, in Europe 244–5,
  249, 258–9, 277
freedom, Middle East
  150–7
Friedman, Aleksandr 6
fundamentalism,
  religions 72, 150–5,
  180
The Future of Europe 278

Gadaffi, Colonel
  Muammar 112–15
galaxies 3–4, 7, 9, 27,
  29–30, 31
  computer simulations
    31–2, 34
Gamow, George 12–15,
  19, 30, 39
gas fields, warfare 121
Gates, Bill 458
de Gaulle, General
  Charles 241, 278, 279
geeks, warfare 129–30
general theory of
  relativity 5–6, 7
genes
  bacteria 419
  defects 344–5
  IVF diagnosis 344–50
  manipulation of
    embryos 365
  new 359–66
  non-invasive approach
    349

Pandora's Box 377
  see also manipulative
    reproduction
Genesis, manipulative
  reproduction 333–4
genetic engineering 473
  see also manipulative
    reproduction
geology 10
germ-line therapy 362,
  365, 366
Germany 261–2, 274,
  275
germs 410–16
Global Positioning
  System (GPS) 104
global village 70
globalisation, Europe 243
glossary, manipulative
  reproduction 378–81
glutinous world 56–61
GNP *see* Gross National
  Product
God 44, 47, 49, 58, 60
  Children of (movement)
    73–4
  cosmos 81
  Islam 54
  Luther 52
  morality 321
  omnipotence 76, 83
  sanctity of life 320
  science 79
going digital 428–30
government, interactive
  media 470–1
GPS *see* Global
  Positioning System
grand unified theory
  (GUT) 20, 21, 35
gravity 18, 21, 23
  inflation 22
  theory of 6, 12, 21
grocery shopping, in
  future 435–6
Gross National Product
  (GNP), Middle East 183
grunts (footsoldiers)
  127–9
guidance
  morals 287
  peremptory 92
Gulf War 99, 108, 112,
  126

European involvement
  239
GUT *see* grand unified
  theory

H-COM *see* household
  communications
  system
haemorrhagic fevers
  397–9
Hanta virus 397, 418
harmonization, Europe
  277, 281
HCG *see* human
  chorionic
  gonadotrophin
healthcare 464–5
heaven 57
Heaven's Gate pact 68
Heisenberg, Werner 16
HFEA *see* Human
  Fertilization
  Embryology Authority
Hinduism 60, 73
history, Middle East
  145–9
HIV-infection 386, 394–5
  see also AIDS
holiness 63, 93
holism 83, 84–5
homes, in future 462–3
homework, in future
  434–5
homosexuality, family
  values 307–9
hormone treatments, IVF
  340–1
hospitals, pathogens 415
hot dark matter (HDM)
  32, 33–4
household
  communications
  system (H-COM)
  433–7, 440
Howard, Michael 278,
  279, 280
Hoyle, Fred 39
HPRT enzyme 348–9
Hubble Constant 9–10,
  11, 36
Hubble, Edwin 3, 5, 6, 9
Hubble Space Telescope
  4, 8
human chorionic

gonadotrophin (HCG) 375, 379
Human Fertilization Embryology Authority (HFEA) 351, 379
human rights, moral values 289–92
humanism 323
Hussein, Saddam 145–6, 159, 163–4
hygiene, diseases 412
hysteria 49

ICSI *see* Intracytoplasmic Sperm Injection
immortals 43
immune system 410
imperialism 146, 148, 184–7
in vitro fertilization (IVF) 337–55
  amino acids 352, 354
  costs 341–2, 351
  culture media 353–5
  embryo selection 350–3
  future 340–55
  genetic diagnosis 344–50
  hormone treatments 340–1
  preimplantation diagnosis 346–7, 348
  success rate 339, 350–1, 360
in vitro maturation of eggs 341–4
India
  break-up of 115–17
  as superpower 186
inequality, media 467–8
infertility
  humans 369–70, 373
  IVF treatment *see in vitro* fertilization
inflation theory (physics) 20, 22, 23
  in universe 24–5, 26, 29
influenza 390–1, 407
information
  electronic 459–60
  revolution 430–1
insects, disease risk 404, 405–7
intelligence, collection of 129–30

interactive media 431, 446, 450–2
international terrorism 214–15
Internet 106, 109, 129, 431
  see also World Wide Web
Intracytoplasmic Sperm Injection (ICSI) 339
IRA terrorism (N. Ireland) 199–200, 208, 209–10, 211, 229, 231
Iran 164, 170–1
Iraq 167
Iron and Steel Community 272
irrigation schemes 174–5
Islam 54, 60, 65–6
  fundamentalism 72, 132–5, 150–2
  laws of war 155
  terrorism 196
Israel 155–7, 158–63
  Arab relations 182–3
  terrorism 219–20, 222–3, 225
Italy 261
  see also Rome
IVF *see in vitro* fertilization

Jacob, Genesis 333
Judaism 53–4, 60

Khomeini, Ayatollah 65–6, 178
Kinkel, Klaus 250–1, 252, 257, 259
Kohl, Chancellor Helmut 239, 261
Kulturkampf (Bismarck) 70, 90
Kurds 169–70, 178

Laban's sheep 333–5
Labour government *see* New Labour Party
Labour Party, Europe 239, 241
Länder states 274
language
  Middle East 150
  religion 80

terrorism 198, 223, 232, 234
lasers 102
Lassa fever 397–8
Lawrence of Arabia 182–3
laws of war, Islam 155
leadership, Europe 241
League of Nations 198
Lebanon 165–6, 220–1
Legionella, air-conditioning systems 414–15
Lemaître, Georges 6
leprosy 391
leukaemia 369
Liberal Democratic Party 242–3
liberalism 70–1, 326–7
Libya 112–15, 165
life
  improvements 466–72
  moral values 317–22
  sanctity 320
live coverage, television 107
logic
  mediatization 109
  religion 80
longevity, religion 79
love, religion 73, 84
LSD 313, 315
Luther, Martin 52, 248–9
  see also Protestantism

Maastricht *see* Treaty of Maastricht
Macchiavelli, Niccoló 249
Magellanic Clouds 9
Major, John 240, 241
malaria 400, 405–6
males *see* men
management, warfare 130
manifestos, Europe 240–3
manipulating fertility 336–55
  see also in vitro fertilization
manipulative
  reproduction 331–81
  cloning humans 367–71
  glossary of terms 378–81
  sex selection 256–8

unpredictable results
364–5
Mariners Southcoast
Church 62
marketing 62, 444–5
marriage, family values
300–1
Marxism 47–8
mass-energy relationship
18, 38
materialism 64, 78–80
MDM *see* mixed dark
matter
measles 386, 408
media 425–72
 consumer control
 449–50
 further reading 478–9
 interactive 431, 446,
 450–2
 printing 453
 reproduction quality
 429
 security 468–9
 voting 471–2
 warfare 107–9
 work 462–3
mediatization 109
medicine 464
 see also diseases
men
 aggression 358
 intractable infertility
 369–70
metabolism,
 measurements 351–2
metaphysics 84
Metaverse structure
 (spacetime) 24
microelectronics *see*
 electronics
Middle East 143–89
 agriculture 174
 centre of 166–71
 democracy 150–1, 156
 faith 150–7
 fundamentalism 150–5
 further reading 476
 greatness 188–9
 Gross National Product
 183
 oil 172–9
 past and future 180–3
 periphery 166–71
 populations 176

return to empire 184–7
 terrorism 214–15,
 219–26
 tourism 178–9
 war and peace 158–65
 water resources 172–9
 women's influence 181
midges, diseases 405
military affairs 100–6,
 147
 see also warfare
Milky Way Galaxy 3, 4,
 5, 6, 7
millenarianism 67–9
Millennium Virus 117
mind reading 472
mixed dark matter
 (MDM) 34
modern history, Middle
 East 145–9
monetary union, Europe
 261–6, 280
Monnet, Jean 252, 255,
 260, 266, 272
monotheism 188
moral heroism 291
Moral Majority 289
moral philosophy 287–8
moral scandals 289
moral values 283–329
 abortion 319–20
 alcohol 313–14
 death 317–22
 dogma 317–22
 drugs 312–16
 ethics 292–3
 further reading 477–8
 great questions 288–9
 homosexuality 307–9
 human rights 289–92
 life/living 317–22
 limits of tolerance
 295–6
 pornography 309–11
 predictions 285–6,
 328–9
 prostitution 307–9
 religion 320–1
 two demands/facts
 293–4
morality 92, 93, 292–3
 crazies 131
 guidance 287
 history 286
 moralization 287–8

Mormonism 67
mosquitoes, diseases
 404–6, 406–7
Muhammad (Islam) 54
multicultural policies 70
Murillo, Bartolomé 58
music, in future 434–5
Muslims *see* Islam
My World Line (Gamow)
 19
mysticism 72, 83

Napoleon *see* Bonaparte
narco-terrorism 224
narrowcasting, television
 447–9
the nation state, Europe
 247–55
NATO *see* North Atlantic
 Treaty Organization
nature, deference to 81
Nazism 47–8, 252
Nelson, Admiral Horatio
 145
neutrinos (physics) 32–4
New Age movement 50,
 72
New Labour Party,
 Europe 241–2, 245–6,
 247, 249
Newton, Isaac 12
New Church 44, 62–4,
 91, 93
non-invasive approach,
 genetic diagnosis 349,
 351
non-renewable resources
 173
North Atlantic Treaty
 Organization (NATO)
 266–8, 271, 279
Northern Ireland,
 terrorism 208, 209–10,
 212, 229–31
nuclear families
 moral values 297,
 298–300
 in year 2010 433–45
nuclear warfare 116, 123,
 137–8

offices, in future 462–3
oil fields 121, 122, 172–9
omnipotence, God 76, 83

one-parent families, moral values 301–2
organ transplantation 370
ova (eggs)
  contraception development 374–6
  In vitro Maturation 341–4
  storage 342
over-population 373–5

paganism 64, 75, 79
Palestine 159, 160, 161
  terrorism 214–15, 219–21, 225
Palestine Liberation Organisation (PLO) 159–60, 215, 219–21, 224
Pandora's Box, genetics 377
parasites 411
parliaments, Europe 263, 267
particle physics 20–1
particles, WIMPs 32, 35
pathogens 402, 411, 413, 414
payment systems, electronic 459
PCs *see* personal Computers
peace, Middle East 158–63
Pearl Harbor, electronic 117–18
personal computers (PCs) 431, 432, 440
personal religion 85–6
personalized intelligent agent (Bob) 433–6, 440–5
philosophy 80, 91, 287
placenta development 372
plagues 372, 388–93, 400–3
Plank, Max 21
PLO *see* Palestine Liberation Organisation
pluralism, society 71
PNV *see* Basque Nationalist Party

policy making, Europe 243–4
political violence 234
Popes 65, 69, 94
population
  explosion 373–6
  Middle East 176
pornography 309–11
post-Cold War era 105, 118, 126
post-war world 200
poverty 78, 258
Powell, Enoch 275–6
power, Europe 258–9
preimplantation diagnosis, IVF 346–7, 348
priests 46
printing 249, 453
privacy, media 469–70
pro-lifers, euthanasia 318
programmes 433–4
promiscuity 394, 413
Prophets 54, 151
prosperity 78–80
prostitution 307–9
Protestantism 44, 69, 85
  eighteenth century 89
  Latin America 72
psychomania 46

quantum physics 16–17, 19–20, 23, 83
quasi-religion 49, 51, 79

rabies 402
recessive genes 334
Red Army Faction *see* Baader-Meinhof group
Red Brigades (Italy) 213
redshift phenomenon 4, 5, 6–7, 8, 9
Reformation 57, 248
relationships, family values 305–7
relativism 79–80
relativity, general theory of 5–6, 7
relaxation 446–53
religion 41–94
  Apes of Faith 46–51
  authoritarianism 70–7
  business success 62–3
  co-operation 87–8
  community 57

corruption 62–6
death 56
further reading 475
glutinous world 56–61
meltdown 87–90
monotheism 188
moral values 320–1
personal 85–6
revival 69
social trap 51, 52–5
traditional 64, 91–4
value of 158–9
warfare 88–90
reproduction
  digital media 429
  manipulative 331–81
resurrection 91–4
rheumatoid arthritis 418
Rifkind, Malcolm 257
rights, laying claim to 290
risks, warfare 139
rivers, damming effects 174–5
rogue state wars 111, 112–15
Rome
  plagues 389
  see also Italy
Russell, Bertrand 321
Russia *see* Union of Soviet Socialist Republics
Russian Commonwealth of States 281

Sampedro, José Luis 47
sanctity 46, 76
sanitation 392
  see also hygiene
Satan *see* Devil; evil
satellites 15, 25, 36
  destruction of 118
  spying 103–4, 120
Saudi Arabia, Kingdom of 168–9
SCAN *see* skin-cancer awareness newsletter
scepticism, religion 79–80
science, materialism 81–3
Scientology, Church of 49
screening, embryos 344–5, 347

secession wars 111, 116
Second World War *see*
World War II
sects
Catholicism 250
religious 73
warfare 115–16
secularism 44, 47, 55, 60,
66
liberalism 70
religion 93–4
security, media 468–9
Séguin, Phillippe 244–5
self-regardingness 295–6
self-satisfaction 84–6
sex
as disease transmitter
413–14
family values 302–5
manipulative
reproduction 356–8
morality 302–3
sheep 333–5, 367
shopping, in future
458–61
Sicarii (terrorists) 196
single currency, Europe
262
singularities (cosmology)
20, 23, 24
smallpox 386, 391, 408
smart weapons 104–5,
135–6
Smolin, Lee 23, 36
social activity, warfare
97–8
Social Chapter, Europe
241, 246
Socialist Parties, Europe
244–5
society 50–1
moral values 324–7
place of sex 303–5
pluralism 71
technology impact 97,
98
South Africa, terrorism
208, 217–18
Soviet Union *see* Union
of Soviet Socialist
Republics
special forces, warfare
128
spectroscopy 4–5
sperm

antibodies 375
cells future target 366
enrichment 357–8
intracytoplasmic
injections 339
Spinoza, Benedict 84, 85
Spiritualism 50, 74
spying, satellites 103–4,
120
starvation 123, 289
state terrorism 219–20
stealth warfare 101–2
subversive violence
206–8, 225, 229
suicide *see* euthanasia
sun 3, 4, 14, 33
superpowers
China 186–7
Europe 258–9
India 186
warfare 110, 111
superstitions 49, 63–4
suprarational faith 91
Supreme Being 43
see also God
surveillance *see* spying
Switzerland, as federation
269
syphilis 390, 392, 413
Syria 163, 164–5, 166–7

taboos 288
technology
marketing 444–5
media 107–9
social impact 97, 98
warfare 99–100, 107–9
telephones 455, 456–7
television
in future 431, 432,
433–4, 447–52
interactive 431, 450–2
live coverage 107
narrowcasting 447–9
plight of humans 289
programmes on demand
433–4
warfare 107–8
terror, definition 233–4
terrorism 131–2, 136–7,
163–235
causalities 204
causes 216
concept 227–8
definitions 227, 233–4

history 196–204
international 214–15
language 198, 223, 232,
234
meaning 197–8, 206–7
Middle East 214–15,
219–26
Northern Ireland 208,
209–10, 212, 229–31
Palestine 214–15
South Africa 208,
217–18
Soviet Union 218–19
USA 218–19, 225–6,
227–8
Terrorism Prevention Act
1996 (USA) 227–8
terrorist states 224
theory of relativity *see*
general theory of
relativity
Thomas, Hugh 237–81
thought reading *see* mind
reading
tissue creation, cloning
369
tolerance 295–6
tools 97–109
totalitarianism 97
tourism 178–9
tradition 91–4
Transcaucasia, oil 172
transcendence 44, 51, 55,
58
death 56
sense of 62
transgenic technology
359–62
transplantation 370
Treaty of Amsterdam
1997 262, 276
Treaty of Maastricht 240,
241, 244, 267, 270, 272
Treaty of Rome 276
TREVI anti-terrorist group
228
tuberculosis 391–2
Turkey 154, 159, 170,
178, 181–2
typhoid 390, 391

UFOs *see* unidentified
flying objects
ulcers 417
UN *see* United Nations

unidentified flying
objects (UFOs) 68
unification of Europe
262, 277–8
Union of Soviet Socialist
Republics (USSR)
110–11
Middle East interest
146–7, 159, 186–7
terrorism 218–19
United Kingdom (UK)
229–32, 268
United Nations (UN)
Commission on Human
Rights 289–90
human rights 289–90
Universal Declaration
289, 290–1
United States of America
(USA)
Europe as shield 258–9
federations 274
Middle East interest 146,
148–9, 185
NATO 267
Navy 119–21
oil dependency 172–3
special relationship
with Europe 253
terrorism 218–19,
225–6, 227–8
warfare 138–41
Universal Declaration of
UN 289, 290–1
Universe 3, 4, 21
see also cosmology
age 10–11, 20
birth 16–22
density 26–8, 29, 31, 34,
36
expansion 6–10, 21–2,
24–6
flat 29–30
inflation 24–5, 26
origins 11–12
present understanding
13
uniformity 25
USA see United States of
America
USSR see Union of Soviet
Socialist Republics
(USSR)

vaccines
for contraception 374–5
DNA 387, 422–4
infectious diseases 391
malaria 400
value projection wars
111–12, 118–21
vancomycin resistance
421
Vibert, Frank 275–6
video phones 456–7
video-clip wars 107–9
violence
crazies 130–2
political 233
subversive 206–8
see also terrorism
virtual friends 437
virulence enigma 410–16
viruses 385–7, 401
drugs against 422
plagues of future 401
voice phones 455–6
voting, media 471–2

war, as terrorism 136–7
warfare 95–141
Asia 121–4, 138–41
categories of wars
111–24
chemical weapons 138
choices 135–41
civilians 133–4
electronics 101, 106
Europe 138–41
further reading 475–6
grunts, geeks and crazies
125–34
nuclear 116, 123
religion 88–90
revolution 100–6
as social activity 97–8
technology 107–9
television 107–8
tools 97–109
USA 138–41
video-clip wars 107–9
zero-casualties 127
wars
against terrorism 228
clean 133–4
Middle East 158–65
water 172–5
water-borne diseases 407

weakly interacting
massive particles
(WIMPs) 32, 35–6
weapons
implications 134
nuclear 116, 137–8
smart 104–5, 135–6
see also warfare
Western European Union
(WEU) 266–8
WEU see Western
European Union
WIMPs see weakly
interacting massive
particles
women
empowerment 373
Middle East 181
work 438–9, 462–3
World War I 198, 313
World War II 99–100,
199, 200–1, 202, 233,
234
World Wide Web
(WWW) 431
worldliness 57, 63, 64
wormholes (cosmology)
24
wrist mounted television
432
WWW see World Wide
Web

X-rays 4

year 2000 68–9
year 2010
household
communications
system 433–7, 440
nuclear family example
433–45
personalized intelligent
agent (Bob) 430–6,
440–5
technologies 439–40
virtual friends 437
working day 438
year 2020, vision 121–4
year 2050+ 472

Zaire see Africa
zero-casualties, warfare
127